Up the Golden Stair

Up the

❦ ELIZABETH YATES

Golden Stair

E. P. Dutton & Co., Inc.   NEW YORK   1966

Grateful acknowledgment is made to the following for permission to quote material:

Friends Journal and Edward Wood for "It Matters Not" by Lydia C. Wood.

Excerpt reprinted from *The Prophet* by Kahlil Gibran with permission of the publisher, Alfred A. Knopf, Inc., copyright 1923 by Kahlil Gibran; renewal copyright 1951 by Administrators C.T.A. of Kahlil Gibran Estate, and Mary G. Gibran.

Golden Quill Press and Winifred Rawlins for "This I Can Now Affirm" from her collection *Fire Within*. Copyright © 1959 by Golden Quill Press.

Harper & Row and Elizabeth Gray Vining for "The Road to Ewelme" from *World in Tune*, copyright 1942, 1952, 1954 by Elizabeth Gary Vining, Harper & Row, publisher, used by permission.

The Macmillan Company, New York, and Macmillan & Co., Ltd., London, for excerpts from "Crossing," LXXI, and from "Gitanjali," XCIII, both from *The Collected Poems and Plays of Rabindranath Tagore*. Copyright, 1918, by The Macmillan Company. Copyright renewed, 1946, by Rabindranath Tagore. Used also by permission of the Trustees of the Tagore Estate and Macmillan & Co., Ltd., London, England.

Louise A. Nickerson for "Continuation (E. to W.)."

Nora S. Unwin for "Within the Nimbus."

❧ Contents

❧ *Foreword*

This book has grown out of necessity, as most books do in any case. I had been asked to think about writing a book that would present the idea of death to children. This stirred me because, for a long time, I had had many thoughts on the subject. So I opened my mind to see what would flow into it and also to examine for their usefulness and validity the ideas that I had been holding over the years.

However, before many weeks had passed, I was called upon to put my long-held thoughts to the test —not of words on paper but in the living of one day after another without the near presence of the one with whom I had shared everything that was life for more than thirty-four years: joy and sorrow, success and despair, high-hearted delight, soul-sounding trials.

The living of the days, the somehow enduring of the nights, was not easy, and I knew within me that there would be many times in the years ahead when it still would not be easy, but I felt that with each day and night I was beginning to make some important aspect of discovery. No matter what books I read, there was something that I had to figure out for myself. No matter what comfort friends gave me, no matter what wisdom others had gained and sought to pass on to me, I had to find my own. In time, what I discovered became part of me. I know now that it is mine forever.

From our first conscious awareness of life, we are obliged to face facts as they confront us. We do this at the various levels of our growing understanding and with the tools we are learning to use. A young child can be realistic about the fact of death if he can be assured that there is still someone left to love and to be loved by. An older person may have a more difficult time. In our tenderness we often try to shield those we love from facing essential facts; we try to spare them suffering. But sorrow, at some time or other in life, is the common lot: to insulate against it may be to deprive ourselves or others of great adventure.

At festive times or particular occasions, we all can rejoice together and then go our separate ways more or less forgetful of those with whom pleasure was shared; but sorrow, in a moment, makes us all one and keeps us mindful of others. It levels us, humbles us, turns us into little children. In our shock and grief and desolation we need to be assured of only one thing, and it is what the young child needs, that there is still love left in the world.

8

As one whom his mother comforteth, so do I comfort you. The ancient words have reached across time and distance with assurance. We are helpless, and we need to be comforted, and we will be. In the way we face the sorrow that has made children of us, we begin to grow up. Strengthened, we turn toward the new adventure: the discovery of the love that is in the world.

A Letter

I ❧ *The Fact*

This may be quite a long letter, for there is so
much that I want to share with you, but I shall write it
slowly as the thoughts come to me, and perhaps you
will read it in the same way. Miles apart as we are, our
thoughts will be meeting, and it will almost be as if we
were clasping hands. We have much to give to each
other, and much to gain from each other, because of the
experience we have both so recently had.

My heart has ached for you in the loss that has
come in your life, and my affection has reached out to
embrace you in the bright busy hours of the day and
even more in the still, lonely hours of the night. This
sorrow that has brought us close together makes us one
with every person who has ever known sorrow. This can
be a kind of special blessing to us all, right now. The
peoples of the world are striving to find and implement
the way to the oneness that is theirs inherently as
human beings, and whatever fosters understanding will

❧ I I

help. Sympathy has within it the power to work a miracle.

No matter how brave we think we are, or think we can be, we must call sorrow by its right name and see it for what it is. Only then can we avail ourselves of the treasure that is hidden in the folds of its dark cloak. I think that we should not, by any twist of the words we use, minimize what we are going through, what anyone goes through, when death enters upon life and removes a member of our circle, family-close or friendship-wide. There will be time enough to ponder the event, to philosophize about it, to discover its significance. Now, the bleak fact stands: a light has gone out; wherever it may be shining, it is here no longer.

Face the dark night then, as a night, but with the knowledge that there is no night so long that dawn does not sometimes end it. When the day comes we shall face it, too, stronger and wiser and, if our prayers have had any breadth to them, far more compassionate. Only those who have gone through a comparable experience know what struggling, what searching, what grasping goes on in the dark. The slow emergence into day may be something like the emergence of a seed as it pushes up through the earth and responds to the sun. A matter of days it may be for some seeds; for others the time may be measured in weeks, or in years.

With growing things, day and night, light and dark, all serve nature's purpose, as does the cold of winter, the warmth of summer, sun and rain and wind.

So much of the work essential to growing is done in the dark, unseen, unnoticed, until the visible evidence of shoot or stalk or sprout appears to break through the crust of earth. Then, with roots established and capable of continuing their holding and their reaching, the top begins to reach in a different way.

A botanist friend told me that with ordinary plants the spread of roots beneath the surface is about equal to the growth that is lifted above the soil. Desert plants do have more roots than top, and in a dry season even lawn grasses will grow deeper roots in their search for needed moisture.

"Do you mean to say," I asked, "that a carrot in the vegetable garden has a root system which, in its way, is equal to that giant maple that shades the house?"

"Yes, the proportion is just about the same," my friend replied, "But it took the maple much, much longer and its roots go not only very deep but very wide."

As the roots of growing things work their way in the dark earth, so have my roots been working, so have yours in another kind of dark.

During these immediate days, and during the next few weeks and months, your friends will be very tender with you and their thoughtfulness will flow around you in many ways. The word *sympathy* will be used often, in speaking and in writing. It is a rich word and conveys much of what one heart would say to another. But only

13

those who know what it is like to have a door close that will never, never open again have learned the true meaning of the word. They are the ones who may give you the most strength, but not always. Affection and imagination working together can create a warm circle with you and your need at its center, and you will find yourself greatly heartened.

"You must be desperately lonely." Those words, when said to me, were deeply comforting. They came from one who knew what companionship was and what the loss of it meant. Yes, it is true, and in loneliness there is an ache that does not cease. Here, again, I hold out my hand to clasp yours. I know that the ache of loneliness will be with me all my days, and I would not have it otherwise, as I know for whom it is. And yet, around the edges of this knowledge, there is a challenge which, if I can accept it, will ennoble my days.

Think with me for a moment: no matter how we enjoy the company of a friend, how we delight in the warmth of good comradeship, there are significant parts of every day that are spent alone. Inner growing and aspiring, even a certain amount of daily doing and planning, are all prompted by or become the result of those times of aloneness. In the quiet times deliberately sought, or in those enforced upon us, we discover ideas that can be put to use when we return again to the busy world of people. If the loneliness is deeper now, it may be that more may be found within it.

So, do not run from it. Escape will not do for you what acceptance will, even though the stark realization of what it is you must accept may shake you again and again.

Let your sorrow find its way out in tears, as often as it must, as often as you need this release. Gradually, something of the numbness that has taken hold of you will be melted down, and the daze of remoteness in which you find yourself will yield. Salty the tears may be, but they are clean and good. Grief is bitter only when through it we reproach ourselves for those things we did not do, or for the something that might have been done had there been time.

If we live our relationships to the full and do all that we can and should within them, there will never come a moment when we will reproach ourselves or feel remorse. There is an old saying that we cannot do a kindness too soon, for we never know when it may be too late. Keep your relationships current. Follow the impulse to do that small kindness for another whenever it comes to you. Then you will never be beset by the thought, Oh, if I had only done it when I thought of it ⟨🖉 15⟩ —— This is one of the discoveries I have made this year: that if the inner promptings of heart and mind are obeyed there will never be an echo of the words "too late."

So give way, my dear, to grief. Let the tears flow and let the hands become fists if need be to beat in rebellion. Yet, even as I say that, I will remind you that too long a rainy season is not good for a garden, and too frequent crying will dim the vision.

There is a story in the Talmud of a man who had a little daughter. She was his only child and when she became sick and died the father was filled with grief. His friends tried to comfort him, but he would not be comforted. Then one night he had a dream. He seemed to be in heaven and many little girls were there, acting their parts in a pageant. Each one carried a lighted candle, except for one whose candle was not lit. Looking more closely, he saw that the child with the unlit candle was his daughter. He took her in his arms and caressed her, then asked her why her candle was not burning like the others. "Often it does light," she answered him, "but your tears keep making it go out."

Mystery and miracle once meant the same thing. Now, as we orient ourselves to a new way of living, those two words may have again the same meaning. There are many things that cannot be explained. To try to force an explanation in pursuit of the mystery may, in this case, lessen the miracle. Don't try to grapple with the event of death with logic, but meet it with faith.

Range the wide world of nature and observe the hints that are there—buds on the trees that move from spring's promise, to summer's fullness, to autumn's brilliance, then fall and return to the earth; the chick who works hard to break out from his protective shell and becomes in time a strong-winged bird; the snake who sloughs his skin; the grub who goes through the various stages to become a butterfly. Always within the case, the covering, the body there is something that is imbued with life. An end of one phase is a new beginning; the form changes to suit the evolving function. Something once visible is no longer to be seen. It might almost be better to say that something tangible can no longer be watched, for much that is best in life is not visible.

"One does not doubt the existence of air because a strong wind is not always blowing," says Aurobindo, "or of sunlight because night intervenes between dusk and dawn."

Something has happened to you, as it has happened to me; something that is the common lot. What shall we do—bow beneath it as if a millstone had fallen on us, or take it in our hands like a key to unlock the gate that opens up the golden stair?

II ❦ *The Adventure*

BARRIE GAVE BRAVE WORDS TO PETER PAN WHEN, alone on the rock as the rising waters were coming nearer, the boy who never wanted to grow up flung back his head and cried, "To die must be an awfully big adventure." And of that we have no slightest doubt; yet, for the one who is left to live on in life it is an equally big adventure.

But—

Can we ever tell, as we stand at the threshold of a new day, just what the day will bring? No matter how carefully planned the hours may be, or how wisely plotted the duties, there are always openings, and through them may come a promise of friendship, a glimpse of beauty, a coin of wisdom's minting, a high clear call of glory. In bed at night, before falling asleep, to go back over the day and weigh the unexpected against the prepared is to realize that there has been more of the former than the latter. There may be a condition here: the courageous spirit and the questing mind are always having adventures. To be ready for the

18 ❦

unexpected is to find it waiting—in people, in places, in daily events: and the one who is ready generally knows how to use and profit by what is encountered.

Adventure sounds like an enterprise involving the body, but often the most meaningful adventures are those that result when mind meets mind and, through words said or written, spirit calls to spirit. Can you remember how the books you read when you were little spoke to your imagination? Without any thought of weighing the ponderables "Will I?" or "Won't I?" you responded and went wherever the words in the book took you.

It was a simple matter to slip down a rabbit hole and have a series of adventures with a certain *Alice;* it was an experience to live at the bottom of the sea and share the joy and the anguish of *The Little Mermaid.* I can recall going to an unspeakably wonderful place called *The Garden Behind the Moon,* and it all seemed so possible. I never questioned; one doesn't with books. Often I went with a lovely lady, who's being I could not define but whose personality I completely understood, to a place called *At the Back of the North Wind.* I traveled between the wings of a wild goose with *Nils* and saw a world that no astronaut today has ever seen. I went on a magic cloak with a *Little Lame Prince,* and the fact that he did this because his legs were useless made no difference at all. Many, many times I accompanied a lonely little girl through the door of a *Cuckoo Clock* and that was ever memorable; so much

19

so that I cannot now hear such a clock tell the hour without thinking of the world behind that little door.

Experiences such as these were like a weaning process for me. I was aware of a mental stretching and expanding as natural as had been an earlier process of which I was quite unaware. Whether a baby likes it or not does not matter in the least, the time comes when milk must be replaced by something more solid. The baby may rebel, scream, spit out the food, make things generally unpleasant, but to no avail. Nothing can alter the fact that if a body is to grow and be the fit habitation for a developing mind, there must be an intake of solid food. The books read and delighted and wondered about in childhood begin to wean us from too great dependence on the world around us as the only world.

I knew there were lands beyond the horizon; and perhaps beyond them there might even be an invisible horizon. It took imagination to get to those far-off lands, but imagination is an act of love of which children find themselves happily capable. Do you remember how easy it was? And, sometimes, still is?

20 ✺ Many of the books read early and often helped me to understand that life was a process of growing; that, in time, it would even grow out of itself into something bigger, certainly different, probably more rarefied, and it was entirely natural that it should do this. Whether I liked it or not, it was the pattern, it was the law. And it was inescapable.

A few years later there were books that went

deeper and gave me a more immediate challenge. An allegory like Bunyan's *Pilgrim's Progress* did exactly that, especially in its last chapter. A story of animals, like *Bambi*, did it in a different way because it made me think of the total picture of life—creatures, trees, flowers, as well as human beings. *Little Women* was a shared experience because the girls were so real and I felt so close to them. In these and other loved books death happened, not only as part of the story but as part of life. Somehow it was right, though tears and heartache went with the reading.

But books, even when they gave experience, were a safe distance away from the actual experience: they could always be closed and returned to the shelf. Then, one day, something happened to me that was not in a book but in my ordinary everyday life; something that brought me right up to the invisible horizon.

Mr. B. was an old man when I knew him and he kept the general store in the small town in which I had been growing up. I must have been in my late teens, but so warm and vital and secure had been the life of our family circle that death had scarcely so much as brushed by our door. A dog that had been everyone's pet for as long as most of us could remember, and that was sixteen years, had died. We gave him a worthy funeral, we mourned appropriately, and in time his place was filled by another dog. What griefs there had been in those early years had been assuaged by tears and ceremony, and life had resumed its course. Then, one morning, the daily paper carried the news that Mrs. B. had died after a brief illness. She had been the music teacher and for many years she had been well known and loved.

That afternoon, when I had occasion to go to the general store, I had not thought to see Mr. B., but he was there, with his long gray work coat on, wrapping up pound packages of tea and sugar. There was no one else in the store and I felt overcome with embarrassment, even something more disturbing that seemed like fear. I simply didn't know how to face Mr. B. or what to say. If I could have done it, I would have backed out of the door and forgotten my purchase. But he had seen me, and, looking up from the small occupation of his hands, he smiled at me.

So I found the item for which I had come to the store, and took it to the counter to pay for it. Knowing I would have to say something, I fumbled for words and mumbled without looking at him, "Mr. B., I'm so sorry about your wife."

He looked at me and somehow drew my eyes to his, then he held my gaze. "Oh, but it was so beautiful!"

Perhaps because I must have appeared ill at ease, perhaps because a wonderful event had become part of him and he felt compelled to share it, he told me of the whole experience.

"It was so beautiful," he repeated. "I was sitting beside her bed last evening when she turned to me and said, 'Can you hear it?' 'Hear what?' I asked. 'The music,' she said, 'the music. Listen!' Her face was aglow, her eyes were shining and she raised her head a little from the pillow as if to hear it better. I listened, but that music was not for me. I knew by the light in her face what joy it was giving her, and when her head slipped back on the pillow I would not have done anything to keep her from hearing that glorious music forever."

"You loved her very much."

"Yes, indeed, for more than forty years, and I love her now more than ever. I know she is in a world of love—of light, too, and of music, but somehow there seems to be more love than ever right here, right now."

Still he held my gaze to his and I saw that his eyes had filled with tears, but his voice was strong and there was triumph in it.

"This I cannot understand now," he said, as he moved his head gently from side to side, "but no doubt I will when my moment comes. 'Can you hear it?' she said. 'It is so beautiful.' "

"But, Mr. B., how can you bear to be here in the store today?"

Surprise swept the tender look of sorrow from his face. "I've still got my work to do," he replied in a matter-of-fact tone.

When I left the store, I knew that a window had been opened in my life, letting in light and a new current of air. The unknown had come close to me for the first time and in it there was nothing to fear, only a

23

beauty beyond describing to be realized someday. And what was this that he had said about love? and what did it really mean? Apparently nothing had happened to the love that Mr. and Mrs. B. had been building through their long lifetime together; if anything, it had grown stronger.

It started me thinking then, and I am still thinking. Like Mr. B. I can say, "This I cannot understand now, but no doubt—"

Yes, *no doubt.*

During the next few days I heard people exclaim more than once, "Poor Mr. B., how lonely he must be!" And whenever I heard such remarks, it took me back to that moment in the store. Lonely, yes, because a dear presence would no longer be a warm and tangible part of his life; but not lonely because he had no one to love. If what Mr. B. said to me was true, love would be multiplied in his life: both in the receiving and in the giving. Through the years, Mr. B.'s "No doubt" has echoed in my mind, at times with comfort, at other times as a challenge.

24

We do not know what the continuing will be; only that it will be. As long as man has had tenure on the earth, he has expressed his faith in that which is beyond present life in some way. Go back through history, far, far back, and the assurance is there among primitive tribes to highly civilized peoples. Pyramids, Indian mounds, present-day memorials speak to their own times and in their own ways. From the earliest writings, through the thinking Greeks and on to today, both within and without the field of religion, the certainty is found. *What* it is no one can say; *that* it is, few have doubted.

The scientific mind may balk at this, the intellectual may lose itself in argument, but the heart holds to an inner knowledge. "Yes," it says, though the weight of "No," may sound against it. In *The Crock of Gold* James Stephens writes, "I have learned that the head does not hear anything until the heart has listened, and that what the heart knows today the head will understand tomorrow."

The books we once read that gave us first adventures out of our bodies made it clear that there was nothing to fear but a great deal to wonder about. It must be so for the one who has slipped out of his skin and moved into a new dimension.

"She is in a world of love," Mr. B. said, "yet there is more love here."

Listening to him, looking into his quiet face and wise, kind eyes, I asked myself if someday I, too, might face what he was facing. Yes, I thought, face it or be ready to, for all who love must know this can happen. It is not the price paid for love; it is a part of love. Mr. B. had learned during the long years just how strong love was. So might I; so might anyone. It took no less courage to live than it did to love, and the two were so intertwined that there was no saying where one began and the other left off; and there was no separating them.

If love is the one thing we can be sure of for another who has gone on, and if it is the thing we know we must have while we are here, then love is the link between the known and the unknown, the visible and the invisible. There are no words to convey this. Words can be used only for the known; for the invisible something other than words is required. Yet, has love at its highest, purest, warmest ever needed words?

"How good that he has his work," people said of Mr. B. as the days and months went on. But the pound packages of tea and sugar that were wrapped, the business of the store that was continued, were not merely to keep hands occupied but to keep love in action. Something new went into the orders that were filled. It was Mr. B.'s secret and it gave a kind of gentle brightness to his days.

"To die must be an awfully big adventure!" said Peter Pan. To live with a new release of love is our adventure now.

26

III ❦ *The Challenge*

STOUTHEARTED AS YOU MAY FEEL, AND READY for the days ahead, the adventure has a way, at times, of turning back upon itself; it is then that it becomes a challenge.

No matter how courageously you learn to set aside your sorrow, keeping it in a secret place to which you alone have recourse; no matter how bravely you free yourself from sentimental ties; there is no guarantee that something will not happen to cause your heart to plummet down to the depths. I think that I guard myself against this, but I know that it can happen. If a limb that has been frostbitten begins to ache, it is a sign that there is life in it; if a heart that has been numbed by loss aches, what does it signify? You know, and you would not have it otherwise.

Sometimes, quite suddenly with me and in a moment of unpreparedness, I find myself affronted—yes, really affronted—that this could have happened: that the one I loved so much has gone from me and, for a

❦ 27

while at least, I cannot follow. Why did it have to happen now? Why?

And who can ever answer that question in any other way than to say that a limit had come to a certain span? When a butterfly moves from a chrysalis, its time of emergence has come; when the setting sun dips below the horizon, it is to flood the dark side of the world with light. Something as orderly as it is inevitable has happened. Yet the questioning persists. Why did it have to happen now when there was so much to live for? so much still to do?

Quite soon, though often not nearly soon enough, when my thinking plummets with a "why" I can retrieve it with a "what." What am I going to do about this so it will be for me, as well, a creative experience? Death has not deprived me of love; if anything, it has made me realize how much there is of it in the world. As love has flowed tenderly toward me during these past months, it can move on from me imaginatively. This is the new imperative in my life.

Seeing this honestly and objectively, things begin to happen. I find myself reaching out to others, more sensitive now of needs other than my own. I know how greatly I must have been upheld in my darkness by the thoughts, the affection, the prayers of my friends. Now, I would return something of this in whatever way presents itself. If I look back over my life, far back down the years, into what it was like before my dear one became a part of it, I can see what his love brought to me, what it did for me. If I look ahead, I can catch a glimpse of what my love, enriched now and chastened, may be able to do for others.

Sometimes the plummeting does not come from within, but from without. Well-meaning and sympathetic as friends may be, there can be moments when their words may seem to pull you down from the high place you have found for yourself. Only you know what struggles were needed for that attainment, and how precarious that height still is. With every good intention, there are people who can convey the impression that you should be sad to do honor to memory. People can be unduly sentimental. People can even hint that you must feel lost physically and spiritually. And how combat these attitudes? Words do little good. They may not come easily and they might sound argumentative. Silence, often the best rebuke, is not wholly right either.

Whatever is said, it is for you to hold valiantly to the reality you have been making yours. You are learning, more from yourself than from anyone else or from anything written, that there is verity and versatility as well as deep abiding in love. That of which you were a visible part for so long has still the power to keep life rich and rewarding. Your manner will convey this to others, though your words may be few.

There are friends, bless them for their presence in the world and cherish them, who have the gift of understanding. One such wrote me, "I am well aware that the holidays will not be easy for you . . . still, when a sadness sneaks up on you in an unguarded moment, or startles you awake in early morning hours, remember that there are understanding hearts (mine among them) that are building up a store of thoughts, love and prayers for you to draw upon." Another wrote to me from a great distance and said, "The fact would tell me that you have now joined the Company of the Greatly Sorrowing, but because of the nature of your life together and because you were so loved, I prefer to think of you as having joined the Company of the Greatly Loving."

A plummeting time comes for me when I let myself wonder if I shall ever see him again, *as I knew him.* My immediate need is for "Yes," but the stark answer that I must give myself is "No." Were I to meet today some friend of my childhood days, or of my school years, neither one would look now as he did then. Yet, no matter what time might have done to us, we would recognize each other. They have been growing and changing as I have, and yet the qualities that first drew us together will be there: stronger, clearer, more radiant than in the early days. And what were they? The list multiplies as I think of those loved-long-ago-and-not-seen-for-years friends: a zest for living, the search for truth, a sharing of beauty. Heart spoke to heart then; heart will ever speak to heart and the language will be understood.

My pocket New Testament opens easily at certain

places. One of the places is Paul's first letter to the Corinthians, chapter thirteen, the Moffat translation—

At present we only see the baffling reflection
   in a mirror,
but then it will be face to face;
at present I am learning bit by bit,
but then I shall understand, as all along I have
   myself been understood.

Fumbling for words to express my thoughts as I have been so often during this past year, I was delighted when a friend put into words what I had been feeling and struggling to say. She wrote, "The possibility of experiencing the nearness of one's beloved must begin, surely, long before he has stepped over, in the quality of love that results from years of understanding and mutual self-discipline. And the continuation of the sense of nearness requires constant practice, just as one practices the presence of God. And this seems to me no sacrilege, inasmuch as love lives on because it is of God."

This I know: my dear one has gone closer to God. This, too, I know: that as I live close to God I shall be near him. Death has made me only more sure of my connectedness. It is in God we live and in God we meet at last. To indulge personal sorrow or the sense of loneliness will not help toward this meeting, but serenity will, and discipline, and inner gladness, and the willingness to yield to the new demands. I have learned that when I keep my life right—and by that I mean responsive, gay, creative, giving—I am most near to my dear one because I am most near to God. If I allow myself to become heavyhearted, I find that I am a long way from him, and it is a weary while to get myself back. Yet, to recognize the fact that this can happen, and probably will continue though in lessening degree, is to be prepared to deal with it.

"We rise to fall—" Browning says in *Asolanda*, and humbly I agree, for I have plummeted again and this time it is with a recurrent pang of remembering that nothing will ever be the same as once it was. Nothing. However long the time may be, wherever events may take me. I can neither change nor mitigate this fact, but I can remind myself of other times in my life about which it could be said that nothing would ever be the same again. There was a time when the play of kindergarten was left for the serious business of the first grade . . . when the eighth grade was preparation for high school . . . when formal education was accounted for and work became the order of the days . . . when relationships widened, intensified, grew, changed. Each new move onward meant that with an opening door, a door behind closed silently. An old way was put aside for a new. And nothing would ever be quite the same again, for if the new way was to be fully realized it demanded all that I had to give to it.

Not really a plummeting, but a dipping of the wings as they meet a fresh current of air, is the uneasy feeling that has come over me at times in the midst of some particular happiness, that I should be enjoying this all by myself. But the current of air is an updraft. The wings yield to it and my spirit soars. If the joy that surrounds me is great, if the beauty of which I am a part is almost beyond description, what must his be now! Bliss. That is the one word I can find that gives me a hint, and only a hint. I say it. I think it. It thinks itself through me, and then I feel right about enjoying the pleasure that has come to me.

If something wonderfully good enters my life, something better than I deserve or have any right to expect, I should not be in the least surprised. He is at one now with all that is good. Friends have a way of saying, "Oh, if he only knew—" But, in a manner beyond imagining, I know that he is aware.

Often I ache for our days of dear companionship and the sharing that went with them—the endless talking and the listening, the philosophizing. Then there was always someone to wonder with, to laugh with. Someone who was keen to discuss the world's events, its woes and its glories. Someone whose wisdom quickened me, whose sympathy never failed me; someone who tempered my enthusiasms, whose ability to see all around a subject helped me to see from more than my one small window. Now, I may catch my breath before a marvel in nature, I may observe something ridiculous that delights me, or serious that stirs me, or wrong that troubles me, and there is no one near to share it with in just the way we had. No one; ever; in our own particular way. And inwardly I ache. But it is the past that has made the present meaningful; and in time that present will be fruitful.

You may often ask yourself from where the strength will come that will enable you to face the days as they go on; it will come, I assure you, sometimes from unexpected sources, sometimes in unlooked-for ways, if you let it come. You have your work to do, and mine is not over yet. To live life fully, to love its every moment, is the only means by which we can ready ourselves for wider living, greater loving. There are two lines from a sonnet of Santayana's that keep echoing in my mind—

> Living you make it goodlier to live,
> Dead you will make it easier to die.

There will be a day when something within me will hear a call like no call ever heard before, sweeter than any thrush that sings at twilight, clearer than any light that flows across the hills at dawn, gentle and utterly demanding. Whatever I am doing, I shall put it down to answer that call and to follow its leading. Nothing else will matter. You will hear such a call one day, in its own time and way, and even so you will answer it. All who are living, *because* they are living, will experience this. I think we will rejoice then as we have never rejoiced before. This is the moment toward which all of life has been tending.

Often in my reading, I find that what I am trying

to say to you has been said so much better by someone else, and so I give you Amiel's words—

> The eternal life is not the future life; it is life in harmony with the true order of things—life in God. We must learn to look upon time as a movement of eternity, as an undulation in the ocean of being. To live, so as to keep this consciousness of ours in perpetual relation with the eternal, is to be wise; to live, so as to personify and embody the eternal, is to be religious.

35

IV ❧ *The Test*

THERE IS A SAYING THAT HE WHO WOULD MAKE A
success of old age must start young; it may also be said
that he who would make a success of dying must do it in
the life he is living. Doctors and ministers know that the
manner of a person's death is often in keeping with his
life. Nurses speak of the expressions on the faces of
those who are approaching death; not always, but often,
those expressions are alive with an eager wonder or
quiet with an inner peace.

Whether our time on earth is of long or short
duration is not nearly so important as the quality of our
living: the service we give in our different ways, the
love we set in motion. When the moment comes and
that secret call is heard, however it reaches the inner
ear, the one who has been living fully and zestfully in
the present will no doubt discover that he is quite ready
for another kind of present. Now, the reach has at last
outdistanced the grasp. When the habitation of the body
is needed no longer, I think that it is as willingly re-

linquished as the bird relinquishes the shell that gave it safe lodging until it was ready to break through it.

When John Quincy Adams, at the age of eighty, was asked one day how he was feeling, he replied, "I thank you, John Quincy Adams is well, sir, quite well. But the house in which he lives at present is becoming dilapidated. . . . The old tenement is becoming almost uninhabitable, and I think John Quincy Adams will have to move out of it soon; but he himself, sir, is quite well, sir, quite well."

But any separation is hard, and it is hardest on the one who is left with memory. I know something of what your sorrow means to you. No doubt your heart feels like an empty room, a well without water, a hurt that will not heal. But nature does not tolerate a vacuum. A raw and gravelly bank beside a new-made road will soon produce an assortment of wild grasses and weeds, some even bearing flowers; a well drained of all its water will begin to fill again from deep springs in the earth; a flesh wound will heal, rebuilding tissue until only a faint scar remains and sometimes even that is absorbed in the new growth.

When I am not blinded by my tears, I can begin to see how much remains for me to do. When I do not bolt the doors of my heart, I can begin to realize how much love there is still left. Slowly, ways of usefulness appear for me; gradually they open other ways through which beauty and tenderness and joy and wonder creep back into my life: as the green covering returns to the earth, as the waters to the well, as healthy tissue to the wound.

Beauty. Tenderness. Joy. Wonder. Let them in, I say to you. Welcome them. Be them. They are all one with love and, as my storekeeper friend said to me, "There is no less love in the world, indeed there is more." More? Because the gift of love is the capacity it creates to love. Look at your own two hands, look at your longing heart: they will be neither useless nor empty if you put them at the disposal of love.

During the years that my life was royally shared with another, I would remind myself occasionally that this would not always be, that to everything there was an end, to everyone a time. He might go first, or I, and one of us would be left. But I had a strong feeling that the deeper our love went and the truer it was, the easier it would be to stand the temporary severance imposed by death. It is not possible to gauge the strength of any feeling until it is put to the test, and this test has been mine during the past year. Because of this, I can say to you now that my feeling has held. When together, we found an ever-flowing though to the eye invisible spring from which we could drink. The spring is still there and its waters are still flowing fresh and clear. To my eye they are invisible, but I think that to him they have become visible.

There are many words that we accept and use freely without actually knowing their meaning, either in their sharpness or in their fullness, until something happens that brings us face to face with them and we are then compelled to find the meaning for ourselves.

One of these is the word *alone*.

Do you remember in *Bambi* that much of the wisdom came from the old stag? He and the young deer were often together and the relationship was rewarding for each one. Near the end of the book there comes a time when the stag will not let Bambi follow him any longer. "In the hour which I am approaching we are all alone," he said, then he went deeper into the forest. Bambi, watching him go, was alone, too; but in a different way.

Sometime or another each one of us will face aloneness. It was only when I did that I began to learn the real meaning of the word that I had read, heard, used for years as part of the English language. It does not matter how rich and rare and satisfying the relationships we have known have been—in families, in friendship, in work, in marriage—there comes a time when each one must see himself as an integer in the Universe: not dependent on or conjoined with anyone else, not needed by or needing anyone else. Something begins to happen then. The only way I know how to say it is that we become aware as never before of our relationship with God, and the actual definition of the word alone— *All plus one*—has a personal meaning.

When this began to work itself through to me, I was acutely conscious of the one; only gradually could I accept the All. But, in time, it became like a great protective mountain rising behind me.

The first year of aloneness is over for me now, and though memory is no less rich it is less poignant. I do not think of what we were doing together a year ago, of what event or festival or holiday we were celebrating, or how we were sharing plain day-by-day experiences. No, a year ago I was already walking the new way, still dazed and numb, still cautiously, though deep within me was a certainty that I knew would prove itself. I know now that I can best honor him as I am most joyfully alive; as I do my work; as I continue to make my discoveries. The future is not my concern, except as the living of one day after another builds the future.

And gratitude for what has been, for what will be, fills my heart with a warmth like that of spring sunshine after the long chilling days of winter.

In Masefield's *Trial of Jesus*, Pilate's wife asks the centurion in charge of the soldiers at the Cross, "Do you think he is dead?

"Centurion: No, lady, I don't.

"Pilate's Wife: Then, where is he?

"Centurion: Let loose in the world, lady, where neither Roman nor Jew can stop his truth."

Love let loose in the world! Is this what has happened, and we called it death?

One day, when I was about ten years old and walking home from school, I stopped to read some words on the notice board outside a church. The capsule sermons

lettered there week after week always drew my attention and gave me much to ponder. But these words
puzzled me. It was hard to make any sense out of
them—

And we are put on earth a little space,
That we may learn to bear the beams of love.

How could something like love that was warm and
comforting, as I had always known it to be, be heavy
like a piece of wood?

The words lodged in my mind. I thought about
them often and began to realize that there was another
kind of beam. A broad shaft of light emitted from a
luminous source was also called a beam. The words
continued to echo within me even though I did not
entirely understand their meaning nor know their source
until a few years later. Reading Blake's poetry, I came
upon them in "The Little Black Boy." The joy in me
rushed out to welcome them as I would welcome the
sudden appearance of an old friend. They said more to
me then, and they have been speaking to me ever since,
but never more clearly than this past year and on one
particular occasion when they helped me to grasp a
point being made by an astronomer in the course of a
lecture.

A great deal of what he was saying I could not begin to understand, and there was much with which I had
to struggle to get any meaning at all out of the words.
Then, in the midst of all the weighty presentation, the

astronomer used the phrase "communication on a beam of light." Suddenly, I knew exactly what he was talking about, but I'm sure that I would not have known had it not been for the discovery that I have made this past year: that love is the link, invisible as the light and strong as the beam; that love is the creative force sweeping into and through and out of life; and that to grow in love is the only continuity of which we can be sure.

The complexities of the Universe were reduced to the simplest possible equation, and I blessed that old astronomer for his words.

Everything that had been fragmented came together for me. It was like the moment when one ceases agitating a kaleidoscope and the pattern made by the many pieces fills eyes and mind with astonishment. Love is the adventure, as it is the challenge and the test. There is nothing new about this. Others have said it; others will say it again. But each one of us has to make the discovery and say it in our own way that it may become valid in our lives.

This has been a long letter. I think it is time now for me to close and say,

God's blessing on you.

P.S. ❧ Others' Words That Have Spoken To Me

This I can now affirm
As I walk through the house of my life
In the middle years.

I never went through a door
And found what I expected.
The room was always lighter
Than had appeared from the corridor,
The furniture more simple,
More carefully brought together
For my entire need,
Than I had ever imagined.
There was often some special delight   ❧ 45
Waiting for me to receive it,
Like a dear animal returned,
Or flowers that suddenly spoke
In a language I understood.

I seldom went into a room
But there was a gathered company
Who paused to greet my entrance,

Whose hands as they moved touched mine
In delicate reassurance;
Across whose faces fell
The shadows from future suns,
Or whose eyes burned dark and kind
Like the ancient teddy bear
I took to bed as a child.

And in the abandoned room
Where no man's footsteps sounded,
Where there was no bed made,
Nor table set with food,
When the door was closed behind me
Even the dust of the floor
Silently blessed my feet,
Even the dying light
Gently caressed my brow,
While a thin flute played in my head
A song I had loved before birth.

Faithfully this has recurred.
Why should I then suppose
It will one day be otherwise?

WINIFRED RAWLINS

There is one way for thee; but one; inform
Thyself of it; pursue it; one way each
Soul hath by which the infinite in reach
Lieth before him; seek and ye shall find:
To each the way is plain; that way the wind
Points all the trees along; that way run down
Loud singing streams; that way pour on and on
A thousand headlands with their cataracts
Of toppling flowers; that way the sun enacts
His travel, and the moon and all the stars
Soar; and the tides move towards it; nothing
       bars
A man who goes the way that he should go;   🖉 47
That which comes soonest is the thing to do.
Thousand light-shadows in the rippling sand
Joy the true soul; the waves along the strand
Whiten beyond his eyes; the trees tossed back
Show him the sky; or, heaped upon his track
In a black wave, wind heaped, point onward still
His one, one way. O joy, joy, joy to fill

The day with leagues! Go thy way, all things
       say,
Thou hast thy way to go; thou hast thy day
To live; thou hast thy need of thee to make
In the hearts of others; do thy thing; yes, slake
The world's great thirst for yet another man!
And be thou sure of this; no other can
Do for thee that appointed thee of God;
Not any light shall shine upon thy road
For other eyes;

      . . .

      Thee the angel calls,
As he calls others; and thy life to thee
Is precious as the greatest's life can be
To him; so live thy life and go thy way.

               RICHARD WATSON DIXON

✿ *Life*

Life! I know not what thou art,
But know that thou and I must part;
And when, or how, or where we met
I own to me's a secret yet.

Life! we've been long together,
Through pleasant and through cloudy
        weather;
'Tis hard to part when friends are dear—
Perhaps 'twill cost a sigh, a tear;
    Then steal away, give little warning,
Choose thine own time;
Say not Good Night,—but in some brighter
      clime
Bid me Good Morning.

                      ✿ 49

ANNA LETITIA BARBAULD

✤ *Within the Nimbus*

We stood in the nimbus of a miracle, you and I,
Knowing that Love, the ONE, had heard that cry.
The only shadow was from God's own hand
Outstretched to save and gird and draw him on.
Their ways are met. Now safe within that grasp
He further goes. Our view dissolves in light.
And still we stand, most surely you and I,
In the nimbus of a rainbow, spanning our morning sky.

NORA S. UNWIN

50 ✤

🌸 *Nature*

As a fond mother, when the day is o'er,
    Leads by the hand her little child to bed,
    Half willing, half reluctant to be led,
    And leaves his broken playthings on the floor,
Still gazing at them through the open door,
    Not wholly reassured and comforted
    By promises of others in their stead,
    Which, though more splendid, may not please him
        more;
So Nature deals with us, and takes away
    Our playthings one by one, and by the hand
    Leads us to rest so gently, that we go
Scarce knowing if we wish to go or stay,   🌿 51
    Being too full of sleep to understand
    How far the unknown transcends the what we
        know.

HENRY WADSWORTH LONGFELLOW

I was alone on that road.
Clouds moved swiftly overhead,
And a light as clear as water
Lay on the horizon. It was May,
The hawthorne white with bloom,
Saint Mary's lace wincing in the wind
Beside the road. A lapwing cried,
Soaring and dipping above the field
Where rabbits huddled in circles,
Brown and bowed their small bodies.

Drenched by sudden rain that swept
Like dim curtains blowing,
I walked toward Ewelme, where
Chaucer's son lay buried,
Where in five centuries the feet of old men
Have hollowed the stone steps between
The almshouse and the church.

I walked alone, wind-buffeted
Feeling the chill fingers of rain

Touch my face, tasting the rain
On my lips, hearing the lapwing's cry,
Smelling the wet, warm earth,
Seeing the storm move toward the world's edge
And the pale sun run after it.
I walked alone in that wide country.

Yet not alone. Oh, not alone!
And I, who hold the dead do not
Return to the living, being free,
Not hovering nostalgic over old scenes,
Not bound even by old loves,
I sang aloud on the empty road,
Exulting, rich at heart, because
You walked there with me.

ELIZABETH GRAY VINING

53

🙿 *It Matters Not*

It matters not, the manner of our going;
Sooner or later comes the Master's call.
In summer's sunshine, or in winter's blowing
The message comes to all.

Perchance our last farewell we may be taking
In calm communion with a loving heart,
Or in fierce winds and sudden waves high breaking,
Our spirits may depart.

It matters not, if only we are ready;
Doing His will, accepted by His grace,
Bearing the banner of our great hope steady,
And standing in our place.

54 🙿

It matters not, the way of life's conclusion,
If by redeeming love we are possessed.
In deepest hush, or wildest storm's confusion,
The Father knoweth best.

LYDIA C. WOOD

✿ When Death Shall Come

When death shall come to summon us at last,
  Some will remember children and the sound
Of little footsteps hallowing the past,
  As driven snowflakes hallow oft the ground;
Some will remember sunlight on a fence;
  And some the breath of blossoms in the rain;
Some will glimpse stars. And all the going hence
  Of these will be a wishing to remain.
But some will think of One who said, "And I,
  If I be lifted up will draw to me
All men." And when these latter come to die,
  With faces lifted to Eternity
They shall go forth with calm, untroubled eyes,
Like children hasting to a glad surprise.   ✿ 55

HELEN FRAZEE-BOWER

✸ *Hope in Him While Thou Livest*

O Friend, hope in Him while thou livest,
    Know Him while thou livest,
For in life is thy release.
If thy bonds be not broken when thou livest,
    What hope of deliverance in death?

It is but an empty dream that the soul must
        pass into union with Him,
Because it has passed from the body.

If He is found now, He is found then:
If not, we go but to dwell in the city of Death.

If thou hast union now, thou shalt have it hereafter.

KABIR

They that love beyond the world,
cannot be separated by it.
   Death cannot kill what never dies.
   Nor can spirits ever be divided that
love and live in the same divine principle;
the root and record of their friendship.
   If absence be not death, neither is theirs.
   Death is but crossing the world, as friends
do the seas; they live in one another still.
   For they must needs be present, that
love and live in that which is omnipresent.
   In this divine glass they see face to face;
and their converse is free as well   57
as pure.
   This is the comfort of friends, that
though they may be said to die, yet their
friendship and society are in the best
sense ever present, because immortal.

                    WILLIAM PENN

🏵 *LXXXIII*

This world is not conclusion;
    A sequel stands beyond,
Invisible, as music,
    But positive, as sound.
It beckons and it baffles;
    Philosophies don't know,
And through a riddle, at the last,
    Sagacity must go.
To guess it puzzles scholars;
    To gain it, men have shown
Contempt of generations,
    And crucifixion known.

58 🏵

🏵 *LXXXV*

They say that "time assuages,"—
    Time never did assuage;

An actual suffering strengthens,
　　As sinews do, with age.

Time is a test of trouble,
　　But not a remedy.
If such it prove, it prove too
　　There was no malady.

❀ *XC*

That such have died enables us
　　The tranquiller to die;
That such have lived, certificate
　　For immortality.

EMILY DICKINSON

❧ 59

Then Almitra spoke, saying, We would ask
now of Death.

And he said:

You would know the secret of death.

But how shall you find it unless you seek it
in the heart of life?

The owl whose night-bound eyes are blind
unto the day cannot unveil the mystery of light.

If you would indeed behold the spirit of death,
open your heart wide unto the body of
life.

For life and death are one, even as the river
and the sea are one.

In the depth of your hopes and desires lies
your silent knowledge of the beyond;

And like seeds dreaming beneath the snow
your heart dreams of spring.

Trust your dreams, for in them is hidden the
gate to eternity.

Your fear of death is but the trembling of the

shepherd when he stands before the king whose
hand is to be laid upon him in honour.

Is the shepherd not joyful beneath his trembling, that he shall wear the mark of the king?

Yet is he not more mindful of his trembling?

For what is it to die but to stand naked in the
wind and to melt into the sun?

And what is it to cease breathing, but to free
the breath from its restless tides, that it may
rise and expand and seek God unencumbered?

Only when you drink from the river of silence
shall you indeed sing.

And when you have reached the mountain
top, then you shall begin to climb.

And when the earth shall claim your limbs,
then shall you truly dance.

KAHLIL GIBRAN

I remember my childhood when the sunrise, like my playfellow, would burst into my bedside with its daily surprise of morning; when the faith in the marvelous bloomed like fresh flowers in my heart every day, looking into the face of the world in simple gladness; when insects, birds and beasts, the common weeds, grass and the clouds had their fullest value of wonder; when the patter of rain at night brought dreams from the fairyland, and mother's voice in the evening gave meaning to the stars.

And then I think of death, and the rise of the curtain and the new morning and my life awakened in its fresh surprise of love.

I have got my leave. Bid me farewell, my brothers! I bow to you all and take my departure.

Here I give back the keys of my door—and I give up all claims to my house. I only ask for the last kind words from you.

We were neighbors for long, but I received more than I could give. Now the day has dawned and the lamp that lit my dark corner is out. A summons has come and I am ready for my journey. . . .

RABINDRANATH TAGORE

63

❧ *Continuation* (E. to W.)

Within my heart's circumference
    You are contained.
My inner ear records your voice;
    Your smile, retained
Will be for all my years ahead
    To know and keep.
And always mine, your love to hold,
I have no need
    To weep.

LOUISE A. NICKERSON

64 ❧

Microbiology
A LABORATORY MANUAL

TENTH EDITION

James G. Cappuccino

Natalie Sherman

PEARSON

Authorized Licensed Edition of the original UK edition, entitled *Microbiology: Pearson New International Edition: A Laboratory Manual, Tenth Edition* by Cappuccino james; Natalie sherman, published by Pearson Education Limited, © 2014 Pearson Education Limited

This Licensed Edition is published by Dorling Kindersley (India) Pvt. Ltd, Copyright © 2014 by arrangement with Pearson Education Ltd, United Kingdom.

ISBN 978-93-325-3519-0

First Impression, 2014

This edition is manufactured in India and is authorized for sale only in India, Bangladesh, Bhutan, Pakistan, Nepal, Sri Lanka and the Maldives. Circulation of this edition outside of these territories is UNAUTHORIZED.

Published by Pearson India Education Services Pvt.Ltd,CIN:U72200TN2005PTC057128.
Formerly known as TutorVista Global Pvt Ltd, licensees of Pearson Education in South Asia

Head Office: 7th Floor, knowledge Boulevard, A-8(A) Sector-62, Noida (U.P) 201309, India

Registered Office: Module G4, Ground Floor, Elnet Software City, TS -140,Block 2 & 9
Rajiv Gandhi Salai, Taramani, Chennai, Tamil Nadu 600113.,Fax: 080-30461003,
Phone: 080-30461060, www.pearson.co.in email id: companysecretary.india@pearson.com

Digitally printed in India by Repro India Ltd. in the year of 2016.

Table of Contents

Basic Laboratory Techniques for Isolation, Cultivation, and Cultural Characterization of Microorganisms

LEARNING OBJECTIVES

Once you have completed the experiments in this section, you should be familiar with

1. The types of laboratory equipment and culture media needed to develop and maintain pure cultures.
2. The types of microbial flora that live on the skin and the effect of hand washing on them.
3. The concept of aseptic technique and the procedures necessary for successful subculturing of microorganisms.
4. Streak-plate and spread-plate inoculation of microorganisms in a mixed microbial population for subsequent pure culture isolation.
5. Cultural and morphological characteristics of microorganisms grown in pure culture.

Introduction

Microorganisms are ubiquitous. They are found in soil, air, water, food, sewage, and on body surfaces. In short, every area of our environment is replete with them. The microbiologist separates these mixed populations into individual species for study. A culture containing a single unadulterated species of cells is called a **pure culture.** To isolate and study microorganisms in pure culture, the microbiologist requires basic laboratory apparatus and the application of specific techniques, as illustrated in **Figure 1.**

Media

The survival and continued growth of microorganisms depend on an adequate supply of nutrients and a favorable growth environment. For survival, most microbes must use soluble low-molecular-weight substances that are frequently derived from the enzymatic degradation of complex nutrients. A solution containing these nutrients is a **culture medium.** Basically, all culture media are liquid, semisolid, or solid. A liquid medium lacks a solidifying agent and is called a **broth medium.** A broth medium supplemented with a solidifying agent called **agar** results in a solid or semisolid medium. Agar, an extract of seaweed, is a complex carbohydrate composed mainly of galactose, and is without nutritional value. Agar serves as an excellent solidifying agent because it liquefies at 100°C and solidifies at 40°C. Because of these properties, organisms, especially pathogens, can be cultivated at temperatures of 37.5°C or slightly higher without fear of the medium liquefying. A completely solid medium requires an agar concentration of about 1.5 to 1.8%. A concentration of less than 1% agar results in a **semisolid medium.** A solid medium has the advantage that it presents a hardened surface on which microorganisms can be grown using specialized techniques for the isolation of discrete colonies. Each colony is a cluster of cells that originates from the multiplication of a single cell and

Basic Laboratory Techniques for Isolation, Cultivation, and Cultural Characterization of Microorganisms

Figure 1 Laboratory apparatus and culture techniques

represents the growth of a single species of microorganism. Such a defined and well-isolated colony is a pure culture. Also, while in the liquefied state, solid media can be placed in test tubes, which are then allowed to cool and harden in a slanted position, producing **agar slants.** These are useful for maintaining pure cultures. Similar tubes that, following preparation, are allowed to harden in the upright position are designated as **agar deep tubes.** Agar deep tubes are used primarily for the study of the gaseous requirements of microorganisms. However, they may be liquefied in a boiling

water bath and poured into Petri dishes, producing **agar plates,** which provide large surface areas for the isolation and study of microorganisms. The various forms of solid media are illustrated in **Figure 2**.

In addition to nutritional needs, the environmental factors must also be regulated, including proper pH, temperature, gaseous requirements, and osmotic pressure.

(a) Agar slants   (b) Agar deep tube   (c) Agar plate

Figure 2 Forms of solid (agar) media

Basic Laboratory Techniques for Isolation, Cultivation, and Cultural Characterization of Microorganisms

Figure 3 Sterilization techniques

Aseptic Technique

Sterility is the hallmark of successful work in the microbiology laboratory, and **sterilization** is the process of rendering a medium or material free of all forms of life. To achieve sterility, it is mandatory that you use sterile equipment and employ **aseptic techniques** when handling bacterial cultures. **Figure 3** is a brief outline of the routine techniques used in the microbiology laboratory.

Culture Tubes and Petri Dishes

Glass **test tubes** and glass or plastic **Petri dishes** are used to cultivate microorganisms. A suitable nutrient medium in the form of broth or agar may be added to the tubes, while only a solid medium is used in Petri dishes. A sterile environment is maintained in culture tubes by various types of closures. Historically, the first type, a cotton plug, was developed by Schröeder and von Dusch in the nineteenth century. Today most laboratories use sleevelike caps (Morton closures) made of metal, such as stainless steel, or heat-resistant plastics. The advantage of these closures over the cotton plug is that they are labor-saving and, most of all, slip on and off the test tubes easily.

Petri dishes provide a larger surface area for growth and cultivation. They consist of a bottom dish portion that contains the medium and a larger top portion that serves as a loose cover.

Petri dishes are manufactured in various sizes to meet different experimental requirements. For routine purposes, dishes approximately 15 cm in diameter are used. The sterile agar medium is dispensed to previously sterilized dishes from molten agar deep tubes containing 15 to 20 ml of medium, or from a molten sterile medium prepared in bulk and contained in 250-, 500-, and 1000-ml flasks, depending on the volume of medium required. When cooled to 40°C, the medium will solidify. Remember that *after inoculation, Petri dishes are incubated in an inverted position* (top down) to prevent condensation formed on the cover during solidification from dropping down onto the surface of the hardened agar. **Figure 4** illustrates some of the culture vessels used in the laboratory. Built-in ridges on tube closures and Petri dishes provide small gaps necessary for the exchange of air.

Transfer Instruments

Microorganisms must be transferred from one vessel to another or from stock cultures to various media for maintenance and study. Such a transfer is called **subculturing** and must be carried out under aseptic conditions to prevent possible contamination.

Wire loops and needles are made from inert metals such as Nichrome or platinum and are inserted into metal shafts that serve as handles. They are extremely durable instruments and are easily sterilized by incineration in the blue (hottest) portion of the Bunsen burner flame.

A. Bacteriological tube
B. Screw cap
C. Plastic closure
D. Metal closure
E. Nonabsorbent cotton

(a) Test tube rack with tubes showing various closures

(b) Petri dish

(c) DeLong shaker flask with closure

Figure 4 Culture vessels

A **pipette** is another instrument used for aseptic transfers. Pipettes are similar in function to straws; that is, they draw up liquids. They are made of glass or plastic drawn out to a tip at one end and with a mouthpiece forming the other end. They are calibrated to deliver different volumes depending on requirements. Pipettes may be sterilized in bulk inside canisters, or they may be wrapped individually in brown paper and sterilized in an autoclave or dry-heat oven.

Figure 5 illustrates these transfer instruments. The proper procedure for the use of pipettes will be demonstrated by your instructor.

⚠ **Pipetting by mouth is not permissible! Pipetting is to be performed with the aid of mechanical pipette aspirators.**

Cultivation Chambers

A prime requirement for the cultivation of microorganisms is that they be grown at their optimum temperature. An incubator is used to maintain optimum temperature during the necessary growth period. It resembles an oven and is thermostatically controlled so that temperature can be varied depending on the requirements of specific microorganisms. Most incubators use dry heat. Moisture is supplied by placing a beaker of water in the incubator during the growth period. A moist environment retards dehydration of the medium and thereby avoids misleading experimental results.

A thermostatically controlled **shaking waterbath** is another piece of apparatus used to

Basic Laboratory Techniques for Isolation, Cultivation, and Cultural Characterization of Microorganisms

(a) Transfer needle

(b) Transfer loop

(c) Blow-out pipette

(d) To-deliver pipette

(e) Micropipette

Mechanical Pipette Aspirators

(f) Plastic pump

(g) Rubber bulb

Figure 5 Transfer instruments

cultivate microorganisms. Its advantage is that it provides a rapid and uniform transfer of heat to the culture vessel, and its agitation provides increased aeration, resulting in acceleration of growth. The single disadvantage of this instrument is that it can be used only for cultivation of organisms in a broth medium.

Refrigerator

A refrigerator is used for a wide variety of purposes such as maintenance and storage of stock cultures between subculturing periods, and storage of sterile media to prevent dehydration. It is also used as a repository for thermolabile solutions, antibiotics, serums, and biochemical reagents.

Effectiveness of Hand Washing

Principle

Each day our hands come in contact with numerous objects and surfaces that are contaminated with microorganisms. These may include door handles, light switches, shopping carts, sinks, toilet seats, books, or even things like compost piles or body fluids, to name a few. The lack of adequate hand washing is a major vehicle in the transmission of microbial infection and disease.

The skin of a human being is sterile while *in utero* and first becomes colonized by a normal microbial flora at birth as it is passed through the birth canal. By the time you reach adulthood, your skin is calculated to contain 10^{12} (1,000,000,000,000), or one trillion, bacteria, most of which are found in the superficial layers of the epidermis and upper hair follicles. This normal flora of microorganisms is called the **resident flora,** the presence of which does not cause negative effects in healthy individuals. In fact, it forms a symbiotic relationship with your skin, which is vital to your health. This beneficial relationship can change in patients who are immunocompromised, or when residential flora accidently gains entrance to the host via inoculating needles, indwelling catheters, lacerations, and the like. Microorganisms that are less permanent and present for only short periods are termed **transient flora.** This latter flora can be removed with good hand washing techniques. The resident flora is more difficult to remove because they are found in the hair follicles and covered by hair, oil, and dead skin cells that obstruct their removal by simple hand washing with soap. Surgical scrubbing is the best means for removal of these organisms from the skin.

Surgical hand washing was introduced into medical practice in the mid-nineteenth century by the Hungarian physician Ignatz Semmelweis while working at an obstetric hospital in Vienna. He observed that the incidence of puerperal fever (child birth fever) was very high, with a death rate of about 20%. He further observed that medical students examining patients and assisting in deliveries came directly from cadaver (autopsy) laboratories without stopping to wash their hands. Upon his insistence, medical students and all medical personnel were required to wash their hands in a chloride of lime (bleach) solution before and after all patient contact. The incidence of death from puerperal fever dropped drastically to around 1%. Semmelweis's effort was responsible for the development of routine surgical scrubbing by surgeons, which has become essential practice for all surgical procedures in modern medicine.

From Experiment 1 of *Microbiology: A Laboratory Manual*, Tenth Edition. James G. Cappuccino, Natalie Sherman.
Copyright © 2014 by Pearson Education, Inc. All rights reserved.

AT THE BENCH

Materials

Media

4 nutrient agar plates per student pair

Equipment

Liquid antibacterial soap, 8 sterile cotton swabs, 2 test tubes of sterile saline, Bunsen burner, glass marking pencil, surgical hand brush, Quebec colony counter, stopwatch.

Procedure Lab One

1. One student will become the washer and the other student the assistant. **The washer must not wash hands before coming to the lab.**

2. The assistant will use the glass marking pencil to label the bottoms of the nutrient agar plates. The assistant will mark two plates as "Water" and two plates as "Soap" and draw a line down the middle of each plate to divide each plate in half. For the "Water" plates, label the halves as R1, R2, R3, and R4. For the "Soap" plates, label the halves as L1, L2, L3, and L4. See **Figure 1**.

3. The assistant will aseptically dip a sterile cotton swab into the first test tube of sterile saline. To do this:

   a. First light the Bunsen burner.

   b. Uncap the test tube; after removing the cap, keep the cap in your hand with the inner aspect of the cap pointed away from your palm. The cap must never be placed on the laboratory bench because doing so would compromise the aseptic procedure.

   c. Flame the neck of the tube by briefly passing it through the flame of the Bunsen burner.

   d. Remove the tube from the flame and dip the swab in the tube, soaking it with saline.

Avoid touching the sides of the tube with the swab.

The assistant will then rub the moistened cotton swab on the pad of the washer's **right** thumb.

4. The assistant will then aseptically inoculate the half of the nutrient agar plate labeled R1 by streaking the far edge of the plate several times then making a zig zag streak only on the half labeled R1. See **Figure 2**. *Caution: Do not gouge the surface of the agar plate.*

5. The assistant will turn on the tap on the lab sink, so that the washer can wash the right hand under warm running water, **without soap,** concentrating on the thumb (rubbing the thumb over the right index and middle finger) for one minute. The assistant will turn off the tap. The washer will shake off the excess water from the hand, but not blot dry. The assistant, using a new, dry (not moistened with saline) sterile cotton swab, will obtain a sample from the right thumb pad and inoculate the section of the nutrient agar plate labeled R2 in the same way that R1 was inoculated.

6. Repeat step 5 two more times, washing the thumb for 2 minutes and then 3 minutes, respectively. The assistant will use a new, dry sterile cotton swab each time, and will aseptically inoculate R3 and R4, respectively. See Table 1.

7. The assistant and washer will now move to the left hand. The assistant will aseptically dip the

Figure 2 Plate inoculation

Figure 1 Plate labeling

TABLE 1	Inoculation of Nutrient Agar Plates		
	WATER—RIGHT THUMB		**SOAP—LEFT THUMB**
R1	No wash, damp cotton swab	L1	No wash, damp cotton swab
R2	Wash 1 minute, dry cotton swab	L2	Wash with soap 1 minute, dry cotton swab
R3	Wash 2 minutes, dry cotton swab	L3	Soap and surgical brush 2 minutes, dry cotton swab
R4	Wash 3 minutes, dry cotton swab	L4	Soap and surgical brush 3 minutes, dry cotton swab

sterile cotton swab into the second test tube of sterile saline (following the process from Step 3) and will rub the moistened cotton swab over the pad of the left thumb and aseptically inoculate L1 as shown in Figure 2.

8. The assistant will turn on the tap of the lab's sink so that the washer can wet the thumb and index finger of the left hand under warm running water. The assistant will apply one or two drops of liquid soap to the thumb and index finger and the washer will wash for 1 minute by rubbing the thumb over the index finger. Rinse well. Shake off water from the hand but do not blot dry. The assistant will turn off the tap. The assistant will then use a dry, sterile cotton swab to obtain a sample from the washed thumb pad and inoculate L2.

9. Repeat step 8 two more times, not only using soap but also scrubbing the thumb with a surgical brush, for 2 minutes and then 3 minutes, respectively. The washer will obtain the surgical brush and the assistant will add saline to the brush to dampen it, and then add one or two drops of soap to the thumb and also the brush. *Caution: Place the brush bristles up on a dry paper towel between washings.* The assistant will use a new, dry sterile cotton swab each time, and will aseptically inoculate L3 and L4, respectively. Refer back to Table 1.

10. Incubate all plates in an inverted position at 37°C for 24 to 48 hours.

Procedure Lab Two

Examine and record the amount of growth found on each nutrient agar plate. Results may be determined by two methods.

1. **Macroscopically.** Visually observe the presence of growth on the surface of each agar plate in each section. Record your results in your Lab Report as 0 = no growth, $1+$ = slight growth, $2+$ = moderate growth, $3+$ = heavy growth, and $4+$ = maximum growth.

2. **Percent Growth Reduction.**

   a. Count the colonies that appear in each section of the agar plates using a Quebec colony counter. If more than 300 colonies are present, label it as "too numerous to count (TNTC)," if fewer than 30 colonies are present, label it as "too few to count (TFTC)."

   b. For sections R2, R3, R4 and L2, L3, L4, calculate the percent growth reduction from the first section, using the following equation:

   Percent reduction = [Colonies (section 1) − Colonies (section x)] ÷ Colonies (section 1)

   X = sections 2, 3, 4 for each hand

9

Observations and Results

1. Record the macroscopic observations in the chart below.

Section (Water—Right Thumb)	Time (min)	Growth (0 = none, 1+ = slight, 2+ = moderate, 3+ = heavy, 4+ = maximum)	Section (Soap—Left Thumb)	Time (min)	Growth (0 = none, 1+ = slight, 2+ = moderate, 3+ = heavy, 4+ = maximum)
R1	0		L1	0	
R2	1		L2	1	
R3	2		L3	2	
R4	3		L4	3	

2. Record the percent growth reduction in the chart below.

Section (Water—Right Thumb)	Time (min)	Number of Colonies	Percent Reduction	Section (Soap—Left Thumb)	Time (min)	Number of Colonies	Percent Reduction
R1	0		—	L1	0		—
R2	1			L2	1		
R3	2			L3	2		
R4	3			L4	3		

Review Questions

1. Compare the effectiveness of hand washing with water, with soap, and with soap and surgical scrubbing.

2. How does the presence of residential flora influence the infectious process?

3. How does hand washing affect residential versus transient flora?

4. Why do you think hand washing is necessary when medical and surgical personnel wear gloves during surgery or when examining patients?

Photo Credit

Credits are listed in order of appearance.

Photo 1: James Cappuccino

Culture Transfer Techniques

LEARNING OBJECTIVES

Once you have completed this experiment, you should be able to

1. Carry out the technique for aseptic removal and transfer of microorganisms for subculturing.
2. Correctly sterilize inoculating instruments in the flame of a Bunsen burner.
3. Correctly manipulate your fingers to re-move and replace the test tube closure.

Principle

Microorganisms are transferred from one medium to another by **subculturing.** This technique is of basic importance and is used routinely in preparing and maintaining stock cultures, as well as in microbiological test procedures.

Microorganisms are always present in the air and on laboratory surfaces, benches, and equipment. They can serve as a source of external contamination and thus interfere with experimental results unless proper aseptic techniques are used during subculturing. Described below are essential steps that you must follow for aseptic transfer of microorganisms. The complete procedure is illustrated in **Figure 1**.

1. Label the tube to be inoculated with the name of the organism and your initials.
2. Hold the stock culture tube and the tube to be inoculated in the palm of your hand, secure with your thumb, and separate the two tubes to form a V in your hand.
3. Sterilize an inoculating needle or loop by holding it in the hottest portion of the Bunsen burner flame, until the wire becomes red hot. Then, rapidly pass the upper portion of the handle through the flame. Once flamed, the loop is never put down but is held in the hand and allowed to cool for 10 to 20 seconds.

4. Uncap the tubes by grasping the first cap with your little finger and the second cap with your next finger and lifting the closure upward. *Note: Once removed, these caps must be kept in the hand that holds the sterile inoculating loop or needle; thus, the inner aspects of the caps point away from the palm of the hand.* They must never be placed on the laboratory bench because doing so would compromise the aseptic procedure.
5. After removing the closures, flame the necks and mouths of the tubes by briefly passing them through the flame two–three times rapidly. The sterile transfer instrument is further cooled by touching it to the sterile inside wall of the culture tube before removing a small sample of the inoculum.
6. Depending on the culture medium, a loop or needle is used for removal of the inoculum. Loops are commonly used to obtain a sample from a broth culture. Either instrument can be used to obtain the inoculum from an agar slant culture by carefully touching the surface of the solid medium in an area exhibiting growth so as not to gouge the agar. A straight needle is always used when transferring microorganisms to an agar deep tube from both solid and liquid cultures.
   a. For a slant-to-broth transfer, obtain inoculum from the slant and lightly shake the loop or needle in the broth culture to dislodge the microorganisms.
   b. For a broth-to-slant transfer, obtain a loopful of broth and place at the base of an agar slant medium. Lightly draw the loop over the hardened surface in a straight or zigzag line, from the base of the agar slant to the top.
   c. For a slant-to-agar deep transfer, obtain the inoculum from the agar slant. Insert a straight needle to the bottom of the tube in a straight line and rapidly withdraw along the line of insertion. This is called a stab inoculation.
7. Following inoculation, remove the instrument and reflame the necks of the tubes.

From Experiment 2 of *Microbiology: A Laboratory Manual*, Tenth Edition. James G. Cappuccino, Natalie Sherman. Copyright © 2014 by Pearson Education, Inc. All rights reserved.

Culture Transfer Techniques

PROCEDURE

1. Label the tube to be inoculated with the name of the organism and your initials.

2. Place the tubes in the palm of your hand, secure with your thumb, and separate to form a V.

3. Flame the needle or loop until the wire is red.

4. With the sterile loop or needle in hand, uncap the tubes.

5. Flame the necks of the tubes by rapidly passing them through the flame once.

6. **Slant-to-broth transfer:** Obtain inoculum from slant and dislodge inoculum in the broth with a slight agitation.

Broth-to-slant transfer: Obtain a loopful of broth and place at base of slant. Withdraw the loop in a zigzag motion.

Slant-to-agar deep transfer: Obtain inoculum from slant. Insert the needle to the bottom of the tube and withdraw along the line of insertion.

7. Flame the necks of the tubes by rapidly passing them through the flame once.

8. Recap the tubes.

9. Reflame the loop or needle.

Figure 1 Subculturing procedure

14

8. Replace the caps on the same tubes from which they were removed.
9. Reflame the loop or needle to destroy any remaining organisms.

In this experiment you will master the manipulations required for aseptic transfer of microorganisms in broth-to-slant, slant-to-broth, and slant-to-agar deep transfers.

CLINICAL APPLICATION

Aseptic Inoculation and Transfer

It's mandatory for those working in a microbiology laboratory to learn and perfect the skill of inoculating bacterial specimens on agar plates, in liquid broth, or in semisolid medium, and subsequently be able to subculture the organism from one medium to another. A sterile inoculating needle or loop is the basic instrument of transfer. It is important that you keep in mind that transferring bacterial cultures requires aseptic or sterile techniques at all times, especially if you are working with pathogens. In short, do not contaminate what you are working with and do not contaminate yourself.

AT THE BENCH

Materials
Cultures

24-hour nutrient broth and nutrient agar slant cultures of *Serratia marcescens*.

Media

Per designated student group: one nutrient broth, one nutrient agar slant, and one nutrient agar deep tube.

Equipment

Bunsen burner, inoculating loop and needle, and glassware marking pencil.

Procedure Lab One

1. Label all tubes of sterile media.
2. Following the procedure outlined and illustrated previously (Figure 1), perform the following transfers:
   a. *S. marcescens* broth culture to a nutrient agar slant, nutrient agar deep tube, and nutrient broth.
   b. *S. marcescens* agar slant culture to a nutrient broth, nutrient agar slant, and nutrient agar deep tube.
3. Incubate all cultures at 25°C for 24 to 48 hours.

Procedure Lab Two

1. Examine all cultures for the appearance of growth, which is indicated by turbidity in the broth culture and the appearance of an orange-red growth on the surface of the slant and along the line of inoculation in the agar deep tube.
2. Record your observations in the chart provided in the Lab Report.

Observations and Results

	Nutrient Broth	Nutrient Agar Slant	Nutrient Agar Deep
Growth (+) or (−)	+	+	+
Orange-red pigmentation (+) or (−)	+	+	+
Draw the distribution of growth.			

Review Questions

1. Explain why the following steps are essential during subculturing:

    a. Flaming the inoculating instrument *prior to and after* each inoculation.

    b. Holding the test tube caps in the hand as illustrated in Figure 1.

c. Cooling the inoculating instrument prior to obtaining the inoculum.

d. Flaming the neck of the tubes immediately after uncapping and before recapping.

2. Describe the purposes of the subculturing procedure.

3. Explain why a straight inoculating needle is used to inoculate an agar deep tube.

4. There is a lack of orange-red pigmentation in some of the growth on your agar slant labeled *S. marcescens*. Does this necessarily indicate the presence of a contaminant? Explain.

5. Upon observation of the nutrient agar slant culture, you strongly suspect that the culture is contaminated. Outline the method you would follow to ascertain whether your suspicion is justified.

Techniques for Isolation of Pure Cultures

In nature, microbial populations do not segregate themselves by species but exist with a mixture of many other cell types. In the laboratory, these populations can be separated into **pure cultures.** These cultures contain only one type of organism and are suitable for the study of their cultural, morphological, and biochemical properties.

In this experiment, you will first use one of the techniques designed to produce discrete colonies. Colonies are individual, macroscopically visible masses of microbial growth on a solid medium surface, each representing the multiplication of a single organism. Once you have obtained these discrete colonies, you will make an aseptic transfer onto nutrient agar slants for the isolation of pure cultures.

PART A   Isolation of Discrete Colonies from a Mixed Culture

LEARNING OBJECTIVE

Once you have completed this experiment, you should be able to

1. Perform the streak-plate and/or the spread-plate inoculation procedure to separate the cells of a mixed culture so that discrete colonies can be isolated.

Principle

The techniques commonly used for isolation of discrete colonies initially require that the number of organisms in the inoculum be reduced. The resulting diminution of the population size ensures that, following inoculation, individual cells will be sufficiently far apart on the surface of the agar medium to separate the different species. The following are techniques that can be used to accomplish this necessary dilution:

1. The **streak-plate** method is a rapid qualitative isolation method. It is essentially a dilution technique that involves spreading a loopful of culture over the surface of an agar plate. Although many types of procedures are performed, the four-way, or quadrant, streak is described. Refer to **Figure 1**, which schematically illustrates this technique.

   a. Place a loopful of culture on the agar surface in Area 1. Flame the loop, cool it by touching an unused part of the agar surface close to the periphery of the plate, and then drag it rapidly several times across the surface of Area 1.

   b. Reflame and cool the loop, and turn the Petri dish 90°. Then touch the loop to a corner of the culture in Area 1 and drag it several times across the agar in Area 2. The loop should never enter Area 1 again.

Figure 1 **Four-way streak-plate technique**

From Experiment 3 of *Microbiology: A Laboratory Manual*, Tenth Edition. James G. Cappuccino, Natalie Sherman. Copyright © 2014 by Pearson Education, Inc. All rights reserved.

Figure 2 **Four-way streak-plate inoculation with** *Serratia marcescens*

Figure 3 **Petri dish turntable**

c. Reflame and cool the loop and again turn the dish 90°. Streak Area 3 in the same manner as Area 2.

d. Without reflaming the loop, again turn the dish 90° and then drag the culture from a corner of Area 3 across Area 4, using a wider streak. Don't let the loop touch any of the previously streaked areas. The flaming of the loop at the points indicated is to dilute the culture so that fewer organisms are streaked in each area, resulting in the final desired separation. A photograph of a streak-plate inoculation is shown in **Figure 2**.

2. The **spread-plate** technique requires that a previously diluted mixture of microorganisms be used. During inoculation, the cells are spread over the surface of a solid agar medium with a sterile, L-shaped bent glass rod while the Petri dish is spun on a "lazy Susan" turntable (**Figure 3**). The step-by-step procedure for this technique is as follows:

a. Place the bent glass rod into a beaker and add a sufficient amount of 95% ethyl alcohol to cover the lower, bent portion.

b. Place an appropriately labeled nutrient agar plate on the turntable. With a sterile pipette, place one drop of sterile water on the center of the plate, followed by a sterile loopful of *Micrococcus luteus*. Mix gently with the loop and replace the cover.

c. Remove the glass rod from the beaker, and pass it through the Bunsen burner flame

with the bent portion of the rod pointing downward to prevent the burning alcohol from running down your arm. Allow the alcohol to burn off the rod completely. Cool the rod for 10 to 15 seconds.

d. Remove the Petri dish cover and spin the turntable.

e. While the turntable is spinning, lightly touch the sterile bent rod to the surface of the agar and move it back and forth. This will spread the culture over the agar surface.

f. When the turntable comes to a stop, replace the cover. Immerse the rod in alcohol and reflame.

g. In the absence of a turntable, turn the Petri dish manually and spread the culture with the sterile bent glass rod.

3. The **pour-plate** technique requires a serial dilution of the mixed culture by means of a loop or pipette. The diluted inoculum is then added to a molten agar medium in a Petri dish, mixed, and allowed to solidify.

AT THE BENCH

Materials

Cultures

24- to 48-hour nutrient broth cultures of a mixture of one part *Serratia marcescens* and three parts *Micrococcus luteus* and a mixture of one part *Escherichia coli* and ten parts *Micrococcus luteus*. For the spread-plate procedure, adjust the cultures to an absorbance (A) of 0.1 at 600 nanometers (nm).

Sources of mixed cultures from the environment could include cultures from a table top, bathroom sink, water fountain, or inside of an incubator. Each student should obtain a mixed culture from one of the environmental sources listed above.

Media

Three Trypticase™ soy agar plates per designated student group for each inoculation technique to be performed.

Equipment

Bunsen burner, inoculating loop, turntable, 95% ethyl alcohol, 500-ml beaker, L-shaped bent glass rod, glassware marking pencil, culture tubes containing 1 ml of sterile water, test tube rack, and sterile cotton swabs.

Procedure Lab One

1. Following the procedures previously described, prepare a spread-plate and/or streak-plate inoculation of each test culture on an appropriately labeled plate.

2. Prepare an environmental mixed culture.

   a. Dampen a sterile cotton swab with sterile water. Wring out the excess water by pressing the wet swab against the walls of the tube.

   b. With the moistened cotton swab, obtain your mixed-culture specimen from one of the selected environmental sources listed in the section on cultures.

   c. Place the contaminated swab back into the tube of sterile water. Mix gently and let stand for 5 minutes.

   d. Perform spread-plate and/or streak-plate inoculation on an appropriately labeled plate.

3. Incubate all plates in an inverted position for 48 to 72 hours at 25°C.

Procedure Lab Two

1. Examine all agar plate cultures to identify the distribution of colonies. In the charts provided in Part A of the Lab Report, complete the following:

   a. Draw the distribution of colonies appearing on each of the agar plate cultures.

   b. On each of the agar plate cultures, select two discrete colonies that differ in appearance. Using Figure 1 as a reference, describe each colony as to its

   Form: Circular, irregular, or spreading.

   Elevation: Flat, slightly raised, or markedly raised.

   Pigmentation.

   Size: Pinpoint, small, medium, or large.

2. Retain the mixed-culture plates to perform Part B of this experiment.

PART B Isolation of Pure Cultures from a Spread-Plate or Streak-Plate Preparation

LEARNING OBJECTIVE

Once you have completed this experiment, you should be able to

1. Prepare a stock culture of an organism using isolates from mixed cultures prepared on an agar streak plate and/or spread plate.

Principle

Once discrete, well-separated colonies develop on the surface of a nutrient agar plate culture, each may be picked up with a sterile needle and transferred to separate nutrient agar slants. Each of these new slant cultures represents the growth of a single bacterial species and is designated as a **pure** or **stock culture.**

CLINICAL APPLICATION

Transferring a Colony of Bacteria Daughter Cells

For identification of a bacterial pathogen, a discrete bacterial colony must be transferred from a streak or spread plate to the new testing media. This new culture will consist of daughter cells that are genetic and metabolic clones of the original bacterial cells that were transferred to the plate. This will allow for identification of the unknown bacterial species through its biochemical and molecular characteristics.

AT THE BENCH

Materials
Cultures

Mixed-culture, nutrient agar streak-plate and/or spread-plate preparations of *S. marcescens* and *M. luteus*, *M. luteus* and *E. coli*, and the environmental specimen plate from Part A.

Media

Four Trypticase soy agar slants per designated student group.

Equipment

Bunsen burner, inoculating needle, and glassware marking pencil.

Procedure Lab One

1. Aseptically transfer, from visibly discrete colonies, the yellow *M. luteus*, the white *E. coli*, the red *S. marcescens*, and a discrete colony from the environmental agar plate specimen to the appropriately labeled agar slants as shown in **Figure 4**.
2. Incubate all slants at 37°C for 18 to 24 hours.

Procedure Lab Two

1. In the chart provided in Part B of the Lab Report, complete the following:
   a. Draw and indicate the type of growth of each pure-culture isolate.
   b. Observe the color of the growth and record its pigmentation.
   c. Indicate the name of the isolated organisms.

PROCEDURE

1. Flame the straight needle until the entire wire is red.

2. After isolating a discrete colony on the agar streak plate, touch the straight needle to the surface of the selected colony.

3. Uncap the agar slant and pass the neck of the tube rapidly over the Bunsen burner flame.

4. Inoculate the slant by drawing the needle upward in a zigzag motion along the surface of the agar. Do not dig into the agar.

5. Flame the neck of the tube and recap.

6. Flame the inoculating needle.

Figure 4 Procedure for the preparation of a pure culture

Observations and Results

PART A: Isolation of Discrete Colonies from a Mixed Culture

	SPREAD-PLATE TECHNIQUE			
	S. marcescens and *M. luteus*		*M. luteus* and *E. coli*	
Draw the colonies that appear on each agar plate.				
Colony description:	Isolate 1	Isolate 2	Isolate 1	Isolate 2
Form	_____	_____	_____	_____
Elevation	_____	_____	_____	_____
Pigmentation	_____	_____	_____	_____
Size	_____	_____	_____	_____

Techniques for Isolation of Pure Cultures

	STREAK-PLATE TECHNIQUE			
	S. marcescens and *M. luteus*		*M. luteus* and *E. coli*	
Draw the colonies that appear on each agar plate.				
Colony description:	Isolate 1	Isolate 2	Isolate 1	Isolate 2
Form	_____	_____	_____	_____
Elevation	_____	_____	_____	_____
Pigmentation	_____	_____	_____	_____
Size	_____	_____	_____	_____

	ENVIRONMENTAL SPECIMEN	
	Spread-Plate Technique	Streak-Plate Technique
Draw the colonies that appear on each agar plate.		
Colony description:		
Form	_____	_____
Elevation	_____	_____
Pigmentation	_____	_____
Size	_____	_____

PART B: Isolation of Pure Cultures from a Spread-Plate or Streak-Plate Preparation

Draw the distribution of growth on the slant surface.				
Type of growth	————	————	————	————
Pigmentation	————	————	————	————
Name of organism	————	————	————	————

Review Questions

1. Can a pure culture be prepared from a mixed-broth or a mixed-agar-slant culture? Explain.

2. Observation of a streak-plate culture shows more growth in Quadrant 4 than in Quadrant 3. Account for this observation.

3. Why is a needle used to isolate individual colonies from a spread plate or streak plate?

4. How can you determine if the colony that you chose to isolate is a pure culture?

Photo Credit

Credits are listed in order of appearance.

Photo 1:   James Cappuccino

Cultural Characteristics of Microorganisms

Once you have completed this experiment, you should be able to

1. Determine the cultural characteristics of microorganisms as an aid in identifying and classifying organisms into taxonomic groups.

Principle

When grown on a variety of media, microorganisms will exhibit differences in the macroscopic appearance of their growth. These differences, called **cultural characteristics,** are used as a basis for separating microorganisms into taxonomic groups. The cultural characteristics for all known microorganisms are contained in *Bergey's Manual of Systematic Bacteriology.* They are determined by culturing the organisms on nutrient agar slants and plates, in nutrient broth, and in nutrient gelatin. The patterns of growth to be considered in each of these media are described below, and some are illustrated in **Figure 1**.

Nutrient Agar Slants

These have a single straight line of inoculation on the surface and are evaluated in the following manner:

1. **Abundance of growth:** The amount of growth is designated as none, slight, moderate, or large.

2. **Pigmentation:** Chromogenic microorganisms may produce intracellular pigments that are responsible for the coloration of the organisms as seen in surface colonies. Other organisms produce extracellular soluble pigments that are excreted into the medium and that also produce a color. Most organisms, however, are nonchromogenic and will appear white to gray.

3. **Optical characteristics:** Optical characteristics may be evaluated on the basis of the amount of light transmitted through the growth. These characteristics are described as **opaque** (no light transmission), **translucent** (partial transmission), or **transparent** (full transmission).

4. **Form:** The appearance of the single-line streak of growth on the agar surface is designated as
   a. **Filiform:** Continuous, threadlike growth with smooth edges.
   b. **Echinulate:** Continuous, threadlike growth with irregular edges.
   c. **Beaded:** Nonconfluent to semiconfluent colonies.
   d. **Effuse:** Thin, spreading growth.
   e. **Arborescent:** Treelike growth.
   f. **Rhizoid:** Rootlike growth.

5. **Consistency:**
   a. **Dry:** Free from moisture.
   b. **Buttery:** Moist and shiny.
   c. **Mucoid:** Slimy and glistening.

Nutrient Agar Plates

These demonstrate well-isolated colonies and are evaluated in the following manner:

1. **Size:** Pinpoint, small, moderate, or large.

2. **Pigmentation:** Color of colony.

3. **Form:** The shape of the colony is described as follows:
   a. **Circular:** Unbroken, peripheral edge.
   b. **Irregular:** Indented, peripheral edge.
   c. **Rhizoid:** Rootlike, spreading growth.

4. **Margin:** The appearance of the outer edge of the colony is described as follows:
   a. **Entire:** Sharply defined, even.
   b. **Lobate:** Marked indentations.
   c. **Undulate:** Wavy indentations.

From Experiment 4 of *Microbiology: A Laboratory Manual,* Tenth Edition. James G. Cappuccino, Natalie Sherman.

Cultural Characteristics of Microorganisms

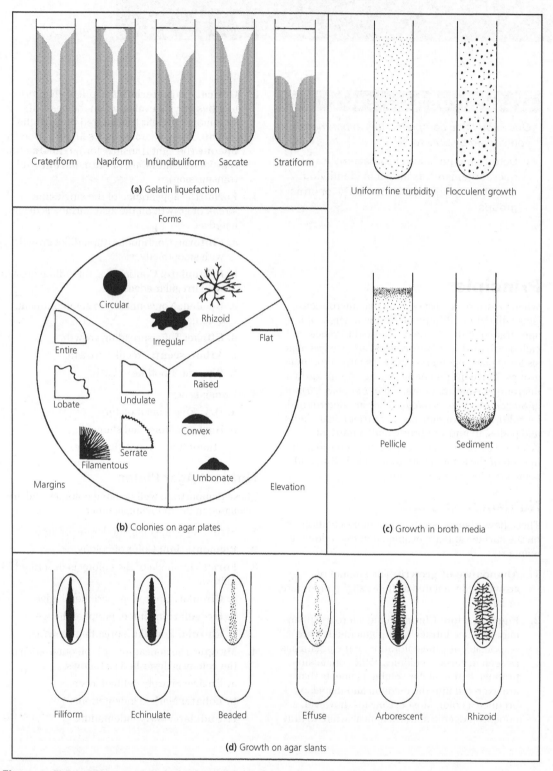

(a) Gelatin liquefaction

Crateriform   Napiform   Infundibuliform   Saccate   Stratiform

Uniform fine turbidity   Flocculent growth

Forms

Circular

Rhizoid

Irregular

Flat

Entire

Raised

Lobate   Undulate

Convex

Filamentous   Serrate

Umbonate

Margins

Elevation

(b) Colonies on agar plates

Pellicle   Sediment

(c) Growth in broth media

Filiform   Echinulate   Beaded   Effuse   Arborescent   Rhizoid

(d) Growth on agar slants

Figure 1   Cultural characteristics of bacteria

d. Serrate: Toothlike appearance.

e. Filamentous: Threadlike, spreading edge.

5. **Elevation:** The degree to which colony growth is raised on the agar surface is described as follows:

   a. Flat: Elevation not discernible.

   b. Raised: Slightly elevated.

   c. Convex: Dome-shaped elevation.

   d. Umbonate: Raised, with elevated convex central region.

Nutrient Broth Cultures

These are evaluated as to the distribution and appearance of the growth as follows:

1. **Uniform fine turbidity:** Finely dispersed growth throughout.
2. **Flocculent:** Flaky aggregates dispersed throughout.
3. **Pellicle:** Thick, padlike growth on surface.
4. **Sediment:** Concentration of growth at the bottom of broth culture may be granular, flaky, or flocculant.

Nutrient Gelatin

This solid medium may be liquefied by the enzymatic action of gelatinase. Liquefaction occurs in a variety of patterns:

1. **Crateriform:** Liquefied surface area is saucer-shaped.
2. **Napiform:** Bulbous-shaped liquefaction at surface.
3. **Infundibuliform:** Funnel-shaped.
4. **Saccate:** Elongated, tubular.
5. **Stratiform:** Complete liquefaction of the upper half of the medium.

CLINICAL APPLICATION

Examining Colony Growth Characteristics to Aid Identification

Bacterial species each have a characteristic pattern of colony growth in a liquid culture or on a solid medium. While not truly a diagnostic tool, recognition of these patterns of characteristics will aid in a clinical lab setting by helping to minimize the list of potential bacterial species to test for.

AT THE BENCH

Materials

Cultures

24-hour nutrient broth cultures of *Pseudomonas aeruginosa, Bacillus cereus, Micrococcus luteus,* and *Escherichia coli.* 72- to 96-hour Trypticase soy broth culture of *Mycobacterium smegmatis.*

Media

Per designated student group: five each of nutrient agar slants, nutrient agar plates, nutrient broth tubes, and nutrient gelatin tubes.

Equipment

Bunsen burner, inoculating loop and needle, and glassware marking pencil.

Procedure Lab One

1. Using aseptic technique, inoculate each of the appropriately labeled media listed below in the following manner:

   a. Nutrient agar slants: With a sterile needle, make a single-line streak of each of the cultures provided, starting at the butt and drawing the needle up the center of the slanted agar surface.

   b. Nutrient agar plates: With a sterile loop, prepare a streak-plate inoculation of each of the cultures for the isolation of discrete colonies.

   c. Nutrient broth cultures: Using a sterile loop, inoculate each organism into a tube of nutrient broth. Shake the loop a few times to dislodge the inoculum.

   d. Nutrient gelatin: Using a sterile needle, prepare a stab inoculation of each of the cultures provided.

2. Incubate all cultures at 37°C for 24 to 48 hours.

Procedure Lab Two

1. Before beginning observation of all the cultures, place the gelatin cultures in a refrigerator for 30 minutes or in a beaker of crushed ice for a few minutes. The gelatin culture will be the last to be observed.

2. Refer to Figure 1 and the descriptions presented in the introductory section of this experiment while making the following observations:

   a. Nutrient agar slants: Observe each of the nutrient agar slant cultures for the amount, pigmentation, form, and consistency of the growth. Record your observations in the chart provided in the Lab Report.

   b. Nutrient agar plates: Observe a single, well-isolated colony on each of the nutrient agar plate cultures and identify its size, elevation, margin, form, and pigmentation.

   Record your observations in the chart provided in the Lab Report.

   c. Nutrient broth cultures: Observe each of the nutrient broth cultures for the appearance of growth (flocculation, turbidity, sediment, or pellicle). Record your observations in the chart provided in the Lab Report.

   d. Nutrient gelatin: Remove gelatin cultures from the refrigerator or beaker of crushed ice, and observe whether liquefaction of the medium has developed and whether the organism has produced gelatinase. Record your observations in the chart provided in the Lab Report.

Observations and Results

Nutrient Agar Slants

	NUTRIENT AGAR SLANT CULTURES				
	M. luteus	*P. aeruginosa*	*M. smegmatis*	*E. coli*	*B. cereus*
Draw the distribution of growth on the slant surface.					
Amount of growth Pigmentation Form Consistency	yellow	blue green		white	

Nutrient Agar Plates

	NUTRIENT AGAR PLATES				
	M. luteus	*P. aeruginosa*	*M. smegmatis*	*E. coli*	*B. cereus*
Draw distribution of colonies.					
Size Elevation Margin Form Pigmentation	yellow				

Cultural Characteristics of Microorganisms

Nutrient Broth Cultures

	NUTRIENT BROTH CULTURES				
	M. luteus	*P. aeruginosa*	*M. smegmatis*	*E. coli*	*B. cereus*
Draw the distribution of growth.					
Appearance of growth	+	+		+	+

Nutrient Gelatin

	NUTRIENT GELATIN CULTURES				
	M. luteus	*P. aeruginosa*	*M. smegmatis*	*E. coli*	*B. cereus*
Draw liquefaction patterns.					
Liquefaction (+) or (−)					
Type of liquefaction					

Photo Credits

Credits are listed in order of appearance.
Photo 1: Elnur Shutterstock
Photo 2: Shutterstock
Photo 3: James Cappuccino
Photo 4: James Cappuccino

Microscopy

Introduction

Microbiology, the branch of science that has so vastly extended and expanded our knowledge of the living world, owes its existence to Antoni van Leeuwenhoek. In 1673, with the aid of a crude microscope consisting of a biconcave lens enclosed in two metal plates, Leeuwenhoek introduced the world to the existence of microbial forms of life. Over the years, microscopes have evolved from the simple, single-lens instrument of Leeuwenhoek, with a magnification of 300×, to the present-day electron microscopes capable of magnifications greater than 250,000×.

Microscopes are designated as either light microscopes or electron microscopes. The former use visible light or ultraviolet rays to illuminate specimens. They include brightfield, darkfield, phase-contrast, and fluorescent instruments. Fluorescent microscopes use ultraviolet radiations whose wavelengths are shorter than those of visible light and are not directly perceptible to the human eye. Electron microscopes use electron beams (instead of light rays) and magnets (instead of lenses) to observe submicroscopic particles.

Essential Features of Various Microscopes

Brightfield Microscope This instrument contains two-lens systems for magnifying specimens: the ocular lens in the eyepiece and the objective lens located in the nosepiece. The specimen is illuminated by a beam of tungsten light focused on it by a substage lens called a condenser; the result is a specimen that appears dark against a bright background. A major limitation of this system is the absence of contrast between the specimen and the surrounding medium, which makes it difficult to observe living cells. Therefore, most brightfield observations are performed on nonviable, stained preparations.

Darkfield Microscope This is similar to the ordinary light microscope; however, the condenser system is modified so that the specimen is not illuminated directly. The condenser directs the light obliquely so that the light is deflected or scattered from the specimen, which then appears bright against a dark background. Living specimens may be observed more readily with darkfield than with brightfield microscopy.

Phase-Contrast Microscope Observation of microorganisms in an unstained state is possible with this microscope. Its optics include special objectives and a condenser that make visible cellular components that differ only slightly in their refractive indexes. As light is transmitted through a specimen with a refractive index different from that of the surrounding medium, a portion of the light is refracted (bent) due to slight variations in density and thickness of the cellular components. The special optics convert the difference between transmitted light and refracted rays, resulting in a significant variation in the intensity of light and thereby producing a discernible image of the structure under study. The image appears dark against a light background.

Fluorescent Microscope This microscope is used most frequently to visualize specimens that are chemically tagged with a fluorescent dye. The source of illumination is an ultraviolet (UV) light obtained from a high-pressure mercury lamp or hydrogen quartz lamp. The ocular lens is fitted with a filter that permits the longer ultraviolet wavelengths to pass, while the shorter wavelengths are blocked or eliminated. Ultraviolet radiations are absorbed by the fluorescent label, and the energy is re-emitted in the form of a different wavelength in the visible light range. The fluorescent dyes absorb at wavelengths between 230 and 350 nanometers (nm) and emit orange, yellow, or greenish light. This microscope is used primarily for the detection of antigen-antibody reactions. Antibodies are conjugated with a fluorescent dye that becomes excited in the presence of ultraviolet light, and the fluorescent portion of the dye becomes visible against a black background.

Electron Microscope This instrument provides a revolutionary method of microscopy, with magnifications up to 1 million×. This permits visualization of submicroscopic cellular particles as well as viral agents. In the electron microscope, the specimen is illuminated by a beam of electrons rather than light, and the focusing is carried out by electromagnets instead of a set of optics. These components are sealed in a tube in which a complete vacuum is established. Transmission electron microscopes require specimens that are prepared as thin filaments, fixed and dehydrated for the electron beam to pass freely through them. As the electrons pass through the specimen, images are formed by directing the electrons onto photographic film, thus making internal cellular structures visible. Scanning electron microscopes are used for visualizing surface characteristics rather than intracellular structures. A narrow beam of electrons scans back and forth, producing a three-dimensional image as the electrons are reflected off the specimen's surface.

While scientists have a variety of optical instruments with which to perform routine laboratory procedures and sophisticated research, the compound brightfield microscope is the "workhorse" and is commonly found in all biological laboratories. Although you should be familiar with the basic principles of microscopy, you probably have not been exposed to this diverse array of complex and expensive equipment. Therefore, only the compound brightfield microscope will be discussed in depth and used to examine specimens.

Microscopic Examination of Stained Cell Preparations

Principle

Microbiology is a science that studies living organisms that are too small to be seen with the naked eye. Needless to say, such a study must involve the use of a good compound microscope. Although there are many types and variations, they all fundamentally consist of a two-lens system, a variable but controllable light source, and mechanical adjustable parts for determining focal length between the lenses and specimen **(Figure 1)**.

Components of the Microscope

Stage A fixed platform with an opening in the center allows the passage of light from an illuminating source below to the lens system above the stage. This platform provides a surface for the placement of a slide with its specimen over the central opening. In addition to the fixed stage, most microscopes have a **mechanical stage** that can be moved vertically or horizontally by means of adjustment controls. Less sophisticated microscopes have clips on the fixed stage, and the slide must be positioned manually over the central opening.

Illumination The light source is positioned in the base of the instrument. Some microscopes are equipped with a built-in light source to provide direct illumination. Others are provided with a reversible mirror that has one side flat and the other concave. An external light source, such as a lamp, is placed in front of the mirror to direct the light upward into the lens system. The flat side of the mirror is used for artificial light, and the concave side for sunlight.

Abbé Condenser This component is found directly under the stage and contains two sets of lenses that collect and concentrate light as it passes upward from the light source into the lens systems. The condenser is equipped with an **iris diaphragm,** a shutter controlled by a lever that is used to regulate the amount of light entering the lens system.

Body Tube Above the stage and attached to the arm of the microscope is the body tube. This structure houses the lens system that magnifies the specimen. The upper end of the tube contains the **ocular** or **eyepiece** lens. The lower portion consists of a movable **nosepiece** containing the **objective lenses.** Rotation of the nosepiece positions objectives above the stage opening. The body tube may be raised or lowered with the aid of **coarse-adjustment** and **fine-adjustment knobs** that are located above or below the stage, depending on the type and make of the instrument.

Theoretical Principles of Microscopy

To use the microscope efficiently and with minimal frustration, you should understand the basic principles of microscopy: magnification, resolution, numerical aperture, illumination, and focusing.

Magnification Enlargement, or magnification, of a specimen is the function of a two-lens system; the **ocular lens** is found in the eyepiece, and the **objective lens** is situated in a

Head

Body tube

Arm

Mechanical stage

Course-adjustment knob

Fine-adjustment knob

Condenser adjustment knob

Base

Ocular (eyepiece) lenses

Nosepiece

Objective lenses

Stage

Condenser

Diaphragm

Substage light

Power switch

Figure 1 A compound microscope

revolving nosepiece. These lenses are separated by the **body tube.** The objective lens is nearer the specimen and magnifies it, producing the **real image** that is projected up into the focal plane and then magnified by the ocular lens to produce the final image.

The most commonly used microscopes are equipped with a revolving nosepiece containing four objective lenses, each possessing a different degree of magnification. When these are combined with the magnification of the ocular lens, the total or overall linear magnification of the specimen is obtained. This is shown in Table 1.

Resolving Power or Resolution Although magnification is important, you must be aware that unlimited enlargement is not possible by merely increasing the magnifying power of the lenses or by using additional lenses, because lenses are limited by a property called **resolving power.** By definition, resolving power is how far

apart two adjacent objects must be before a given lens shows them as discrete entities. When a lens cannot discriminate, that is, when the two objects appear as one, it has lost resolution. Increased magnification will not rectify the loss and will, in fact, blur the object. The resolving power of a lens is dependent on the wavelength of light used and the **numerical aperture,** which is a characteristic of each lens and imprinted on each objective. The numerical aperture is defined as a function of the diameter of the objective lens in relation to its focal length. It is doubled by use of the substage condenser, which illuminates the object with rays of light that pass through the specimen obliquely as well as directly. Thus, resolving power is expressed mathematically as follows:

$$\text{resolving power} = \frac{\text{wavelength of light}}{2 \times \text{numerical aperture}}$$

TABLE 1	Overall Linear Magnification	
MAGNIFICATION		**TOTAL MAGNIFICATION**
OBJECTIVE LENSES	**OCULAR LENS**	**OBJECTIVE MULTIPLIED BY OCULAR**
Scanning 4×	10×	40×
Low-power 10×	10×	100×
High-power 40×	10×	400×
Oil-immersion 100×	10×	1000×

Based on this formula, the shorter the wavelength, the greater the resolving power of the lens. Thus, for the same numerical aperture, short wavelengths of the electromagnetic spectrum are better suited for higher resolution than are longer wavelengths.

However, as with magnification, resolving power also has limits. You might rationalize that merely decreasing the wavelength will automatically increase the resolving power of a lens. Such is not the case, because the visible portion of the electromagnetic spectrum is very narrow and borders on the very short wavelengths found in the ultraviolet portion of the spectrum.

The relationship between wavelength and numerical aperture is valid only for increased resolving power when light rays are parallel. Therefore, the resolving power is also dependent on another factor, the **refractive index.** This is the bending power of light passing through air from the glass slide to the objective lens. The refractive index of air is lower than that of glass; as light rays pass from the glass slide into the air, they are bent or refracted so that they do not pass into the objective lens. This would cause a loss of light, which would reduce the numerical aperture and diminish the resolving power of the objective lens. Loss of refracted light can be compensated for by interposing mineral oil, which has the same refractive index as glass, between the slide and the objective lens. In this way, decreased light refraction occurs and more light rays enter directly into the objective lens, producing a vivid image with high resolution **(Figure 2).**

Illumination Effective illumination is required for efficient magnification and resolving power. Since the intensity of daylight is an uncontrolled variable, artificial light from a tungsten lamp is the most commonly used light source in microscopy. The light is passed through the condenser located beneath the stage. The condenser contains

two lenses that are necessary to produce a maximum numerical aperture. The height of the condenser can be adjusted with the **condenser knob.** Always keep the condenser close to the stage, especially when using the oil-immersion objective.

Between the light source and the condenser is the iris diaphragm, which can be opened and closed by means of a lever, thereby regulating the amount of light entering the condenser. Excessive illumination may actually obscure the specimen because of lack of contrast. The amount of light entering the microscope differs with each objective lens used. A rule of thumb is that *as the magnification of the lens increases,*

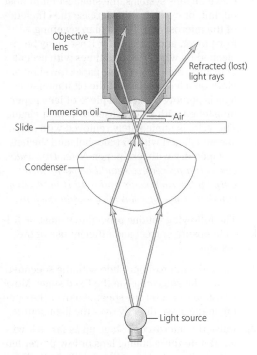

Figure 2 Refractive index in air and in mineral oil

39

the distance between the objective lens and slide, called working distance, decreases, whereas the numerical aperture of the objective lens increases (**Figure 3**).

Use and Care of the Microscope

You will be responsible for the proper care and use of microscopes. Since microscopes are expensive, you must observe the following regulations and procedures.

The instruments are housed in special cabinets and must be moved by users to their laboratory benches. The correct and only acceptable way to do this is to grip the microscope arm firmly with the right hand and the base with the left hand, and lift the instrument from the cabinet shelf. Carry it close to the body and gently place it on the laboratory bench. This will prevent collision with furniture or coworkers and will protect the instrument against damage.

Once the microscope is placed on the laboratory bench, observe the following rules:

1. Remove all unnecessary materials (such as books, papers, purses, and hats) from the laboratory bench.

2. Uncoil the microscope's electric cord and plug it into an electrical outlet.

3. Clean all lens systems; the smallest bit of dust, oil, lint, or eyelash will decrease the efficiency of the microscope. The ocular, scanning, low-power, and high-power lenses may be cleaned by wiping several times with acceptable lens tissue. Never use paper toweling or cloth on a lens surface. If the oil-immersion lens is gummy or tacky, a piece of lens paper moistened with xylol is used to wipe it clean. The xylol is immediately removed with a tissue moistened with 95% alcohol, and the lens is wiped dry with lens paper. *Note: This xylol cleansing procedure should be performed only by the instructor and only if necessary; consistent use of xylol may loosen the lens.*

The following routine procedures must be followed to ensure correct and efficient use of the microscope.

1. Place the microscope slide with the specimen within the stage clips on the fixed stage. Move the slide to center the specimen over the opening in the stage directly over the light source.

2. Raise the microscope stage up as far as it will go. Rotate the scanning lens or low-power lens into position. Lower the body tube with the coarse-adjustment knob to its lowest position. *Note: Never lower the body tube while looking through the ocular lens.*

3. While looking through the ocular lens, use the fine-adjustment knob, rotating it back and forth slightly, to bring the specimen into sharp focus.

4. Adjust the substage condenser to achieve optimal focus.

5. Routinely adjust the light source by means of the light-source transformer setting, and/or the iris diaphragm, for optimum illumination for each new slide and for each change in magnification.

6. Most microscopes are **parfocal,** which means that when one lens is in focus, other lenses will also have the same focal length and can be rotated into position without further major adjustment. In practice, however, usually a half-turn of the fine-adjustment knob in either direction is necessary for sharp focus.

7. Once you have brought the specimen into sharp focus with a low-powered lens, preparation may be made for visualizing the specimen under oil immersion. Place a drop of oil on the slide directly over the area to be viewed. Rotate the nosepiece until the oil-immersion objective locks into position. *Note: Care should be taken not to allow the high-power objective to touch the drop of oil.* The slide is observed from the side as the objective is rotated slowly into position. This will ensure that the objective will be properly immersed in the oil. The fine-adjustment knob is readjusted to bring the image into sharp focus.

8. During microscopic examination of microbial organisms, it is always necessary to observe several areas of the preparation. This is accomplished by scanning the slide without the application of additional immersion oil. *Note: This will require continuous, very fine adjustments by the slow, back-and-forth rotation of the fine-adjustment knob only.*

On completion of the laboratory exercise, return the microscope to its cabinet in its original condition. The following steps are recommended:

1. Clean all lenses with dry, clean lens paper. *Note: Use xylol to remove oil from the stage only.*

2. Place the low-power objective in position and lower the body tube completely.

3. Center the mechanical stage.

Objective	Working Distance	Diaphragm Opening
Scanning 4×	4× 9–10 mm Slide	Reduced
Low power 10×	10× 5–8 mm Slide	Not fully opened
High power 40×	40× 0.5–0.7 mm Slide	Not fully opened
Oil immersion 100×	100× 0.13–0.18 mm Slide	Fully opened

Figure 3 Relationship between working distance, objective, and diaphragm opening

4. Coil the electric cord around the body tube and the stage.

5. Carry the microscope to its position in its cabinet in the manner previously described.

CLINICAL APPLICATION

Using Microscopic Examination in the Diagnosis of Tuberculosis

The visualization of stained bacterial cells using a compound light microscope can be the first step in diagnosing microbial infections. For example, a rapid diagnosis for tuberculosis can be made by identifying the unique characteristics of *Mycobacterium tuberculosis* in a stained sample of patient sputum.

AT THE BENCH

Materials

Slides

Commercially prepared slides of *Staphylococcus aureus, Bacillus subtilis, Aquaspirillum itersonii, Saccharomyces cerevisiae*, and a human blood smear.

Equipment

Compound microscope, lens paper, and immersion oil.

Procedure

1. Review the parts of the microscope, making sure you know the names and understand the function of each of these components.

2. Review instructions for the use of the microscope, giving special attention to the use of the oil-immersion objective.

3. Examine the prepared slides, noting the shapes and the relative sizes of the cells under the high-power (also called high-dry, because it is the highest power that does not use oil) and oil-immersion objectives.

4. Record your observations in the Lab Report.

Lab Report

Observations and Results

Draw several cells from a typical microscopic field as viewed under each magnification, and give the total magnification for each objective.

	High Power – 40x	Oil Immersion – 100x
S. aureus 3 Magnification _____		
B. subtilis 4 Magnification _____		
A. itersonii 2 spirillum Magnification _____		
S. cerevisiae 5 Magnification _____		
Blood smear 1 Magnification _____		

Review Questions

1. Explain why the body tube of the microscope should not be lowered while you are looking through the ocular lens.

2. For what purpose would you adjust each of the following microscope components during a microscopy exercise?

   a. Iris diaphragm:

   b. Coarse-adjustment knob:

   c. Fine-adjustment knob:

   d. Condenser:

   e. Mechanical stage control:

3. As a beginning student in the microbiology laboratory, you experience some difficulties in using the oil-immersion lens. Describe the steps you would take to correct the following problems:

   a. Inability to bring the specimen into sharp focus.

   b. Insufficient light while viewing the specimen.

   c. Artifacts in the microscopic field.

Photo Credit

Credits are listed in order of appearance.

Photo 1:   Charles D. Winters Photo Reseachers, Inc

Microscopic Examination of Living Microorganisms Using a Hanging-Drop Preparation or a Wet Mount

LEARNING OBJECTIVES

Once you have completed this experiment, you should know how to

1. Microscopically examine living microorganisms.
2. Make a hanging-drop preparation or wet mount to view living microorganisms.

Principle

Bacteria, because of their small size and a refractive index that closely approximates that of water, do not lend themselves readily to microscopic examination in a living, unstained state. Examination of living microorganisms is useful, however, to do the following:

1. Observe cell activities such as motility and binary fission.
2. Observe the natural sizes and shapes of the cells, considering that **heat fixation** (the rapid passage of the smear over the Bunsen burner flame) and exposure to chemicals during staining cause some degree of distortion.

In this experiment you will use individual cultures of *Pseudomonas aeruginosa*, *Bacillus cereus*, *Staphylococcus aureus*, and *Proteus vulgaris* for a hanging-drop preparation or a wet mount. Hay infusion or pond water may be substituted or used in addition to the above organisms. **Figure 1** illustrates several organisms commonly found in pond water and hay infusions.

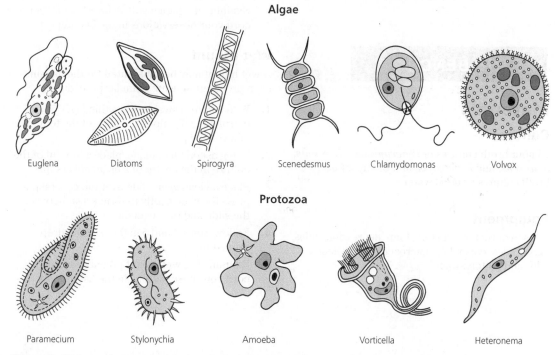

Algae

Euglena   Diatoms   Spirogyra   Scenedesmus   Chlamydomonas   Volvox

Protozoa

Paramecium   Stylonychia   Amoeba   Vorticella   Heteronema

Figure 1 Algae and protozoa commonly found in natural infusions and pond water (drawings are not to scale)

From Experiment 6 of *Microbiology: A Laboratory Manual*, Tenth Edition. James G. Cappuccino, Natalie Sherman.

You will observe the preparation(s) microscopically for differences in the sizes and shapes of the cells, as well as for motility, a self-directed movement. It is essential to differentiate between actual motility and **Brownian movement,** a vibratory movement of the cells due to their bombardment by water molecules in the suspension. Hanging-drop preparations and wet mounts make the movement of microorganisms easier to see because they slow down the movement of water molecules.

CLINICAL APPLICATION

Observation of Living Bacteria and the Diagnosis of Syphilis

Some microorganisms are difficult or unable to be stained. One such bacteria is *Treponema pallidum,* the causative agent for syphilis. Special stains must be used to stain this bacterium; however, it can be viewed unstained and alive using a darkfield microscope. Under those conditions, its characteristic shape and motility can be observed, leading to a diagnosis of syphilis.

AT THE BENCH

Materials

Cultures

24-hour broth cultures of *P. aeruginosa, B. cereus, S. aureus,* and *P. vulgaris;* and/or hay infusion broth cultures or pond water.

Equipment

Bunsen burner, inoculating loop, depression slides, glass slides, coverslips, microscope, petroleum jelly, and cotton swabs.

Procedure

Hanging-Drop Preparation

Perform the following steps for each culture provided in this experiment. Steps 1–4 are illustrated in **Figure 2**.

1. With a cotton swab, apply a ring of petroleum jelly around the concavity of the depression slide.

2. Using aseptic technique, place a loopful of the culture in the center of a clean coverslip.

3. Place the depression slide, with the concave surface facing down, over the coverslip so that the depression covers the drop of culture. Press the slide gently to form a seal between the slide and the coverslip.

4. Quickly turn the slide right side up so that the drop continues to adhere to the inner surface of the coverslip.

5. For microscopic examination, first focus on the drop culture under the low-power objective (10×) and reduce the light source by adjusting the Abbé condenser. Repeat using the high-power objective (40×).

6. Examine the hanging-drop preparation and record your observations in the Lab Report.

Wet Mount

A wet mount may be substituted for the hanging-drop preparation using a similar procedure:

1. With a cotton swab apply a thin layer of petroleum jelly along the edge of the four sides of a coverslip.

2. Using aseptic technique, place a loopful of the culture in the center of a clean coverslip.

3. Place a clean glass slide over the coverslip and press the slide gently to form a seal between the slide and the coverslip.

4. Follow Steps 4 and 5 in the hanging-drop procedure.

5. Examine the wet-mount preparation and record your observations in the Lab Report.

Microscopic Examination of Living Microorganisms Using a Hanging-Drop Preparation or a Wet Mount

PROCEDURE

1. Spread a ring of petroleum jelly around the concavity of the depression slide.

2. Place a loopful of the bacterial culture in the center of the coverslip.

3. Lower the depression slide, with the concavity facing down, onto the coverslip. Press gently to form a seal.

4. Turn the hanging-drop preparation over so that the culture drop adheres to the coverslip.

Figure 2 Hanging-drop preparation

Name: _____

Date: _____ Section: _____

Observations and Results

1. Examine the hanging-drop or wet-mount preparation to determine shape
    and motility of the different bacteria present. Record your results in the
    chart below.

Organisms	Shape	True Motility or Brownian Movement?
S. aureus		
P. aeruginosa		
B. cereus		
P. vulgaris		

2. Draw a representative field of each of the above organisms.

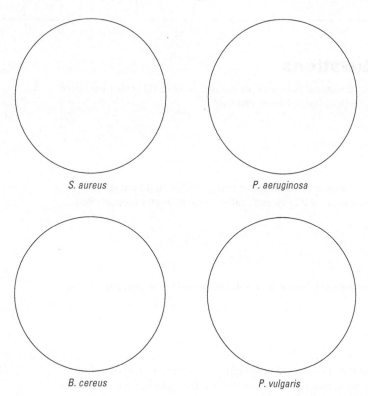

S. aureus   P. aeruginosa

B. cereus   P. vulgaris

3. Draw representative fields of pond water and hay infusion if you used them. Try to identify some of the organisms that you see by referring to Figure 1. Note the shape and type of movement in the chart below.

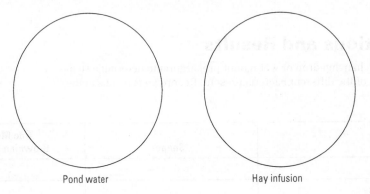

Pond water   Hay infusion

	Pond Water			Hay Infusion		
Shape						
True motility or Brownian movement?						
Organism						

Review Questions

1. Why are living, unstained bacterial preparations more difficult to observe microscopically than stained preparations?

2. What is the major advantage of using living cell preparations (hanging-drop or wet mount) rather than stained preparations?

3. How do you distinguish between true motility and Brownian movement?

4. During the microscopic observation of a drop of stagnant pond water, what criteria would you use to distinguish viable organisms from nonviable suspended debris?

The Microscopic Measurement of Microorganisms

Principle

Determination of microbial size is not as simple as you might assume. Before an accurate measurement of cells can be made, the diameter of the microscopic field must be established by means of optic devices, namely, an ocular micrometer and a stage micrometer. The **ocular micrometer (Figure 1a)**, which is placed on a circular shelf inside the eyepiece, is a glass disc with graduations etched on its surface. The distance between these graduations will vary depending on the objective being used, which determines the size of the field. This distance is determined by using a **stage micrometer (Figure 1b)**, a special glass slide with etched graduations that are 0.01 mm, or 10 micrometers (μm), apart.

The calibration procedure for the ocular micrometer requires that the graduations on both micrometers be superimposed on each other **(Figure 1c)**. This is accomplished by rotating the ocular lens. A determination is then made of the number of ocular divisions per known distance on the stage micrometer. Finally, the calibration factor for one ocular division is calculated as follows:

$$\text{One division on ocular micrometer in mm} = \frac{\text{Known distance between two lines on stage micrometer}}{\text{Number of divisions on ocular micrometer}}$$

Example: If 13 ocular divisions coincide with two stage divisions (2×0.01 mm = known distance of 0.02 mm), then:

$$\text{one ocular division} = \frac{0.02\,\text{mm}}{13}$$

$$= 0.00154\,\text{mm, or}\,1.54\,\mu\text{m}$$

Once the ocular micrometer is calibrated, the size of a microorganism can easily be determined, first by counting the number of spaces occupied by the organism **(Figure 1d)** and second by

(a) Ocular micrometer: Graduations must be calibrated for each objective on the microscope.

(b) Stage micrometer: Graduations are spaced 0.01 mm (10 μm) apart.

(c) Superimposed ocular micrometer over stage micrometer: Thirteen graduations on the ocular micrometer coincide with two graduations on the stage micrometer.

(d) Measurement of microorganisms with the calibrated micrometer: Each cell occupies five divisions on the ocular micrometer.

Figure 1 Calibration and use of the ocular micrometer

multiplying this number by the calculated calibration factor for one ocular division.

Example: If an organism occupies five spaces on the ocular micrometer, then:

length of = number of ocular divisions occupied × calibration factor for one ocular division
organism

$$= 5 \times 1.54 \ \mu m = 7.70 \ \mu m$$

In this experiment, you will calibrate an ocular micrometer for the oil-immersion objective and determine the sizes of microorganisms such as bacteria, yeast, and protozoa.

AT THE BENCH

Materials

Slides

Prepared slides of yeast cells, protozoa, and bacterial cocci and bacilli.

Equipment

Ocular micrometer, stage micrometer, microscope, immersion oil, and lens paper.

Procedure

1. With the assistance of a laboratory instructor, carefully place the ocular micrometer into the eyepiece.

2. Place the stage micrometer on the microscope stage and center it over the illumination source.

3. With the stage micrometer in clear focus under the low-power objective, slowly rotate the eyepiece to superimpose the ocular micrometer graduations over those of the stage micrometer.

4. Add a drop of immersion oil to the stage micrometer, bring the oil-immersion objective into position, and focus, if necessary, with the *fine-adjustment knob only.*

5. Move the mechanical stage so that a line on the stage micrometer coincides with a line on the ocular micrometer at one end. Find another line on the ocular micrometer that coincides with a line on the stage micrometer. Determine the distance on the stage micrometer (number of divisions × 0.01 mm) and the corresponding number of divisions on the ocular micrometer.

6. Determine the value of the calibration factor for the oil-immersion objective.

7. Remove the stage micrometer from the stage.

8. To determine the size of the cocci on the prepared slides under the oil-immersion objective, do the following:

   a. Calculate the number of ocular divisions occupied by each of three separate cocci. Record the data in the readings columns of the first observation chart in the Lab Report.

   b. Determine and record the average of the three measurements.

   c. Determine the size by multiplying the average by your calculated calibration factor, and record this value.

9. Determine and record the size of the other microorganisms by observing the remaining prepared slides under oil immersion as outlined in Step 8. Since these organisms are not round, both length and width measurements are required.

10. Check that your observations are complete in the Lab Report.

Lab Report

Observations and Results

1. Calibration of ocular micrometer for the oil-immersion objective:

    Distance on stage micrometer _____

    Divisions on ocular micrometer _____

    Calibration factor for one ocular division _____

2. Use the charts below to record your observations and measurements of the microorganisms studied.

	WIDTH OF MICROORGANISMS IN MICROMETERS (μm)				
	Number of ocular divisions				
	Readings				
Organism	**1**	**2**	**3**	**Average $\times$ Calibration Factor $=$ Size**	
Cocci					
Bacilli					
Yeast					
Protozoa					

	LENGTH OF MICROORGANISMS IN MICROMETERS (μm)				
	Number of ocular divisions				
	Readings				
Organism	**1**	**2**	**3**	**Average $\times$ Calibration Factor $=$ Size**	
Bacilli					
Yeast					
Protozoa					

Review Questions

1. Can the same calibration factor be used to determine the size of a microorganism under all objectives? Explain.

2. If one stage micrometer division contains 12 ocular divisions, then the distance between two lines on the ocular micrometer is _____. Show your calculations.

3. If 1 mm is equal to 1/25,400 inch, convert the size of a bacterium measuring 3 μm $\times$ 1.5 μm to inches. Show your calculations.

4. A comparative study of microbial size, using a stage micrometer, requires that you measure *Bacillus subtilis* in both the stained and unstained states.

   a. Would you expect the measurements to be comparable in both preparations?

   b. If a variation in size is expected, how would you account for this difference?

Photo Credits

Credits are listed in order of appearance.

Photo 1: Charles D. Winters Photo Reseachers, Inc

Bacterial Staining

LEARNING OBJECTIVES

Once you have completed the experiments in this section, you should be familiar with

1. The chemical and theoretical basis of biological staining.
2. Manipulative techniques of smear preparation.
3. Procedures for simple staining and negative staining.
4. The method for performing differential staining procedures, such as the Gram, acid-fast, capsule, and spore stains.

Introduction

Visualization of microorganisms in the living state is quite difficult, not only because they are minute, but also because they are transparent and practically colorless when suspended in an aqueous medium. To study their properties and to divide microorganisms into specific groups for diagnostic purposes, biological stains and staining procedures in conjunction with light microscopy have become major tools in microbiology.

Chemically, a stain (dye) may be defined as an organic compound containing a benzene ring plus a chromophore and an auxochrome group (**Figure 1**).

The stain picric acid may be used to illustrate this definition (**Figure 2**).

The ability of a stain to bind to macromolecular cellular components such as proteins or nucleic acids depends on the electrical charge found on the chromogen portion, as well as on the cellular component to be stained.

Acidic stains are anionic, which means that, on ionization of the stain, the chromogen portion exhibits a negative charge and therefore has a strong affinity for the positive constituents of the cell. Proteins, positively charged cellular components, will readily bind to and accept the color of the negatively charged, anionic chromogen of an acidic stain. Structurally, picric acid is an example of an acidic stain that produces an anionic chromogen, as illustrated in **Figure 3**.

Basic stains are cationic, because on ionization the chromogen portion exhibits a positive charge and therefore has a strong affinity for the negative constituents of the cell. Nucleic acids, negatively charged cellular components, will

Figure 1 Chemical composition of a stain

From Part 3 of *Microbiology: A Laboratory Manual*, Tenth Edition. James G. Cappuccino, Natalie Sherman.

Bacilli Staining

Figure 2 Chemical formation of picric acid

Benzene
colorless

Nitro groups
chromophore

Trinitrobenzene
chromogen, yellow
in color due to the
presence of
chromophores

Auxochrome

Trinitrohydroxybenzene
(picric acid) yellow stain

Picric acid

Anionic chromogen

Ionization

Figure 3 Picric acid: an acidic stain

Methylene blue

Cationic chromogen

Ionization

Figure 4 Methylene blue: a basic stain

readily bind to and accept the color of the positively charged, cationic chromogen of a basic stain. Structurally, methylene blue is a basic stain that produces a cationic chromogen, as illustrated in **Figure 4**.

Figure 5 is a summary of acidic and basic stains.

Basic stains are more commonly used for bacterial staining. The presence of a negative charge on the bacterial surface acts to repel most acidic stains and thus prevent their penetration into the cell.

Numerous staining techniques are available for visualization, differentiation, and separation of bacteria in terms of morphological characteristics and cellular structures. A summary of commonly used procedures and their purposes is outlined in **Figure 6**.

56

Bacterial Staining

Figure 5 Acidic and basic stains

Figure 6 Staining techniques

Preparation of Bacterial Smears

Principle

Bacterial smears must be prepared prior to the execution of any of the staining techniques. Although not difficult, the preparation requires adequate care. Meticulously follow the rules listed below.

1. **Preparation of the glass microscope slide:** Clean slides are essential for the preparation of microbial smears. Grease or oil from the fingers on slides must be removed by washing the slides with soap and water or scouring powders such as Bon Ami®, followed by a water rinse and a rinse of 95% alcohol. After cleaning, dry the slides and place them on laboratory towels until ready for use. *Note: Remember to hold the clean slides by their edges.*

2. **Labeling of slides:** Proper labeling of the slide is essential. The initials of the organism can be written on either end of the slide with a glassware marking pencil on the surface on which the smear is to be made. Care should be taken that the label does not come into contact with staining reagents.

3. **Preparation of smear:** It is crucial to avoid thick, dense smears. A thick or dense smear occurs when too much of the culture is used in its preparation, which concentrates a large number of cells on the slide. This type of preparation diminishes the amount of light that can pass through and makes it difficult to visualize the morphology of single cells.

Note: Smears require only a small amount of the bacterial culture. A good smear is one that, when dried, appears as a thin whitish layer or film. The print of your textbook should be legible through the smear. Different techniques are used depending on whether the smear is made from a broth or solid-medium culture.

a. **Broth cultures:** Resuspend the culture by tapping the tube with your finger. Depending on the size of the loop, one or two loopfuls should be applied to the center of the slide with a sterile inoculating loop and spread evenly over an area about the size of a dime. Set the smears on the laboratory table and allow to air-dry.

b. **Cultures from solid medium:** Organisms cultured in a solid medium produce thick, dense surface growth and are not amenable to direct transfer to the glass slide. These cultures must be diluted by placing one or two loopfuls of water on the center of the slide in which the cells will be emulsified. Transfer of the cells requires the use of a sterile inoculating loop or a needle, if preferred. Only the tip of the loop or needle should touch the culture to prevent the transfer of too many cells. Suspension is accomplished by spreading the cells in a circular motion in the drop of water with the loop or needle. This helps to avoid cell clumping. The finished smear should occupy an area about the size of a nickel and should appear as a translucent, or semitransparent, confluent whitish film **(Figure 1)**. At this point the smear should be allowed to dry completely. *Note: Do not blow on slide or wave it in the air.*

4. **Heat fixation:** Unless fixed on the glass slide, the bacterial smear will wash away during the staining procedure. This is avoided by heat fixation, during which the bacterial proteins are coagulated and fixed to

---

From Experiment 8 of *Microbiology: A Laboratory Manual*, Tenth Edition. James G. Cappuccino, Natalie Sherman.

Figure 1 A bacterial smear following fixation

the glass surface. Heat fixation is performed by the rapid passage of the air-dried smear two or three times over the flame of the Bunsen burner.

The preparation of a bacterial smear is illustrated in **Figure 2**.

CLINICAL APPLICATION

Proper Slide Preparation

Before any staining or visualization of a bacterial sample can take place, a proper smear must be prepared. A smear that is too thick may give a false result due to retention of dye that should have been rinsed away or because the thickness may prevent dye penetration. A smear that is too thin may have too few cells, increasing the time and energy to find the bacteria under magnification. Inconclusive results due to improperly prepared slides may have an impact on patient treatment and outcomes. Good smears are those which allow newsprint to be read through the smear.

AT THE BENCH

Materials

Cultures

24-hour nutrient agar slant culture of *Bacillus cereus* and a 24-hour nutrient broth culture of *Staphylococcus aureus*.

Equipment

Glass microscope slides, Bunsen burner, inoculating loop and needle, and glassware marking pencil.

Procedure

Smears from a Broth Medium

Label three clean slides with the initials of the organism, and number them 1, 2, and 3. Resuspend the sedimented cells in the broth culture by tapping the culture tube with your finger. The next four steps of this procedure are illustrated in Figure 2a and c:

1. With a sterile loop, place one loopful of culture on Slide 1, two loopfuls on Slide 2, and three loopfuls on Slide 3, respectively.

2. With a circular movement of the loop, spread the cell suspension into an area approximately the size of a dime.

3. Allow the slide to air-dry completely.

4. Heat fix the preparation. *Note: Pass the air-dried slide through the outer portion of the Bunsen flame to prevent overheating, which can distort the morphology through plasmolysis of the cell wall.*

Examine each slide for the confluent, whitish film or haze and record your results in the Lab Report.

Smears from a Solid Medium

Label four clean slides with the initials of the organism. Label Slides 1 and 2 with an L for loop, and Slides 3 and 4 with an N for needle. The next four steps of this procedure are illustrated in Figure 2b and c:

1. Using a loop, place one to two loops of water on each slide.

2. With a sterile loop, touch the entire loop to the culture and emulsify the cells in water on Slide 1. Then, with a sterile loop, just touch the tip of the loop to the culture and emulsify it in the water on Slide 2. Repeat Steps 1 and 2 using a sterile inoculating needle on Slides 3 and 4.

3. Allow all slides to air-dry completely.

4. Heat fix the preparation.

Examine each slide for the confluent, whitish film or haze and record your results in the Lab Report.

Preparation of Bacterial Smears

Figure 2 **Bacterial smear preparation**

Observations and Results

Select the preparation that you think is best and ask your instructor to comment on your choice. Remember that printed material should be legible through a good smear. Indicate by slide number the consistency of smears from both broth and solid cultures that you considered best.

Broth culture _____   Solid culture: Loop _____   Needle _____

Review Questions

1. Why are thick or dense smears less likely to provide a good smear preparation for microscopic evaluation?

2. Why is it essential that smears be air-dried? Why can't they be gently heated over a flame to speed up the drying process?

3. Why should you be careful not to overheat the smear during the heat-fixing process?

4. Why do you think the presence of grease or dirt on a glass slide will result in a poor smear preparation? Cite two or three reasons.

Photo Credit

Credits are listed in order of appearance.

Photo 1: Experiment performed and photographed by L. Brent Selinger, Department of Biological Sciences, University of Lethbridge, Pearson Education

Simple Staining

Principle

In **simple staining,** the bacterial smear is stained with a single reagent, which produces a distinctive contrast between the organism and its background. Basic stains with a positively charged chromogen are preferred because bacterial nucleic acids and certain cell wall components carry a negative charge that strongly attracts and binds to the cationic chromogen. The purpose of simple staining is to elucidate the morphology and arrangement of bacterial cells **(Figure 1)**. The most commonly used basic stains are methylene blue, crystal violet, and carbol fuchsin.

CLINICAL APPLICATION

Quick and Simple Stain

Simple stains are relatively quick and useful methods of testing for the presence of, determining the shape of, or determining the numbers of bacteria present in a sample. Generally involving a single staining step, simple staining methods are not considered differential or diagnostic and will have limited uses. However, this is a quick procedure for determining whether a clinical sample has the presence of a foreign bacterial pathogen.

AT THE BENCH

Materials

Cultures

24-hour nutrient agar slant cultures of *Escherichia coli* and *Bacillus cereus* and a 24-hour nutrient broth culture of *Staphylococcus aureus.*

Cocci are spherical in shape.

	(a) Diplococcus	Diplo = pair
	(b) Streptococcus	Strepto = chain
	(c) Staphylococcus	Staphylo = cluster
	(d) Tetrad	Tetrad = packet of 4
	(e) Sarcina	Sarcina = packet of 8

Bacilli are rod-shaped.

	(a) Diplobacillus	Diplo = pair
	(b) Streptobacillus	Strepto = chain

Spiral bacteria are rigid or flexible.

	(a) Vibrios are curved rods.
	(b) Spirilla are helical and rigid.
	(c) Spirochetes are helical and flexible.

Figure 1 Bacterial shapes and arrangements

From Experiment 9 of *Microbiology: A Laboratory Manual*, Tenth Edition. James G. Cappuccino, Natalie Sherman.

Reagents

Methylene blue, crystal violet, and carbol fuchsin.

Equipment

Bunsen burner, inoculating loop, staining tray, microscope, lens paper, bibulous (highly absorbent) paper, and glass slides.

Procedure

1. Prepare separate bacterial smears of the organisms. *Note: All smears must be heat fixed prior to staining.*

Simple Staining

The following steps are illustrated in **Figure 2**.

1. Place a slide on the staining tray and flood the smear with one of the indicated stains, using the appropriate exposure time for each: carbol fuchsin, 15 to 30 seconds; crystal violet, 20 to 60 seconds; methylene blue (shown in Figure 2), 1 to 2 minutes.

2. *Gently* wash the smear with tap water to remove excess stain. During this step, hold the slide parallel to the stream of water; in this way you can reduce the loss of organisms from the preparation.

3. Using bibulous paper, blot dry but *do not* wipe the slide.

4. Repeat this procedure with the remaining two organisms, using a different stain for each.

5. Examine all stained slides under oil immersion.

6. In the chart provided in the Lab Report, complete the following:

   a. Draw a representative field for each organism.

   b. Describe the morphology of the organisms with reference to their shapes (bacilli, cocci, spirilla) and arrangements (chains, clusters, pairs). Refer to the photographs in **Figure 3**.

PROCEDURE

1 Place slide on the staining tray and flood the smear with methylene blue. Allow 1 to 2 minutes of exposure to the stain.

2 Gently wash the smear with tap water.

3 Blot the slide dry with bibulous paper.

Figure 2 Simple staining procedure

Diplobacilli

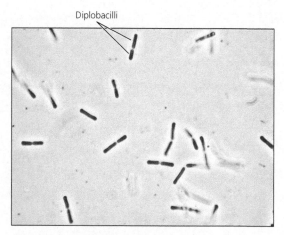

(a) Bacilli and diplobacilli (rod-shaped) bacteria

(b) Spirilla (spiral-shaped) bacteria

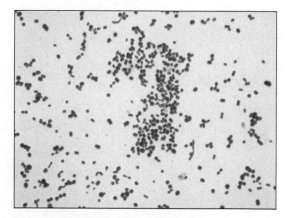

(c) Cocci (spherical-shaped) bacteria: *Staphylococcus*

Figure 3 **Micrographs showing bacteria morphology**

Observations and Results

	Methylene Blue	Crystal Violet	Carbol Fuchsin
Draw a representative field.	◯	◯	◯

Organism
Cell morphology:
  Shape
  Arrangement
Cell color
	_____
	
	_____
	_____
	_____
		_____
		
		_____
		_____
		_____
			_____
			
			_____
			_____
			_____

Review Questions

1. Why are basic dyes more effective for bacterial staining than acidic dyes?

2. Can simple staining techniques be used to identify more than the morphological characteristics of microorganisms? Explain.

3. During the performance of the simple staining procedure, you failed to heat fix your *E. coli* smear preparation. Upon microscopic examination, how would you expect this slide to differ from the correctly prepared slides?

4. During a coffee break, your friend spills coffee on your lab coat and the fabric is discolored. Is this a true biological stain or simply a compound capable of imparting color? Explain your rationale.

Photo Credits

Credits are listed in order of appearance.

Photo 1:   Experiment performed and photographed by L. Brent Selinger, Department of Biological Sciences, University of Lethbridge, Pearson Education

Photo 2:   Jennifer M. Warner, Biology Department, University of North Carolina at Charlotte

Photo 3:   Michael Abbey Photo Reseachers, Inc.

Negative Staining

CLINICAL APPLICATION

Detecting Encapsulated Invaders

The principle application of negative staining is to determine if an organism possesses a capsule (a gelatinous outer layer that makes the microorganism more virulent), although it can also be used to demonstrate spore formation. The technique is frequently used in the identification of fungi such as *Cryptococcus neoformans,* an important infectious agent found in bird dropping that is linked to meningeal and lung infections in humans.

Principle

Negative staining requires the use of an acidic stain such as India ink or nigrosin. The acidic stain, with its negatively charged chromogen, will not penetrate the cells because of the negative charge on the surface of bacteria. Therefore, the unstained cells are easily discernible against the colored background.

The practical application of negative staining is twofold. First, since heat fixation is not required and the cells are not subjected to the distorting effects of chemicals and heat, their natural size and shape can be seen. Second, it is possible to observe bacteria that are difficult to stain, such as some spirilla. Because heat fixation is not done during the staining process, keep in mind that the organisms are not killed and *slides should be handled with care.* **Figure 1** shows a negative stain of bacilli.

AT THE BENCH

Materials
Cultures

24-hour agar slant cultures of *Micrococcus luteus, Bacillus cereus,* and *Aquaspirillum itersonii.*

Reagent

Nigrosin.

Equipment

Bunsen burner, inoculating loop, staining tray, glass slides, lens paper, and microscope.

Procedure

Steps 1–4 are illustrated in **Figure 2**.

1. Place a small drop of nigrosin close to one end of a clean slide.
2. Using aseptic technique, place a loopful of inoculum from the *M. luteus* culture in the drop of nigrosin and mix.

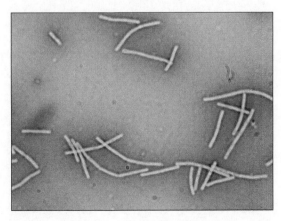

Figure 1 **Negative staining:** *Bacilli* (1000 ×)

From Experiment 10 of *Microbiology: A Laboratory Manual,* Tenth Edition. James G. Cappuccino, Natalie Sherman.

3. Place a slide against the drop of suspended organisms at a 45° angle and allow the drop to spread along the edge of the applied slide.

4. Push the slide away from the drop of suspended organisms to form a thin smear. Air-dry. *Note: Do not heat fix the slide.*

5. Repeat Steps 1–4 for slide preparations of *B. cereus* and *A. itersonii.*

6. Examine the slides under oil immersion, and record your observations in the Lab Report.

PROCEDURE

❶ Place a drop of nigrosin at one end of the slide.

❷ Place a loopful of the inoculum into the drop of stain and mix with the loop.

❸ Place a slide against the drop of suspended organisms at a 45° angle and allow the drop to spread along the edge of the applied slide.

❹ Push the slide away from the previously spread drop of suspended organisms, forming a thin smear. Air-dry the slide.

Figure 2 Negative staining procedure

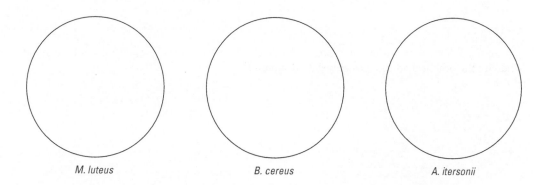

Name: _____

Date: _____ Section: _____

Observations and Results

1. Draw representative fields of your microscopic observations.

M. luteus	*B. cereus*	*A. itersonii*

2. Describe the microscopic appearance of the different bacteria using the chart below.

Organism	*M. luteus*	*B. cereus*	*A. itersonii*
Shape			
Arrangement			
Magnification			

Review Questions

1. Why can't methylene blue be used in place of nigrosin for negative staining? Explain.

2. What are the practical advantages of negative staining?

3. Why doesn't nigrosin penetrate bacterial cells?

Photo Credit

Credits are listed in order of appearance.

Photo 1: Experiment performed and photographed by L. Brent Selinger, Department of Biological Sciences, University of Lethbridge, Pearson Education

Gram Stain

Gram-positive cells have a thick peptidoglycan layer, whereas the peptidoglycan layer in gram-negative cells is much thinner and surrounded by outer lipid-containing layers. Peptidoglycan is mainly a polysaccharide composed of two chemical subunits found only in the bacterial cell wall. These subunits are *N*-acetylglucosamine and *N*-acetylmuramic acid. With some organisms, as the adjacent layers of peptidoglycan are formed, they are cross-linked by short chains of peptides by means of a transpeptidase enzyme, resulting in the shape and rigidity of the cell wall. In the case of gram-negative bacteria and several of the gram-positive such as the *Bacillus*, the cross-linking of the peptidoglycan layer is direct because the

Principle

Differential staining requires the use of at least four chemical reagents that are applied sequentially to a heat-fixed smear. The first reagent is called the **primary stain.** Its function is to impart its color to all cells. The second stain is a mordant used to intensify the color of the primary stain. In order to establish a color contrast, the third reagent used is the decolorizing agent. Based on the chemical composition of cellular components, the **decolorizing agent** may or may not remove the primary stain from the entire cell or only from certain cell structures. The final reagent, the counterstain, has a contrasting color to that of the primary stain. Following decolorization, if the primary stain is not washed out, the **counterstain** cannot be absorbed and the cell or its components will retain the color of the primary stain. If the primary stain is removed, the decolorized cellular components will accept and assume the contrasting color of the counterstain. In this way, cell types or their structures can be distinguished from each other on the basis of the stain that is retained.

The most important differential stain used in bacteriology is the **Gram stain,** named after Dr. Hans Christian Gram. It divides bacterial cells into two major groups, gram-positive and gram-negative, which makes it an essential tool for classification and differentiation of microorganisms. **Figure 1** shows gram-positive and gram-negative stained cells. The Gram stain reaction is based on the difference in the chemical composition of bacterial cell walls.

(a) Gram-positive stain of streptococci

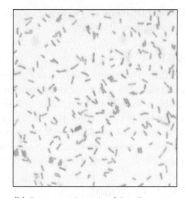

(b) Gram-negative stain of *E. coli*

Figure 1 Gram-stained cells

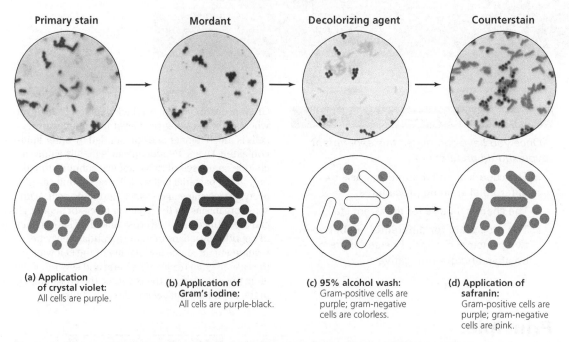

Primary stain | Mordant | Decolorizing agent | Counterstain

(a) Application of crystal violet: All cells are purple.

(b) Application of Gram's iodine: All cells are purple-black.

(c) 95% alcohol wash: Gram-positive cells are purple; gram-negative cells are colorless.

(d) Application of safranin: Gram-positive cells are purple; gram-negative cells are pink.

Figure 2 Microscopic observation of cells following steps in the Gram staining procedure

bacteria do not have short peptide tails. Early experiments have shown that a gram-positive cell denuded of its cell wall by the action of lysozyme or penicillin will stain gram-negative.

The Gram stain uses four different reagents. Descriptions of these reagents and their mechanisms of action follow. **Figure 2** shows the microscopic appearance of cells at each step of the Gram staining procedure.

Primary Stain

Crystal Violet (Hucker's) This violet stain is used first and stains all cells purple.

Mordant

Gram's Iodine This reagent serves not only as a killing agent but also as a mordant, a substance that increases the cells' affinity for a stain. It does this by binding to the primary stain, thus forming an insoluble complex. The resultant crystal-violet–iodine (CV-I) complex serves to intensify the color of the stain. At this point, all cells will appear purple-black.

Decolorizing Agent

Ethyl Alcohol, 95% This reagent serves a dual function as a protein-dehydrating agent and as a lipid solvent. Its action is determined by two factors, the concentration of lipids and the thickness of the peptidoglycan layer in bacterial cell walls. In gram-negative

cells, the alcohol increases the porosity of the cell wall by dissolving the lipids in the outer layers. Thus, the CV-I complex can be more easily removed from the thinner and less highly cross-linked peptidoglycan layer. Therefore, the washing-out effect of the alcohol facilitates the release of the unbound CV-I complex, leaving the cells colorless or unstained. The much thicker peptidoglycan layer in gram-positive cells is responsible for the more stringent retention of the CV-I complex, as the pores are made smaller due to the dehydrating effect of the alcohol. Thus, the tightly bound primary stain complex is difficult to remove, and the cells remain purple. *Note: Be careful not to over-decolorize the smear with alcohol.*

Counterstain

Safranin This is the final reagent, used to stain pink those cells that have been previously decolorized. Since only gram-negative cells undergo decolorization, they may now absorb the counterstain. Gram-positive cells retain the purple color of the primary stain.

The preparation of adequately stained smears requires that you bear in mind the following precautions:

1. The most critical phase of the procedure is the decolorization step, which is based on the ease with which the CV-I complex is released from the cell. Remember that over-decolorization will result in loss of the primary stain, causing

gram-positive organisms to appear gram-negative. Under-decolorization, however, will not completely remove the CV-I complex, causing gram-negative organisms to appear gram-positive. Strict adherence to all instructions will help remedy part of the difficulty, but individual experience and practice are the keys to correct decolorization.

2. It is imperative that, between applications of the reagents, slides be thoroughly washed under running water or water applied with an eyedropper. This removes excess reagent and prepares the slide for application of the subsequent reagent.

3. The best Gram-stained preparations are made with fresh cultures, that is, not older than 24 hours. As cultures age, especially in the case of gram-positive cells, the organisms tend to lose their ability to retain the primary stain and may appear to be **gram-variable;** that is, some cells will appear purple, while others will appear pink.

CLINICAL APPLICATION

Gram Staining: The First Diagnostic Test

The Gram stain is a diagnostic staining procedure that can be done on body fluids, tissue biopsies, throat cultures, samples from abscesses when infection is suspected, and more. Clinically important results are obtained much more rapidly from staining than from culturing the specimen. The results of the Gram stain will aid a clinical lab in determining which additional tests may be required for identification of the bacterial strain in question. Once the bacterial gram type, shape, and orientation are determined, it expedites the appropriate choice of antibiotic needed to treat the patient.

AT THE BENCH

Materials

Cultures

24-hour nutrient agar slant cultures of *Escherichia coli*, *Staphylococcus aureus*, and *Bacillus cereus*.

Reagents

Crystal violet, Gram's iodine, 95% ethyl alcohol, and safranin.

Equipment

Bunsen burner, inoculating loop or needle, staining tray, glass slides, bibulous paper, lens paper, and microscope.

Procedure

Smear Preparation

1. Obtain four clean glass slides.

2. Using aseptic technique, prepare a smear of each of the three organisms and on the remaining slide prepare a smear consisting of a mixture of *S. aureus* and *E. coli*. Do this by placing a drop of water on the slide, and then transferring each organism separately to the drop of water with a sterile, cooled loop. Mix and spread both organisms by means of a circular motion of the inoculating loop.

3. Allow smears to air-dry and then heat fix in the usual manner.

Gram Staining

The following steps are shown in **Figure 3**.

1. *Gently* flood smears with crystal violet and let stand for 1 minute.

2. *Gently* wash with tap water.

3. *Gently* flood smears with the Gram's iodine mordant and let stand for 1 minute.

4. *Gently* wash with tap water.

5. Decolorize with 95% ethyl alcohol. *Note: Do not over-decolorize.* Add reagent drop by drop until the alcohol runs almost clear, showing only a blue tinge.

6. *Gently* wash with tap water.

7. Counterstain with safranin for 45 seconds.

8. *Gently* wash with tap water.

9. Blot dry with bibulous paper and examine under oil immersion.

10. As you observe each slide under oil immersion, complete the chart provided in the Lab Report.

    a. Draw a representative microscopic field.

    b. Describe the cells according to their morphology and arrangement.

    c. Describe the color of the stained cells.

    d. Classify the organism as to the Gram reaction: gram-positive or gram-negative.

Gram Stain

PROCEDURE

1. Gently stain with crystal violet for 1 minute.

2. Gently wash off the stain with tap water.

3. Gently apply Gram's iodine for 1 minute.

4. Gently wash off the Gram's iodine with tap water.

5. Add 95% alcohol drop by drop until the alcohol runs almost clear.

6. Gently wash off the 95% alcohol with tap water.

7. Counterstain with safranin for 45 seconds.

8. Gently wash off the safranin with tap water.

9. Blot dry with bibulous paper.

Figure 3 Gram staining procedure

Observations and Results

	E. coli	*B. cereus*	*S. aureus*	*Mixture*
Draw a representative field.	◯	◯	◯	◯
Cell morphology: Shape	_____	_____	_____	_____
Arrangement	_____	_____	_____	_____
Cell color	_____	_____	_____	_____
Gram reaction	_____	_____	_____	_____

Review Questions

1. What are the advantages of differential staining procedures over the simple staining technique?

2. Cite the purpose of each of the following reagents in a differential staining procedure.

   a. Primary stain:

   b. Mordant:

c. Decolorizing agent:

d. Counterstain:

3. Why is it essential that the primary stain and the counterstain be of contrasting colors?

4. Which is the most crucial step in the performance of the Gram staining procedures? Explain.

5. Because of a snowstorm, your regular laboratory session was canceled and the Gram staining procedure was performed on cultures incubated for a longer period of time. Examination of the stained *B. cereus* slides revealed a great deal of color variability, ranging from an intense blue to shades of pink. Account for this result.

Photo Credits

Credits are listed in order of appearance.

Photo 1: James Cappuccino

Photo 2: Centers for Disease Control and Prevention

Photo 3: David Alexander, University of Portland

Acid-Fast Stain

LEARNING OBJECTIVES

Once you have completed this experiment, you should understand

1. The chemical basis of the acid-fast stain.
2. The procedure for differentiating bacteria into acid-fast and non–acid-fast groups.

Principle

While the majority of bacterial organisms are stainable by either simple or Gram staining procedures, a few genera, particularly the members of the genus *Mycobacterium*, are visualized much better by the **acid-fast** method. Since *M. tuberculosis* and *M. leprae* represent bacteria that are pathogenic to humans, the stain is of diagnostic value in identifying these organisms.

The characteristic difference between mycobacteria and other microorganisms is the presence of a thick, waxy (lipoidal) wall that makes penetration by stains extremely difficult. The mycobacteria tend to clump together, and it is difficult to identify individual cells in stained preparations if this clumping effect occurs. To avoid or minimize this phenomenon requires careful preparation of the smear. Place a small drop of water on the slide, suspend the culture in the water, and mix the suspension thoroughly to dislodge and disperse some of the cells. Once the stain has penetrated, however, it cannot be readily removed even with the vigorous use of acid-alcohol as a decolorizing agent (unlike the 95% ethyl alcohol used in the Gram stain). Because of this property, these organisms are called acid-fast, while all other microorganisms, which are easily decolorized by acid-alcohol, are non–acid-fast.

The acid-fast stain uses three different reagents.

Primary Stain

Carbol Fuchsin Unlike cells that are easily stained by ordinary aqueous stains, most species of mycobacteria are not stainable with common dyes such as methylene blue and crystal violet. Carbol fuchsin, a dark red stain in 5% phenol that is soluble in the lipoidal materials that constitute most of the mycobacterial cell wall, does penetrate these bacteria and is retained. Penetration is further enhanced by the application of heat, which drives the carbol fuchsin through the lipoidal wall and into the cytoplasm. This application of heat is used in the **Ziehl-Neelsen method.** The **Kinyoun method,** a modification of the Ziehl-Neelsen method, circumvents the use of heat by addition of a wetting agent (Tergitol®) to this stain, which reduces surface tension between the cell wall of the mycobacteria and the stain. Following application of the primary stain, all cells will appear red.

Decolorizing Agent

Acid-Alcohol (3% HCl + 95% Ethanol) Prior to decolorization, the smear is cooled, which allows the waxy cell substances to harden. On application of acid-alcohol, acid-fast cells will be resistant to decolorization since the primary stain is more soluble in the cellular waxes than in the decolorizing agent. In this event, the primary stain is retained and the mycobacteria will stay red. This is not the case with non–acid-fast organisms, which lack cellular waxes. The primary stain is more easily removed during decolorization, leaving these cells colorless or unstained.

Counterstain

Methylene Blue This is used as the final reagent to stain previously decolorized cells. As only non–acid-fast cells undergo decolorization, they may now absorb the counterstain and take on its blue color, while acid-fast cells retain the red of the primary stain.

Acid-Fast Stain

PROCEDURE

1a **Heat method:** Apply carbol fuchsin and steam over a beaker of boiling water that is placed on a hot plate for 5 minutes. Do not allow the stain to evaporate.

or

1b **Heatless method:** Apply carbol fuchsin with Tergitol® for 5 to 10 minutes.

2 Cool and wash off stain with tap water.

3 Add acid-alcohol drop by drop until the alcohol runs almost clear.

4 Wash off the acid-alcohol with tap water.

5 Counterstain with methylene blue for 2 minutes.

6 Wash off the methylene blue with tap water.

7 Blot the slide dry with bibulous paper.

Figure 1 Acid-fast staining procedure

Diagnosing Leprosy and Lung Infections

The cell walls of bacteria belonging to the genera *Mycobacterium* or *Nocardia* contain mycolic acid and are resistant to penetration by water-soluble stains such as the Gram stain, which can lead to a "false" gram-positive result. The medical importance of the acid-fast stain is for the diagnosis of the *Mycobacterium* species, which cause tuberculosis, leprosy, and other infections. The genus *Nocardia*, which is the causative agent for lung infections, will also be identified by the acid-fast staining method.

AT THE BENCH

Materials
Cultures
72- to 96-hour Trypticase soy broth culture of *Mycobacterium smegmatis* and 18- to 24-hour culture of *Staphylococcus aureus*.

Reagents
Carbol fuchsin, acid-alcohol, and methylene blue.

Equipment
Bunsen burner, hot plate, 250-ml beaker, inoculating loop, glass slides, bibulous paper, lens paper, staining tray, and microscope.

Procedure
Smear Preparation

1. Obtain three clean glass slides.
2. Using aseptic technique, prepare a bacterial smear of each organism plus a third mixed smear of *M. smegmatis* and *S. aureus*.
3. Allow smears to air-dry and then heat fix in the usual manner.

Acid-Fast Staining
Steps 1–7 are pictured in **Figure 1**.

1. **a.** Flood smears with carbol fuchsin and place over a beaker of water on a warm hot plate, allowing the preparation to steam for 5 minutes. *Note: Do not allow stain to evaporate; replenish stain as needed. Also, prevent stain from boiling by adjusting the hot-plate temperature.*
   b. For a heatless method, flood the smear with carbol fuchsin containing Tergitol® for 5 to 10 minutes.
2. Wash with tap water. Heated slides must be cooled prior to washing.
3. Decolorize with acid-alcohol, adding the reagent drop by drop until the alcohol runs almost clear with a slight red tinge.
4. Wash with tap water.
5. Counterstain with methylene blue for 2 minutes.
6. Wash smear with tap water.
7. Blot dry with bibulous paper and examine under oil immersion.
8. In the chart provided in the Lab Report, complete the following:
   a. Draw a representative microscopic field for each preparation.
   b. Describe the cells according to their shapes and arrangements.
   c. Describe the color of the stained cells.
   d. Classify the organisms as to reaction: acid-fast or non–acid-fast.

Refer to **Figure 2** for a photograph of an acid-fast stain.

Figure 2 **Acid-fast stain of mycobacteria**

Observations and Results

	M. smegmatis	*S. aureus*	Mixture
Draw a representative field.	◯	◯	◯

Cell morphology:
  Shape
  Arrangement
Cell color
Acid-fast reaction
	_____
	_____
	_____
	_____
		_____
		_____
		_____
		_____
			_____
			_____
			_____
			_____

Review Questions

1. Why must heat or a surface-active agent be used with application of the primary stain during acid-fast staining?

2. Why is acid-alcohol rather than ethyl alcohol used as a decolorizing agent?

3. What is the specific diagnostic value of this staining procedure?

4. Why is the application of heat or a surface-active agent not required during the application of the counterstain in acid-fast staining?

5. A child presents symptoms suggestive of tuberculosis, namely a respiratory infection with a productive cough. Microscopic examination of the child's sputum reveals no acid-fast rods. However, examination of gastric washings reveals the presence of both acid-fast and non–acid-fast bacilli. Do you think the child has active tuberculosis? Explain.

Photo Credit

Credits are listed in order of appearance.

Photo 1:   James Cappuccino

Differential Staining for Visualization of Bacterial Cell Structures

PART A Spore Stain (Schaeffer-Fulton Method)

Principle

Members of the anaerobic genera *Clostridium* and *Desulfotomaculum* and the aerobic genus *Bacillus* are examples of organisms that have the capacity to exist either as metabolically active **vegetative cells** or as highly resistant, metabolically inactive cell types called **spores.** When environmental conditions become unfavorable for continuing vegetative cellular activities, particularly with the exhaustion of a nutritional carbon source, these cells have the capacity to undergo **sporogenesis** and give rise to a new intracellular structure called the **endospore,** which is surrounded by impervious layers called spore coats. As conditions continue to worsen, the endospore is released from the degenerating vegetative cell and becomes an independent cell called a **free spore.** Because of the chemical composition of spore layers, the spore is resistant to the damaging effects of excessive heat, freezing, radiation, desiccation, and chemical agents, as well as to the commonly employed microbiological stains. With the return of favorable environmental conditions, the free spore may revert to a metabolically active and less resistant vegetative cell through **germination** (see **Figure 1**). It should be emphasized that sporogenesis and germination are not means of reproduction but merely mechanisms that ensure cell survival under all environmental conditions.

In practice, the spore stain uses two different reagents.

Primary Stain

Malachite Green Unlike most vegetative cell types that stain by common procedures, the free spore, because of its impervious coats, will not accept the primary stain easily. For further penetration, the application of heat is required. After the primary stain is applied and the smear is heated, both the vegetative cell and spore will appear green.

Decolorizing Agent

Water Once the spore accepts the malachite green, it cannot be decolorized by tap water, which removes only the excess primary stain. The spore remains green. On the other hand, the stain does not demonstrate a strong affinity for vegetative cell components; the water removes it, and these cells will be colorless.

Counterstain

Safranin This contrasting red stain is used as the second reagent to color the decolorized vegetative cells, which will absorb the counterstain and

Differential Staining for Visualization of Bacterial Cell Structures

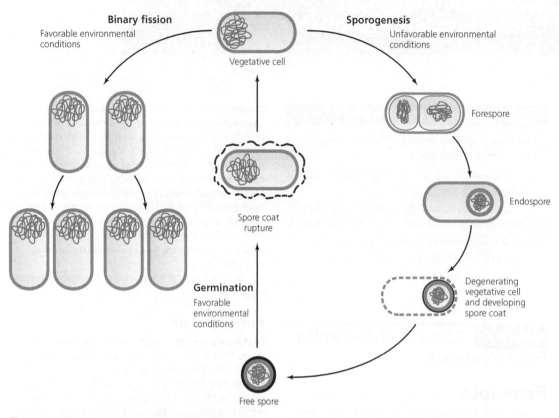

Figure 1 Life cycle of a spore-forming bacterium

appear red. The spores retain the green of the primary stain. A micrograph of spore-stained cells appears in **Figure 2**.

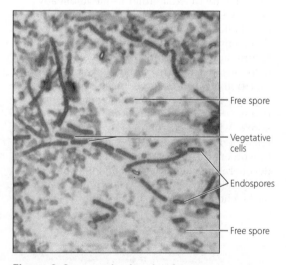

Figure 2 Spore stain showing free spores and vegetative bacilli

AT THE BENCH

Materials
Cultures
48- to 72-hour nutrient agar slant culture of *Bacillus cereus* and thioglycollate culture of *Clostridium sporogenes*.

Reagents
Malachite green and safranin.

Equipment
Bunsen burner, hot plate, staining tray, inoculating loop, glass slides, bibulous paper, lens paper, and microscope.

Procedure
Smear Preparation

1. Obtain two clean glass slides.
2. Make individual smears in the usual manner using aseptic technique.
3. Allow smear to air-dry, and heat fix in the usual manner.

Spore Staining
Steps 1–5 are illustrated in **Figure 3**.

1. Flood smears with malachite green and place on top of a beaker of water sitting on a warm hot plate, allowing the preparation to steam for 2 to 3 minutes. *Note: Do not allow stain to evaporate; replenish stain as needed.* Prevent the stain from boiling by adjusting the hot plate temperature.
2. Remove slides from hot plate, cool, and wash under running tap water.
3. Counterstain with safranin for 30 seconds.
4. Wash with tap water.
5. Blot dry with bibulous paper and examine under oil immersion.
6. In the chart provided in the Lab Report, complete the following:

    a. Draw a representative microscopic field of each preparation.

    b. Describe the location of the endospore within the vegetative cell as central, subterminal, or terminal on each preparation.

    c. Indicate the color of the spore and vegetative cell on each preparation.

PART B Capsule Stain (Anthony Method)

Principle
A **capsule** is a gelatinous outer layer that is secreted by the cell and that surrounds and adheres to the cell wall. It is not common to all organisms. Cells that have a heavy capsule are generally virulent and capable of producing disease, since the structure protects bacteria against the normal phagocytic activities of host cells. Chemically, the capsular material is composed mainly of complex polysaccharides such as levans, dextrans, and celluloses.

Capsule staining is more difficult than other types of differential staining procedures because the capsular materials are water-soluble and may be dislodged and removed with vigorous washing. Smears should not be heated because the resultant cell shrinkage may create a clear zone around the organism that is an artifact that can be mistaken for the capsule.

The capsule stain uses two reagents.

Primary Stain
Crystal Violet (1% aqueous) A violet stain is applied to a non–heat-fixed smear. At this point, the cell and the capsular material will take on the dark color.

Decolorizing Agent
Copper Sulfate (20%) Because the capsule is nonionic, unlike the bacterial cell, the primary stain adheres to the capsule but does not bind to it. In the capsule staining method, copper sulfate is used as a decolorizing agent rather than water. The copper sulfate washes the purple primary stain out of the capsular material without removing the stain bound to the cell wall. At the same time, the decolorized capsule absorbs the copper sulfate, and the capsule will now appear blue in contrast to the deep purple color of the cell.

Figure 4 shows the presence of a capsule as a clear zone surrounding the darker-stained cell.

Differential Staining for Visualization of Bacterial Cell Structures

PROCEDURE

1 Flood smears with malachite green and steam over a beaker of water placed on a hot plate.

2 Cool and wash off stain with tap water. The water also serves as the decolorizing agent.

3 Counterstain with safranin for 30 seconds.

4 Wash off the safranin with tap water.

5 Blot the slide dry with bibulous paper.

Figure 3 **Spore-staining procedure**

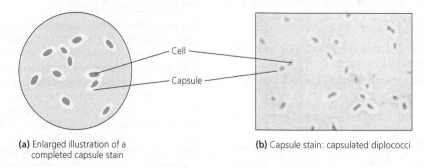

Cell

Capsule

(a) Enlarged illustration of a completed capsule stain

(b) Capsule stain: capsulated diplococci

Figure 4 **Capsule stain**

Encapsulated Bacterial Pneumonia

The virulence of an organism is increased by the presence of a capsule, since the capsule protects the organism from phagocytosis by white blood cells and inhibits antibody or complement fixation. The water-soluble polysaccharide and/or the polypeptide composition of the bacterial capsule makes staining this feature difficult. Gram-negative bacteria that form capsules include *Haemophilus influenzae* and *Klebsiella pneumoniae*. Gram-positive bacteria that form capsules include *Bacillus anthracis* and *Streptococcus pneumoniae*. If a bacterial infection is not being cleared or responding to antibiotic therapy as expected, staining of isolated organisms to determine the presence of a capsule may be warranted.

AT THE BENCH

Materials

Cultures

48-hour-old skimmed milk cultures of *Alcaligenes viscolactis*, *Leuconostoc mesenteroides*, and *Enterobacter aerogenes*.

Reagents

1% crystal violet and 20% copper sulfate ($CuSO_4 \cdot 5H_2O$).

Equipment

Bunsen burner, inoculating loop or needle, staining tray, bibulous paper, lens paper, glass slides, and microscope.

Procedure

Steps 1–5 are pictured in **Figure 5**.

1. Obtain one clean glass slide. Place several drops of crystal violet stain on the slide.

2. Using aseptic technique, add three loopfuls of a culture to the stain and *gently* mix with the inoculating loop.

3. With a clean glass slide, spread the mixture over the entire surface of the slide to create a very thin smear. Let stand for 5 to 7 minutes. Allow smears to air-dry. *Note: Do not heat fix.*

4. Wash smears with 20% copper sulfate solution.

5. *Gently* blot dry and examine under oil immersion.

6. Repeat Steps 1–5 for each of the remaining test cultures.

7. In the chart provided in the Lab Report, complete the following:

   a. Draw a representative microscopic field of each preparation.

   b. Record the comparative size of the capsule; that is, small, moderate, or large.

   c. Indicate the color of the capsule and of the cell on each preparation.

Differential Staining for Visualization of Bacterial Cell Structures

PROCEDURE

1 Place several drops of crystal violet stain on a clean glass slide.

2 Aseptically transfer 3 loopfuls of culture to the stain and gently mix with the loop.

3 With a clean glass slide, spread mixture to form a thin smear. Air-dry.

4 Wash smear with 20% copper sulfate solution.

5 Gently blot dry with bibulous paper.

Figure 5 **Capsule staining procedure**

Observations and Results

PART A: Spore Stain

	C. sporogenes	*B. cereus*
Draw a representative field.		
Color of spores	_____	_____
Color of vegetative cells	_____	_____
Location of endospore	_____	_____

PART B: Capsule Stain

	A. viscolactis	*L. mesenteroides*	*E. aerogenes*
Draw a representative field.			
Capsule size	_____	_____	_____
Color of capsule	_____	_____	_____
Color of cell	_____	_____	_____

Review Questions

1. Why is heat necessary in spore staining?

2. Explain the function of water in spore staining.

3. Assume that during the performance of this exercise you made several errors in your spore-staining procedure. In each of the following cases, indicate how your microscopic observations would differ from those observed when the slides were prepared correctly.

   a. You used acid-alcohol as the decolorizing agent.

   b. You used safranin as the primary stain and malachite green as the counterstain.

    c. You did not apply heat during the application of the primary stain.

4. Explain the medical significance of a capsule.

5. Explain the function of copper sulfate in this procedure.

Photo Credits

Credits are listed in order of appearance.

Photo 11:   Steven R. Spilatro, Department of Biology, Marietta College, Marietta, Ohio

Photo 12:   James Cappuccino

Cultivation of Microorganisms: Nutritional and Physical Requirements, and Enumeration of Microbial Populations

LEARNING OBJECTIVES

Once you have completed the experiments in this section, you should be familiar with

1. The basic nutritional and environmental requirements for the cellular activities of all forms of life.

2. The principles associated with the use of routine and special-purpose media for microbial cultivation.

3. The diversified physical factors essential for microbial cultivation.

4. Specialized techniques for the cultivation of anaerobic microorganisms.

5. The serial dilution–agar plate technique for enumeration of viable microorganisms.

6. The growth dynamics of bacterial populations.

Introduction

As do all other living organisms, microorganisms require certain basic nutrients and physical factors for the sustenance of life. However, their particular requirements vary greatly. Understanding these needs is necessary for successful cultivation of microorganisms in the laboratory.

Nutritional Needs

Nutritional needs of microbial cells are supplied in the laboratory through a variety of media. The following list illustrates the nutritional diversity that exists among microbes.

1. **Carbon:** This is the most essential and central atom common to all cellular structures and functions. Among microbial cells, two carbon-dependent types are noted:

   a. **Autotrophs:** These organisms can be cultivated in a medium consisting solely of inorganic compounds; specifically, they use inorganic carbon in the form of carbon dioxide.

   b. **Heterotrophs:** These organisms cannot be cultivated in a medium consisting solely of inorganic compounds; they must be supplied with organic nutrients, primarily glucose.

2. **Nitrogen:** This is also an essential atom in many cellular macromolecules, particularly proteins and nucleic acids. Proteins serve as the structural molecules forming the so-called fabric of the cell and as functional molecules, enzymes, that are responsible for the metabolic activities of the cell. Nucleic acids include DNA, the genetic basis of cell life, and RNA, which plays an active role in protein synthesis within the cell. Some microbes use atmospheric nitrogen, others rely on inorganic compounds such as ammonium or nitrate salts, and still others require nitrogen-containing organic compounds such as amino acids.

3. **Nonmetallic elements:** Two major nonmetallic ions are used for cellular nutrition:

   a. **Sulfur** is integral to some amino acids and is therefore a component of proteins.

From Part 4 of *Microbiology: A Laboratory Manual*, Tenth Edition. James G. Cappuccino, Natalie Sherman.

Sources include organic compounds such as sulfur-containing amino acids, inorganic compounds such as sulfates, and elementary sulfur.

b. **Phosphorus** is necessary for the formation of the nucleic acids DNA and RNA and also for synthesis of the high-energy organic compound adenosine triphosphate (ATP). Phosphorus is supplied in the form of phosphate salts for use by all microbial cells.

4. **Metallic elements: Ca^{2+}, Zn^{2+}, Na^+, K^+, Cu^{2+}, Mn^{2+}, Mg^{2+}, Fe^{2+}, and Fe^{3+}** are some of the metallic ions necessary for continued efficient performance of varied cellular activities. Some of these activities are osmoregulation, regulation of enzyme activity, and electron transport during biooxidation. Remember that these ions are micronutrients and are required in trace concentrations only. Inorganic salts supply these materials.

5. **Vitamins:** These organic substances contribute to cellular growth and are essential in minute concentrations for cell activities. They are also sources of coenzymes, which are required for the formation of active enzyme systems. Some microbes require vitamins to be supplied in a preformed state for normal metabolic activities. Some possess extensive vitamin-synthesizing pathways, whereas others can synthesize only a limited number from other compounds present in the medium.

6. **Water:** All cells require distilled water in the medium so that the low-molecular-weight nutrients can cross the cell membrane.

7. **Energy:** Active transport, biosynthesis, and biodegradation of macromolecules are the metabolic activities of cellular life. These activities can be sustained only if there is a constant availability of energy within the cell. Two bioenergetic types of microorganisms exist:

a. **Phototrophs** use radiant energy as their sole energy source.

b. **Chemotrophs** depend on oxidation of chemical compounds as their energy source. Some microbes use organic molecules such as glucose; others utilize inorganic compounds such as H_2S or $NaNO_2$.

Physical Factors

Three of the most important physical factors that influence the growth and survival of cells are temperature, pH, and the gaseous environment. An understanding of the roles they play in cell metabolism is essential.

1. **Temperature** influences the rate of chemical reactions through its action on cellular enzymes. Bacteria, as a group of organisms, exist over a wide range of temperatures. However, individual species can exist only within a narrower spectrum of temperatures. Low temperatures slow down or inhibit enzyme activity, thereby slowing down or inhibiting cell metabolism and, consequently, cell growth. High temperatures cause coagulation and thus irreversibly denature thermolabile enzymes. Although enzymes differ in their degree of heat sensitivity, generally temperatures in the range of 70°C destroy most essential enzymes and cause cell death.

2. **The pH of the extracellular environment** greatly affects cells' enzymatic activities. Most commonly, the optimum pH for cell metabolism is in the neutral range of 7. An increase in the hydrogen ion concentration resulting in an acidic pH (below 7) or a decrease in the hydrogen ion concentration resulting in an alkaline pH (above 7) is often detrimental. Either increase or decrease will slow down the rate of chemical reactions because of the destruction of cellular enzymes, thereby affecting the rate of growth and, ultimately, survival.

3. **The gaseous requirement** in most cells is atmospheric oxygen, which is necessary for the biooxidative process of respiration. Atmospheric oxygen plays a vital role in ATP formation and the availability of energy in a utilizable form for cell activities. Other cell types, however, lack the enzyme systems for respiration in the presence of oxygen and therefore must use an anaerobic form of respiration or fermentation.

The following exercises will demonstrate the diversity of nutritional and environmental requirements among microorganisms.

Nutritional Requirements: Media for the Routine Cultivation of Bacteria

Principle

To satisfy the diverse nutritional needs of bacteria, bacteriologists employ two major categories of media for routine cultivation.

Chemically Defined Media

These are composed of known quantities of chemically pure, specific organic and/or inorganic compounds. Their use requires knowledge of the organism's specific nutritional needs. The following two chemically defined media are used in this exercise:

1. **Inorganic synthetic broth:** This completely inorganic medium is prepared by incorporating the following salts per 1000 ml of water:

Sodium chloride (NaCl)	5.0 g
Magnesium sulfate ($MgSO_4$)	0.2 g
Ammonium dihydrogen phosphate ($NH_4H_2PO_4$)	1.0 g
Dipotassium hydrogen phosphate (K_2HPO_4)	1.0 g
Atmospheric carbon dioxide (CO_2)	

2. **Glucose salts broth:** This medium is composed of salts incorporated into the inorganic synthetic broth medium plus **glucose,** 5 g per liter, which serves as the sole organic carbon source.

Complex Media

The exact chemical composition of these media is not known. They are made of extracts of plant and animal tissue and are variable in their chemical composition. Most contain abundant amino acids, sugars, vitamins, and minerals; however, the quantities of these constituents are not known. They are capable of supporting the growth of most heterotrophs. The following two complex media are used in this exercise.

1. **Nutrient broth:** This basic complex medium is prepared by incorporating the following ingredients per 1000 ml of distilled water:

Peptone	5.0 g
Beef extract	3.0 g

   Peptone, a semidigested protein, is primarily a nitrogen source. The **beef extract,** a beef derivative, is a source of organic carbon, nitrogen, vitamins, and inorganic salts.

2. **Yeast extract broth:** This is composed of the basic artificial medium ingredients used in the nutrient broth plus **yeast extract,** 5 g per liter, which is a rich source of vitamin B and provides additional organic nitrogen and carbon compounds.

   The yeast extract broth is an example of an **enriched medium** and is used for the cultivation of **fastidious** microorganisms, organisms that have highly elaborate and specific nutritional needs. These bacteria do not grow or grow poorly on a basic artificial medium and require the addition of one or more growth-supporting substances, enrichments such as additional plant or animal extracts, vitamins, or blood.

Measuring Turbidity

In this experiment you will evaluate (1) the abilities of media to support the growth of different species of bacteria, and (2) the nutritional needs of the bacteria. You will observe the amount of growth, measured by turbidity, present in each culture following incubation. To evaluate more accurately the amount

From Experiment 14 of *Microbiology: A Laboratory Manual*, Tenth Edition. James G. Cappuccino, Natalie Sherman.
Copyright © 2014 by Pearson Education, Inc. All rights reserved.

Figure 1 Schematic diagram of a spectrophotometer

of growth, a Bausch & Lomb Spectronic 20 spectrophotometer will be used.

This instrument measures the amount of light transmitted (T) or absorbed (A). It transmits a beam of light at a single wavelength (monochromatic light) through a liquid culture. The cells suspended in the culture interrupt the passage of light, and the amount of light energy transmitted through the suspension is measured on a photoelectric cell and converted into electrical energy. The electrical energy is then recorded on a galvanometer as 0% to 100% T. A schematic representation of a spectrophotometer is shown in **Figure 1**.

In practice, the density of a cell suspension is expressed as absorbance (A) rather than percent T, since A is directly proportional to the concentration of cells, whereas percent T is inversely proportional to the concentration of suspended cells. Therefore, as the turbidity of a culture increases, the A increases and percent T decreases, indicating growth of the cell population in the culture. For example, in comparing three cultures with A readings of 0.10 (percent T = 78), 0.30 (percent T = 49), and 0.50 (percent T = 30), the A reading of 0.50 would be indicative of the most abundant growth, and the 0.10 reading would be indicative of the least amount of growth. **Figure 2** shows the Bausch & Lomb Spectronic 20 spectrophotometer.

CLINICAL APPLICATION

The Purpose of Specialized Media

The successful cultivation of bacteria requires the use of culture media containing the nutritional and biochemical requirements capable of supporting growth. There is no single medium that can support the growth of all microorganisms. This challenge has been met by the development of a variety of specialized media. For example, the streptococci require media supplemented with blood in order to determine certain properties that are necessary for isolation and species identification. Another example is the thioglycollate medium, which contains thioglycolic acid that removes oxygen from the medium to encourage the growth of certain anaerobic bacteria.

AT THE BENCH

Materials

Cultures

Saline suspension of 24-hour Trypticase soy broth cultures, adjusted to 0.05 absorbance at a wavelength of 600 nm, of *Escherichia coli*, *Alcaligenes faecalis*, and *Streptococcus mitis*.

Figure 2 **The Bausch & Lomb Spectronic 20 spectrophotometer**

Media

Per designated student group: three test tubes
(13 × 100 mm) of each type of broth: inorganic
synthetic broth, glucose salts broth, nutrient broth,
and yeast extract broth.

Equipment

Bunsen burner, sterile 1-ml serological pipettes,
mechanical pipetting device, glassware marking pencil, test tube rack, and Bausch & Lomb
Spectronic 20 spectrophotometer.

Procedure Lab One

1. Using a sterile 1-ml pipette, add 0.1 ml of the
   E. coli culture to one test tube of each of the
   appropriately labeled media.
2. Repeat Step 1 for inoculation with *A. faecalis*
   and *S. mitis*.
3. Incubate the test cultures for 24 to 48 hours at
   37°C.

Procedure Lab Two

Follow the instructions below and refer to
Figure 2 for the use of the spectrophotometer
to obtain the absorbance readings of all your
cultures.

1. Turn the instrument on 10 to 15 minutes prior
   to use.
2. Set wavelength at 600 nm.
3. Set percent transmittance to 0% (A to 2) by
   turning the knob on the left.

4. Read the four yeast extract broth cultures as
   follows:
   a. Wipe clean the provided test tube of
      sterile yeast broth that will serve as the
      blank for the yeast broth culture readings.
      Fingerprints on the test tube will obscure
      the light path of the spectrophotometer.
   b. Insert the yeast extract broth blank into the
      tube holder, close the cover, and set the A
      to 0 (percent T = 100) by turning the knob
      on the right.
   c. Shake lightly or tap one of the tubes of
      yeast extract broth culture to resuspend the
      bacteria, wipe the test tube clean, and allow
      it to sit for several seconds for the equilibra-
      tion of the bacterial suspension.
   d. Remove the yeast extract broth blank from
      the tube holder.
   e. Insert a yeast extract broth culture into the
      tube holder, close the cover, and read and
      record the optical density reading in the
      chart provided in the Lab Report.
   f. Remove the yeast extract broth culture
      from the tube holder.
   g. Reset the spectrophotometer to an A of 2
      with the tube holder empty and to an A of 0
      with the yeast extract broth blank.
   h. Repeat Steps c through g to read and record
      the absorbance of the remaining yeast ex-
      tract broth cultures.
5. Repeat Step 4 (a–h) to read and record the
   absorbance of the nutrient broth cultures. Use
   the provided nutrient broth blank to set the
   spectrophotometer to an A of 0.

6. Repeat Step 4 (a–h) to read and record the absorbance of the glucose salts broth cultures. Use the provided glucose salts broth blank to set the spectrophotometer to an A of 0.

7. Repeat Step 4 (a–h) to read and record the absorbance of the inorganic synthetic broth cultures. Use the provided inorganic synthetic broth blank to set the spectrophotometer to an A of 0.

8. At the end of the experiment, return all cultures to the area designated for their disposal.

9. Complete the Lab Report.

Name: _____

Date: _____ Section: _____

Observations and Results

Optical Density Readings

	Yeast Extract Broth	Nutrient Broth	Glucose Broth	Inorganic Synthetic Broth
E. coli				
A. faecalis				
S. mitis				

1. On the basis of the above data, list the media in order (from best to worst) according to their ability to support the growth of bacteria.

2. List the three bacterial species in order of their increasing fastidiousness.

3. Why did the most fastidious organism grow poorly in the chemically defined medium?

Review Questions

1. Explain the advantages of using A readings rather than percent T as a means of estimating microbial growth.

2. Explain the reason for the use of different medium blanks in adjusting the spectrophotometer prior to obtaining A readings.

3. Why are complex media preferable to chemically defined media for routine cultivation of microorganisms?

4. Would you expect a heterotrophic organism to grow in an inorganic synthetic medium? Explain.

5. A soil isolate is found to grow poorly in a basic artificial medium. You suspect that a vitamin supplement is required.

   a. What supplement would you use to enrich the medium to support and maintain the growth of the organisms? Explain.

   b. Outline the procedure you would follow to determine the specific vitamins required by the organism to produce a more abundant growth.

Photo Credit

Credits are listed in order of appearance.

Photo 1: L. Brent Selinger, Department of Biological Sciences, University of Lethbridge, Pearson Education

Use of Differential, Selective, and Enriched Media

Principle

Numerous special-purpose media are available for functions including the following:

1. Isolation of bacterial types from a mixed population of organisms.

2. Differentiation among closely related groups of bacteria on the basis of macroscopic appearance of the colonies and biochemical reactions within the medium.

3. Enumeration of bacteria in sanitary microbiology, such as in water and sewage, and also in food and dairy products.

4. Assay of naturally occurring substances such as antibiotics, vitamins, and products of industrial fermentation.

5. Characterization and identification of bacteria by their abilities to produce chemical changes in different media.

In addition to nutrients necessary for the growth of all bacteria, special-purpose media contain both nutrients and chemical compounds important for specific metabolic pathways in different types of bacteria. In this exercise, three types of media will be studied and evaluated.

Selective Media

These media are used to select (isolate) specific groups of bacteria. They incorporate chemical substances that inhibit the growth of one type of bacteria while permitting growth of another, thus facilitating bacterial isolation.

1. **Phenylethyl alcohol agar:** This medium is used for the isolation of most gram-positive organisms. The phenylethyl alcohol is partially inhibitory to gram-negative organisms, which may form visible colonies whose size and number are much smaller than on other media.

2. **Crystal violet agar:** This medium is selective for most gram-negative microorganisms. Crystal violet dye exerts an inhibitory effect on most gram-positive organisms.

3. **7.5% sodium chloride agar:** This medium is inhibitory to most organisms other than halophilic (salt-loving) microorganisms. It is most useful in the detection of members of the genus *Staphylococcus*.

Figure 1 is a photo illustrating the selective effect of phenylethyl alcohol agar, which inhibits the gram-negative organism *E. coli* and selects for the gram-positive organism *S. aureus*.

Differential/Selective Media

These media can distinguish among morphologically and biochemically related groups of organisms. They incorporate chemical compounds that, following inoculation and incubation, produce a characteristic change in the appearance of bacterial growth and/or the medium surrounding the colonies, which permits differentiation.

Sometimes differential and selective characterisctics are combined in a single medium. MacConkey agar is a good example of this because it contains bile salts and crystal violet, which inhibit gram-positive organisms and allow gram-negatives to grow. In addition, it contains the substrate lactose and the pH indicator neutral red, which differentiates the red lactose-fermenting colonies from the translucent nonfermenting colonies. The following media are examples of this type of media:

1. **Mannitol salt agar:** This medium contains a high salt concentration, 7.5% NaCl, which is inhibitory to the growth of most, but not all,

(a) Nutrient agar   (b) Phenylethyl alcohol agar

Figure 1 Selective effect of phenylethyl alcohol agar reduces the growth of *E. coli* and selects for *S. aureus*

bacteria other than the staphylococci. The medium also performs a differential function: It contains the carbohydrate mannitol, which some staphylococci are capable of fermenting, and phenol red, a pH indicator for detecting acid produced by mannitol-fermenting staphylococci. These staphylococci exhibit a yellow zone surrounding their growth; staphylococci that do not ferment mannitol will not produce a change in coloration.

2. **MacConkey agar:** The inhibitory action of crystal violet on the growth of gram-positive organisms allows the isolation of gram-negative bacteria. Incorporation of the carbohydrate lactose, bile salts, and the pH indicator neutral red permits differentiation of enteric bacteria on the basis of their ability to ferment lactose. On this basis, enteric bacteria are separated into two groups:

    a. **Coliform bacilli** produce acid as a result of lactose fermentation. The bacteria exhibit a red coloration on their surface. *Escherichia coli* produce greater quantities of acid from lactose than other coliform species. When this occurs, the medium surrounding the growth also becomes pink because of the action of the acid that precipitates the bile salts, followed by absorption of the neutral red.

    b. **Dysentery, typhoid, and paratyphoid bacilli** are not lactose fermenters and therefore do not produce acid. The colonies appear tan and frequently transparent.

3. **Eosin–methylene blue agar (Levine):** Lactose and the dyes eosin and methylene blue permit differentiation between enteric lactose fermenters and nonfermenters as well as identification of the colon bacillus, *E. coli*. The *E. coli* colonies are blue-black with a metallic green sheen caused by the large quantity of acid that is produced and that precipitates the dyes onto the growth's surface. Other coliform bacteria, such as *Enterobacter aerogenes*, produce thick, mucoid, pink colonies on this medium. Enteric bacteria that do not ferment lactose produce colorless colonies, which, because of their transparency, appear to take on the purple color of the medium. This medium is also partially inhibitory to the growth of gram-positive organisms, and thus gram-negative growth is more abundant.

A photographic representation of the effects of selective/differential media is presented in **Figure 2**.

Enriched Media

Enriched media are media that have been supplemented with highly nutritious materials, such as blood, serum, or yeast extract, for the purpose of cultivating fastidious organisms.

For example, in **blood agar,** the blood incorporated into the medium is an enrichment ingredient for the cultivation of fastidious organisms such as the *Streptococcus* spp. The blood also permits demonstration of the hemolytic properties of some microorganisms, particularly the streptococci,

(a) Mannitol salt agar   (b) MacConkey agar   (c) Eosin–methylene blue agar

Figure 2 Effects of selective/differential media

whose hemolytic activities are classified as follows:

1. **Gamma hemolysis:** No lysis of red blood cells results in no significant change in the appearance of the medium surrounding the colonies.

2. **Alpha hemolysis:** Incomplete lysis of red blood cells, with reduction of hemoglobin to methemoglobin, results in a greenish halo around the bacterial growth.

3. **Beta hemolysis:** Lysis of red blood cells with complete destruction and use of hemoglobin by the organism results in a clear zone surrounding the colonies. This hemolysis is produced by two types of beta hemolysins,

namely **streptolysin O,** an antigenic, oxygen-labile enzyme, and **streptolysin S,** a nonantigenic, oxygen-stable lysin. The hemolytic reaction is enhanced when blood agar plates are streaked and simultaneously stabbed to show subsurface hemolysis by streptolysin O in an environment with reduced oxygen tension. Based on the hemolytic patterns on blood agar, the pathogenic beta-hemolytic streptococci may be differentiated from other streptococci.

Figure 3 shows the different types of hemolysis exhibited by different species of the genus *Streptococcus* on blood agar.

(a) Gamma hemolysis   (b) Alpha hemolysis   (c) Beta hemolysis

Figure 3 Types of hemolysis exhibited on a blood agar plate

CLINICAL APPLICATION

First Steps in Infected Wound Diagnosis

Wounds that have become infected may be swabbed or surgically processed to remove tissue. Once stained samples have revealed infectious agents, cultures are typically made on (1) blood agar for isolation of staphylococci and streptrococci bacteria, (2) MacConkey agar for gram-negative rods, and (3) enriched media that can support aerobes or anaerobes, such as thioglycollate broth. Additional media may be used, depending on what was observed microscopically, including Sabouraud dextrose agar for fungi and Löwenstein-Jensen medium for acid-fast rods. Once the microbes are isolated, further tests (which you will learn soon!) would likely be needed for complete identification.

AT THE BENCH

Materials

Cultures

24- to 48-hour Trypticase soy broth cultures of *Enterobacter aerogenes*, *Escherichia coli*, *Streptococcus* var. Lancefield Group E, *Streptococcus mitis*, *Enterococcus faecalis*, *Staphylococcus aureus*, *Staphylococcus epidermidis*, and *Salmonella typhimurium*.

Media

Per designated student group: one each of phenyl-ethyl alcohol agar, crystal violet agar, 7.5% sodium chloride agar, mannitol salt agar, MacConkey agar, eosin–methylene blue agar, and blood agar.

Equipment

Bunsen burner, inoculating loop, and glassware marking pencil.

Procedure Lab One

1. Using the bacterial organisms listed in Step 2, prepare and inoculate each of the plates in the following manner:

   a. Appropriately label the cover of each plate.

   b. Divide each of the Petri dishes into the required number of sections (one section for each different organism) by marking the *bottom of the dish*. Label each section with the name of the organism to be inoculated, as illustrated in **Figure 4a**.

   c. Using aseptic technique, inoculate all plates, except the blood agar plate, with the designated organisms by making a single line of inoculation of each organism in its appropriate section (**Figure 4b**). Be sure to close the Petri dish and flame the inoculating needle between inoculations of the different organisms.

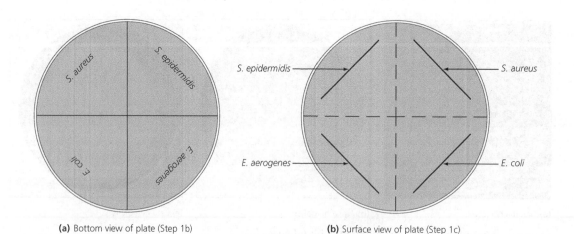

(a) Bottom view of plate (Step 1b)   (b) Surface view of plate (Step 1c)

Figure 4 Mannitol salt agar plate preparation and inoculation procedure

d. Using aseptic technique, inoculate the blood agar plate as described in Step 1c. Upon completion of each single line of inoculation, use the inoculating loop and make three or four stabs at a 45° angle across the streak.

2. Inoculate each of the different media with the following:

   a. Phenylethyl alcohol agar: *E. coli, S. aureus,* and *E. faecalis.*

   b. Crystal violet agar: *E. coli, S. aureus,* and *E. faecalis.*

   c. 7.5% sodium chloride agar: *S. aureus, S. epidermidis,* and *E. coli.*

   d. Mannitol salt agar: *S. aureus, S. epidermidis, E. aerogenes,* and *E. coli.*

   e. MacConkey agar: *E. coli, E. aerogenes, S. typhimurium,* and *S. aureus.*

   f. Eosin–methylene blue agar: *E. coli, E. aerogenes, S. typhimurium,* and *S. aureus.*

   g. Blood agar: *E. faecalis, S. mitis,* and *Streptococcus* var. Lancefield Group E.

3. Incubate the phenylethyl alcohol agar plate in an inverted position for 48 to 72 hours at 37°C. Incubate the remaining plates in an inverted position for 24 to 48 hours at 37°C.

Procedure LabTwo

1. Carefully examine each of the plates. In the chart provided in the Lab Report, note and record the following:

   a. Amount of growth along line of inoculation as follows: 0 = none; 1+ = scant; and 2+ = moderate to abundant.

   b. Appearance of the growth: coloration, transparency.

   c. Change in the appearance of the medium surrounding the growth: coloration, transparency indicative of hemolysis.

Lab Report

Observations and Results

Type of Medium	Medium	Bacterial Species	Amount of Growth	Appearance of Growth	Appearance of Medium
Selective	Phenylethyl alcohol agar	E. coli	1	white	white
		S. aureus	2	yellow	white
		E. faecalis	2	yellow	white
	Crystal violet agar	E. coli	1	purple	no
		S. aureus	~~X~~ 0	~~XXX~~ no	no
		E. faecalis	1	purple	no
	7.5% sodium chloride agar	E. coli			
		S. aureus			
		S. epidermidis			
Differential/ Selective	Mannitol salt agar	E.coli	0	no	red
		E.aerogenes	0	no	red
		S. aureus	2	yellow	yellow
		S. epidermidis	2	white	red
	MacConkey agar	E. coli	2	pink	pink
		E. aerogenes	2	pink	clear
		S. typhimurium	2	Pink	clear
		S. aureus	2	pink	clear
	Eosin–methylene blue agar	E. coli	2	~~XXX~~ green	red
		E. aerogenes	2	~~XXX~~	red
		S. typhimurium	2	~~XXX~~ purple	red
		~~S. aureus~~ Kp	2/2	~~XXX~~ purple	red
Enriched	Blood agar	~~S. mitis~~ Sa	2	~~XXX~~ white	white
		E. faecalis	2	~~XXX~~ white	white
		~~Streptococcus~~ Sp var. Lancefield Group E	2	~~XXX~~ white	white
		Ea	2	~~XXX~~ white	no change

Indicate the specific selective and/or differential purpose of each of the following media:

    a. Phenylethyl alcohol agar:

    b. Crystal violet agar:

    c. 7.5% sodium chloride agar:

    d. Mannitol salt agar:

    e. MacConkey agar:

f. Eosin–methylene blue agar (Levine):

g. Blood agar:

Review Questions

1. Explain the purpose of the following:
   a. Crystal violet in the MacConkey agar medium:

   b. Blood in the blood agar medium:

   c. Eosin and methylene blue dyes in the eosin–methylene blue agar medium:

d. High salt concentration in the mannitol salt agar medium:

e. Lactose in the MacConkey agar medium:

f. Phenylethyl alcohol in the phenylethyl alcohol agar medium:

2. Why are crystal violet agar and 7.5% sodium chloride agar considered selective media?

3. A patient exhibits a boil on his neck. You, as a microbiology technician, are asked to identify the causative organism and determine whether it is pathogenic. Describe the procedure that you would follow to make this determination.

Photo Credits

Credits are listed in order of appearance.

Photo 1:   Experiment performed and photographed by L. Brent Selinger, Department of Biological Sciences, University of Lethbridge, Pearson Education

Photo 2:   James Cappuccino

Photo 3:   Experiment performed and photographed by L. Brent Selinger, Department of Biological Sciences, University of Lethbridge, Pearson Education

Photo 4:   James Cappuccino

Photo 5:   Experiment performed and photographed by L. Brent Selinger, Department of Biological Sciences, University of Lethbridge, Pearson Education

Photo 6:   James Cappuccino

Physical Factors: Temperature

Principle

Microbial growth is directly dependent on how temperature affects cellular enzymes. With increasing temperatures, enzyme activity increases until the three-dimensional configuration of these molecules is lost because of denaturation of their protein structure. On the other hand, as the temperature is lowered toward the freezing point, enzyme inactivation occurs and cellular metabolism gradually diminishes. At 0°C, biochemical reactions cease in most cells.

Bacteria, as a group of living organisms, are capable of growth within an overall temperature range of minus 5°C to 80°C. Each species, however, requires a narrower range that is determined by the heat sensitivity of its enzyme systems. Specific temperature ranges consist of the following **cardinal (significant) temperature points** (**Figure 1**):

1. **Minimum growth temperature:** The lowest temperature at which growth will occur. Below this temperature, enzyme activity is inhibited and the cells are metabolically inactive so that growth is negligible or absent.

2. **Maximum growth temperature:** The highest temperature at which growth will occur. Above this temperature, most cell enzymes are destroyed and the organism dies.

3. **Optimum growth temperature:** The temperature at which the rate of reproduction is most rapid; however, it is not necessarily optimum or ideal for all enzymatic activities of the cell.

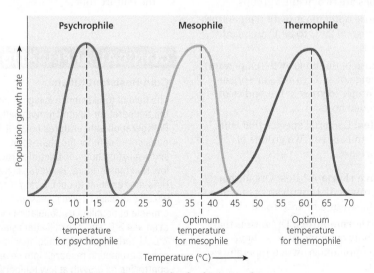

Figure 1 The effect of temperature on the growth of microorganisms

Figure 2 **Effect of temperature on bacterial growth and pigmentation**

Figure 2 shows the effects of temperature on bacterial growth and pigment production.

All bacteria can be classified into one of three major groups, depending on their temperature requirements:

1. **Psychrophiles:** Bacterial species that will grow within a temperature range of –5°C to 20°C. The distinguishing characteristic of all psychrophiles is that they will grow between 0° and 5°C.

2. **Mesophiles:** Bacterial species that will grow within a temperature range of 20°C to 45°C. The distinguishing characteristics of all mesophiles are their ability to grow at human body temperature (37°C) and their inability to grow at temperatures above 45°C. Included among the mesophiles are two distinct groups:

   a. Those whose optimum growth temperature is in the range of 20°C to 30°C are plant saprophytes.

   b. Those whose optimum growth temperature is in the range of 35°C to 40°C are organisms that prefer to grow in the bodies of warm-blooded hosts.

3. **Thermophiles:** Bacterial species that will grow at 35°C and above. Two groups of thermophiles exist:

   a. Facultative thermophiles: Organisms that will grow at 37°C, with an optimum growth temperature of 45°C to 60°C.

   b. Obligate thermophiles: Organisms that will grow only at temperatures above 50°C, with optimum growth temperatures above 60°C.

The ideal temperature for specific enzymatic activities may not coincide with the optimum growth temperature for a given organism. To understand this concept, you will investigate pigment production and carbohydrate fermentation by selected organisms at a variety of incubation temperatures.

1. The production of an endogenous red or magenta pigment by *Serratia marcescens* is determined by the presence of an orange to deep red coloration on the surface of the colonial growth.

2. Carbohydrate fermentation by *Saccharomyces cerevisiae* is indicated by the presence of gas, one of the end products of this fermentative process. Detection of this accumulated gas may be noted as an air pocket, of varying size, in an inverted inner vial (Durham tube) within the culture tube.

CLINICAL APPLICATION

Cold-Resistant Killers

The field of food science is highly concerned with the temperature-related growth patterns of bacteria. Refrigeration temperatures below 4.4°C are generally considered safe for the short-term storage of food, since most pathogenic bacteria grow very slowly below that temperature. However, some dangerous bacteria are resistant to cold. *Listeria monocytogenes*, which causes a flu-like illness and can be deadly, is capable of doubling its population every 36 hours, even at 4.2°C, and can still attain slow growth below 2°C. Listeria's cold tolerance may be due to adaptive genes, prompting research into novel methods of controlling its growth at low temperatures.

Materials

Cultures

24- to 48-hour nutrient broth cultures of *Escherichia coli*, *Bacillus stearothermophilus*, *Pseudomonas savastanoi*, *Serratia marcescens*, and Sabouraud broth culture of *Saccharomyces cerevisiae*.

Media

Per designated student group: four Trypticase soy agar plates and four Sabouraud broth tubes containing inverted Durham tubes.

Equipment

Bunsen burner, inoculating loop, refrigerator set at 4°C, two incubators set at 37°C and 60°C, sterile Pasteur pipette, test tube rack, and glassware marking pencil.

Procedure Lab One

1. Score the underside of all plates into four quadrants with a glassware marker. Label each section with the name of the test organism to be inoculated. When labeling the cover of each plate, include the temperature of incubation (4°C, 20°C, 37°C, or 60°C).

2. Aseptically inoculate each of the plates with *E. coli*, *B. stearothermophilus*, *P. savastanoi*, and *S. marcescens* by means of a single line of inoculation of each organism in its appropriately labeled section.

3. Appropriately label the four Sabouraud broth tubes, including the temperatures of incubation as indicated above.

4. Gently shake the *S. cerevisiae* culture to suspend the organisms. Using a sterile Pasteur pipette, aseptically add one drop of the culture into each of the four tubes of broth media.

5. Incubate all plates in an inverted position and the broth cultures at each of the four experimental temperatures (4°C, 20°C, 37°C, or 60°C) for 24 to 48 hours.

Procedure Lab Two

1. In the chart provided in the Lab Report, complete the following:

   a. Observe all the cultures for the presence of growth. Record your observations: (1+) for scant growth; (2+) for moderate growth; (3+) for abundant growth; and (–) for the absence of growth. Evaluate the amount of growth in the *S. cerevisiae* cultures by noting the degree of developed turbidity.

   b. Observe the *S. marcescens* growth on all the plate cultures for the presence or absence of orange to deep red pigmentation. Record the presence of pigment on a scale of 1+ to 3+, and enter (–) for the absence of pigmentation.

   c. Observe the *S. cerevisiae* cultures for the presence of a gas pocket in the Durham tube, which is indicative of carbohydrate fermentation. Record your observations using the following designations: (1+) for a minimal amount of gas; (2+) for a moderate amount of gas; (3+) for a large amount of gas; and (–) for the absence of gas.

   d. Record and classify the cultures as psychrophiles, mesophiles, facultative thermophiles, or obligate thermophiles.

Lab Report

Observations and Results

Temperature	*Serratia marcescens* Pigment	*Serratia marcescens* Growth	*Pseudomonas savastanoi* Growth	*Escherichia coli* Growth	*Bacillus stearothermophilus* Growth	*Saccharomyces cerevisiae* Growth	*Saccharomyces cerevisiae* Gas
4°C (refrig.)	~~red~~	~~3+~~		—	—		
20°C (room temp.)	red	3+		+1	+1		
37°C (body temp.)	white	3+		+2	+1		
60°C	—	—		—	+1		
Classification							

Based on your observations of the *S. marcescens* and *S. cerevisiae* cultures, is the optimum growth temperature the ideal temperature for all cell activities? Explain.

Review Questions

1. In the following chart, indicate the types of organisms that would grow preferentially in or on various environments, and indicate the optimum temperature for their growth.

Environment	Type of Organism	Optimum Temperature
Ocean bottom near shore		
Ocean bottom near hot vent		
Hot sulfur spring		
Compost pile (middle)		
High mountain lake		
Center of an abscess		
Antarctic ice		

2. Explain the effects of temperatures above the maximum and below the minimum growth temperatures on cellular enzymes.

3. If an organism grew at 20°C, explain how you would determine experimentally whether the organism was a psychrophile or a mesophile.

4. Is it possible for thermophilic organisms to induce infections in warm-blooded animals? Explain.

Photo Credit

Credits are listed in order of appearance.

Photo 1: David Alexander, University of Portland

Physical Factors: pH of the Extracellular Environment

Principle

Growth and survival of microorganisms are greatly influenced by the pH of the environment, and all bacteria and other microorganisms differ as to their requirements. Based on their pH optima, microorganisms may be classified as acidophiles, neutrophiles, or alkalophiles (**Figure 1**). Each species has the ability to grow within a specific pH range, which may be broad or limited, with the most rapid growth occurring within a narrow optimum range. These specific pH needs reflect the organisms' adaptations to their natural environment. For example, enteric bacteria are capable of survival within a broad pH range, which is characteristic of their natural habitat, the digestive system. Bacterial blood parasites, on the other hand, can tolerate only a narrow range; the pH of the circulatory system remains fairly constant at approximately 7.4.

Despite this diversity and the fact that certain organisms can grow at extremes of the pH scale, generalities can be made. The specific range for bacteria is between 4 and 9, with the optimum being 6.5 to 7.5. Fungi (molds and yeasts) prefer an acidic environment, with optimum activities at a pH of 4 to 6.

Because a neutral or nearly neutral environment is generally advantageous to the growth of microorganisms, the pH of the laboratory medium is frequently adjusted to approximately 7. Metabolic activities of the microorganism will result in the production of wastes, such as acids from carbohydrate degradation and alkali from protein breakdown, and these will cause shifts in pH that can be detrimental to growth.

To retard this shift, chemical substances that act as **buffers** are frequently incorporated when the medium is prepared. A commonly used **buffering system** involves the addition of equimolar concentrations of K_2HPO_4, a salt of a weak base, and KH_2PO_4, a salt of a weak acid. In a medium that has become acidic, the K_2HPO_4 absorbs

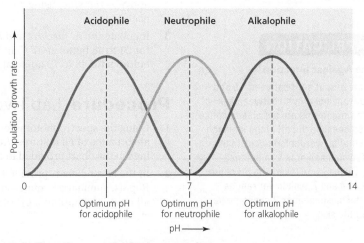

Figure 1 The effect of pH on the growth of microorganisms

excess H^+ to form a weakly acidic salt and a potassium salt with the anion of the strong acid.

$$K_2HPO_4 \ + \ HCL \ \rightarrow \ KH_2PO_4 \ + \ KCL$$

| Salt of a weak base | Strong acid | Salt of a weak acid | Potassium chloride salt |

In a medium that has become alkaline, KH_2PO_4 releases H^+, which combines with the excess OH^- to form water, and the remaining anionic portion of the weakly acidic salt combines with the cation of the alkali.

$$KH_2PO_4 \ + \ KOH \ \rightarrow \ K_2HPO_4 \ + \ H_2O$$

| Salt of a weak acid | Strong base | Salt of a weak base | Water |

Most media contain amino acids, peptones, and proteins, which can act as natural buffers because of their amphoteric nature. For example, amino acids are zwitterions, molecules in which the amino group and the carboxyl group ionize to form dipolar ions. These behave in the following manner:

CLINICAL APPLICATION

pH as a Defense Against Infection

Most bacteria grow best at a pH between 6.5 and 7.5, and fungi show optimal growth between a pH of 4 and 6. Many microorganisms are not able to cause stomach infections because the pH of the stomach is 2.0, resembling that of hydrochloric acid. In this way, the acid of the stomach acts as a defense against infection. By the same token, the pH of the skin varies between 4 and 7, with lower ranges (around 5) being the most common, helping prevent many infections of the skin.

AT THE BENCH

Materials

Cultures

Saline suspensions of 24-hour nutrient broth cultures, adjusted to an absorbance (A) of 0.05 at a wavelength of 600 nm, of *Alcaligenes faecalis*, *Escherichia coli*, and *Saccharomyces cerevisiae*.

Media

Per designated student group: 12 Trypticase soy broth (TSB) tubes, three at each of the following pH designations: 3, 6, 7, and 9. The pH has been adjusted with 1N sodium hydroxide or 1N hydrochloric acid.

Equipment

Bunsen burner, sterile 1-ml pipettes, mechanical pipetting device, Bausch & Lomb Spectronic 20 spectrophotometer, test tube rack, and glassware marking pencil.

Procedure Lab One

1. Using a sterile pipette, inoculate a series of the appropriately labeled TSB tubes of media, pH values of 3, 6, 7, and 9, with *E. coli* by adding 0.1 ml of the saline culture to each.

2. Repeat Step 1 for the inoculation of *A. faecalis* and *S. cerevisiae*, using a new sterile pipette each time.

3. Incubate the *A. faecalis* and *E. coli* cultures for 24 to 48 hours at 37°C and the *S. cerevisiae* cultures for 48 to 72 hours at 25°C.

Procedure Lab Two

1. Using the spectrophotometer determine the absorbance of all cultures. Record the readings in the chart provided in the Lab Report.

2. In the second chart provided in the Lab Report, summarize your results as to the overall range and optimum pH of each organism studied.

Observations and Results

Absorbance Readings

Microbial Species	ABSORBANCE READINGS			
	pH 3	pH 6	pH 7	pH 9
E. coli				
A. faecalis				
S. cerevisiae				

pH Summary

Microbial Species	pH Range	Optimum pH
E. coli		
A. faecalis		
S. cerevisiae		

Review Questions

1. Explain the mechanism by which buffers prevent radical shifts in pH.

2. Explain why it is necessary to incorporate buffers into media in which microorganisms are grown.

3. Why are proteins and amino acids considered to be natural buffers?

4. Explain why microorganisms differ in their pH requirements.

5. Will all microorganisms grow optimally at a neutral pH? Explain.

6. You are instructed to grow *E. coli* in a chemically defined medium containing glucose and NH_4Cl as the carbon and nitrogen sources and also in nutrient broth that contains beef extract and peptone. Both media are adjusted to a pH of 7. With turbidity as an index for the amount of growth in each of the cultures, the following spectrophotometric readings are obtained following incubation:

	ABSORBANCE READINGS	
Time (hours)	Chemically Defined Medium	Nutrient Broth Medium
6	0.100	0.100
12	0.300	0.500
18	0.275	0.900
24	0.125	1.500

Based on the above data, explain why *E. coli* ceased growing in the chemically defined medium but continued to grow in the nutrient broth.

Physical Factors: Atmospheric Oxygen Requirements

LEARNING OBJECTIVES

Once you have completed this experiment, you should be familiar with

1. The diverse atmospheric oxygen requirements of microorganisms.

Principle

Microorganisms exhibit great diversity in their ability to use free oxygen (O_2) for cellular respiration. These variations in O_2 requirements reflect the differences in biooxidative enzyme systems present in the various species. Microorganisms can be classified into one of five major groups according to their O_2 needs:

1. **Aerobes** require the presence of atmospheric oxygen for growth. Their enzyme system necessitates use of O_2 as the final hydrogen (electron) acceptor in the complete oxidative degradation of high-energy molecules such as glucose.

2. **Microaerophiles** require limited amounts of atmospheric oxygen for growth. Oxygen in excess of the required amount appears to block the activities of their oxidative enzymes and results in death.

3. **Obligate anaerobes** require the absence of free oxygen for growth because their oxidative enzyme system requires the presence of molecules other than O_2 to act as the final hydrogen (electron) acceptor. In these organisms, as in aerobes, the presence of atmospheric oxygen results in the formation of toxic metabolic end products, such as superoxide, O_2, a free radical of oxygen. However, these organisms lack the enzymes superoxide dismutase

and catalase, whose function is to degrade the superoxide to water and oxygen as follows:

$$2O_2^- + 2H^+ \xrightarrow{\text{Superoxide dismutase}} H_2O_2 + O_2$$

$$2H_2O_2 \xrightarrow{\text{Catalase}} 2H_2O + O_2$$

In the absence of these enzymes, small amounts of atmospheric oxygen are lethal, and these organisms are justifiably called obligate anaerobes.

4. **Aerotolerant anaerobes** are fermentative organisms, and therefore they do not use O_2 as a final electron acceptor. Unlike the obligate anaerobes, they produce catalase and/or superoxide dismutase, and thus they are not killed by the presence of O_2. Hence, these organisms are anaerobes that are termed aerotolerant.

5. **Facultative anaerobes** can grow in the presence or absence of free oxygen. They preferentially use oxygen for aerobic respiration. However, in an oxygen-poor environment, cellular respiration may occur anaerobically, utilizing such compounds as nitrates (NO_3^-) or sulfates (SO_4^{2-}) as final hydrogen acceptors, or via a fermentative pathway.

The oxygen needs of microorganisms can be determined by noting their growth distributions following a **shake-tube inoculation.** This procedure requires introduction of the inoculum into a melted agar medium, shaking of the test tube to disperse the microorganisms throughout the agar, and rapid solidification of the medium to ensure that the cells remain dispersed. Following incubation, the growth distribution indicates the organisms' oxygen requirements. Aerobes exhibit surface growth, whereas anaerobic growth is limited to the bottom of the deep tube. Facultative anaerobes, because of their indifference to the presence or absence of oxygen, exhibit growth throughout the medium. Microaerophiles grow in a zone slightly below the surface. **Figure 1** illustrates the shake-tube inoculation procedure and the distribution of growth following an appropriate incubation period.

CLINICAL APPLICATION

Differentiating Aerobes and Anaerobes

Samples suspected of containing anaerobes need to be handled carefully and transported promptly to a lab, where they are typically inoculated onto anaerobic blood agar plates and anaerobic broth, as well as onto MacConkey agar and an aerobic blood plate. Growth on aerobic or anaerobic agars will determine oxygen requirements, while comparable growth on both aerobic and anaerobic media suggests a facultative anaerobe.

AT THE BENCH

Materials

Cultures

24- to 48-hour nutrient broth cultures of *Staphylococcus aureus*, *Corynebacterium xerosis*, and *Enterococcus faecalis*; 48- to 72-hour Sabouraud broth cultures of *Saccharomyces cerevisiae* and *Aspergillus niger*; and a 48-hour thioglycollate broth culture of *Clostridium sporogenes*.

Media

Six brain heart infusion agar deep tubes per designated student group.

Equipment

Bunsen burner, waterbath, iced waterbath, thermometer, sterile Pasteur pipettes, test tube rack, and glassware marking pencil.

Procedure Lab One

1. Liquefy the sterile brain heart infusion agar by boiling in a waterbath at 100°C.
2. Cool molten agar to 45°C; check temperature with a thermometer inserted into the waterbath.

Determining Oxygen Requirements

1. Using aseptic technique, inoculate each experimental organism by introducing two drops of the culture from a sterile Pasteur pipette into the appropriately labeled tubes of molten agar.
2. Vigorously rotate the freshly inoculated molten infusion agar between the palms of the hands to distribute the organisms.
3. Place inoculated test tubes in an upright position in the iced waterbath to solidify the medium rapidly.
4. Incubate the *S. aureus*, *C. xerosis*, *E. faecalis*, and *C. sporogenes* cultures for 24 to 48 hours at 37°C and the *A. niger* and *S. cerevisiae* cultures for 48 to 72 hours at 25°C.

Procedure Lab Two

1. Observe each of the experimental cultures for the distribution of growth in each tube.
2. Record your observations and your determination of the oxygen requirements for each of the experimental species in the chart provided in the Lab Report.

PROCEDURE

1 Transfer two drops of inoculum from the test culture into a melted agar deep tube.

2 Disperse the organisms throughout the molten agar medium by rapidly rotating the tube between the palms of your hands.

3 Cool rapidly by immersion in an iced waterbath.

4 Incubate at 37°C.

Distribution of Growth

Oxygen concentration

High

Low

Aerobic

Microaerophilic

Facultative anaerobic

Aerotolerant

Anaerobic

Figure 1 Procedure for determination of oxygen requirements

Observations and Results

Species	Distribution of Growth	Classification According to Oxygen Requirement
S. aureus	top	aerobic
C. xerosis	top	aerobic
E. faecalis	below surface	microaerophilic
A. niger	throughout	facultative anaer
S. cerevisiae	top-zone throu	aerobic
C. sporogenes	hole	aerotolerant

Review Questions

1. Why is it necessary to place the inoculated molten agar cultures in an iced waterbath for their rapid solidification?

2. As indicated by its oxygen requirements, which group of microorganisms has the most extensive bioenergetic enzyme system? Explain.

3. Account for the inability of aerobes to grow in the absence of O_2.

4. Account for the subsurface growth of microaerophiles in a shake-tube culture.

5. Consider the culture type in which growth was distributed throughout the entire medium and explain why the growth was more abundant toward the surface of the medium in some cultures, whereas other cultures showed an equal distribution of growth throughout the tubes.

6. Account for the fact that the *C. sporogenes* culture showed a separation within the medium or an elevation of the medium from the bottom of the test tube.

7. Your instructor asks you to explain why the *Streptococcus* species that are catalase negative are capable of growth in the presence of oxygen. How would you respond?

Techniques for the Cultivation of Anaerobic Microorganisms

LEARNING OBJECTIVES

Once you have completed this experiment, you should be familiar with

1. The methods for cultivation of anaerobic organisms.

Principle

Microorganisms differ in their abilities to use oxygen for cellular respiration. **Respiration** involves the oxidation of substrates for energy necessary to life. A substrate is **oxidized** when it loses a hydrogen ion and its electron (H^+e^-). Since the H^+e^- cannot remain free in the cell, it must immediately be picked up by an electron acceptor, which becomes reduced. Therefore reduction means gaining the H^+e^-. These are termed **oxidation-reduction (redox)** reactions. Some microorganisms have enzyme systems in which oxygen can serve as an electron acceptor, thereby being reduced to water. These cells have high oxidation-reduction potentials; others have low potentials and must use other substances as electron acceptors.

The enzymatic differences in microorganisms are explained more fully in the section dealing with metabolism. This discussion is limited to cultivation of the strict anaerobes, which cannot be cultivated in the presence of atmospheric oxygen (**Figure 1**). The procedure is somewhat more difficult because it involves sophisticated equipment and media enriched with substances that lower the redox potential. **Figure 2** shows some of the methods available for anaerobic cultivation.

The following experiment uses fluid thioglycollate medium and the GasPak™ anaerobic system.

Figure 1 Illustration of redox potentials in an agar deep tube

In the figure:

Redox potential — High ↕ Low

- Free exchange of oxygen
- Decreased exchange of oxygen
- Complete absence of oxygen

Aerobic cells
$2H^+e^- + O_2 \longrightarrow H_2O$
Reduction: oxygen final electron acceptor

Facultatively anaerobic cells
$2H^+e^- \longrightarrow$ Electron acceptors other than oxygen

Strictly anaerobic cells
$2H^+e^- \longrightarrow$ Electron acceptors other than oxygen

CLINICAL APPLICATION

Oxygen as a Treatment?

The causative agent of gas gangrene, *Clostridium perfringens,* is an anaerobic bacterium that thrives in wounds deprived of circulation and oxygen and can cause limb loss and death. Treatment may involve amputation or surgical removal of infected tissue. Doctors may also prescribe therapy using enriched oxygen delivered to the patient in a hyperbaric chamber. This allows the blood to carry more oxygen to the wounds, slowing the growth of anaerobic microbes. Patients typically undergo five 90-minute sessions lying in a chamber pressurized to 2.5 atmospheres, possibly alleviating the need for surgery.

Techniques for the Cultivation of Anaerobic Microorganisms

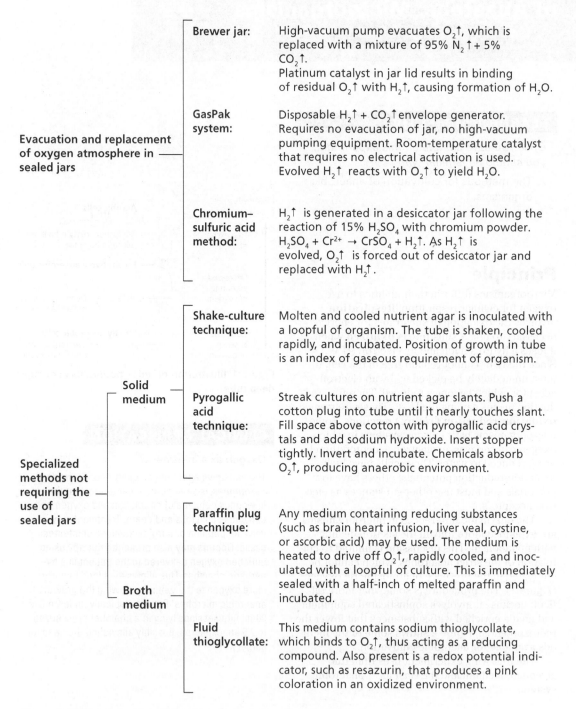

Evacuation and replacement of oxygen atmosphere in sealed jars

Brewer jar: High-vacuum pump evacuates $O_2\uparrow$, which is replaced with a mixture of 95% $N_2\uparrow$ + 5% $CO_2\uparrow$.
Platinum catalyst in jar lid results in binding of residual $O_2\uparrow$ with $H_2\uparrow$, causing formation of H_2O.

GasPak system: Disposable $H_2\uparrow$ + $CO_2\uparrow$ envelope generator. Requires no evacuation of jar, no high-vacuum pumping equipment. Room-temperature catalyst that requires no electrical activation is used. Evolved $H_2\uparrow$ reacts with $O_2\uparrow$ to yield H_2O.

Chromium–sulfuric acid method: $H_2\uparrow$ is generated in a desiccator jar following the reaction of 15% H_2SO_4 with chromium powder. $H_2SO_4 + Cr^{2+} \rightarrow CrSO_4 + H_2\uparrow$. As $H_2\uparrow$ is evolved, $O_2\uparrow$ is forced out of desiccator jar and replaced with $H_2\uparrow$.

Specialized methods not requiring the use of sealed jars

Solid medium

Shake-culture technique: Molten and cooled nutrient agar is inoculated with a loopful of organism. The tube is shaken, cooled rapidly, and incubated. Position of growth in tube is an index of gaseous requirement of organism.

Pyrogallic acid technique: Streak cultures on nutrient agar slants. Push a cotton plug into tube until it nearly touches slant. Fill space above cotton with pyrogallic acid crystals and add sodium hydroxide. Insert stopper tightly. Invert and incubate. Chemicals absorb $O_2\uparrow$, producing anaerobic environment.

Broth medium

Paraffin plug technique: Any medium containing reducing substances (such as brain heart infusion, liver veal, cystine, or ascorbic acid) may be used. The medium is heated to drive off $O_2\uparrow$, rapidly cooled, and inoculated with a loopful of culture. This is immediately sealed with a half-inch of melted paraffin and incubated.

Fluid thioglycollate: This medium contains sodium thioglycollate, which binds to $O_2\uparrow$, thus acting as a reducing compound. Also present is a redox potential indicator, such as resazurin, that produces a pink coloration in an oxidized environment.

Figure 2 Methods for the cultivation of anaerobic microorganisms

Materials
Cultures
24- to 48-hour nutrient broth cultures of *Bacillus cereus, Escherichia coli,* and *Micrococcus luteus;* and 48-hour thioglycollate broth culture of *Clostridium sporogenes.*

Media
Per designated student group: four screw-cap tubes of fluid thioglycollate medium and four nutrient agar plates.

Equipment
Bunsen burner, inoculating loop, GasPak anaerobic system, test tube rack, and glassware marking pencil.

Procedure Lab One
Fluid Thioglycollate Medium
1. For the performance of this procedure, the fluid thioglycollate medium must be fresh. Freshness is indicated by the absence of a pink color in the upper one-third of the medium. If this coloration is present, loosen the screw caps and place the tubes in a boiling water bath for 10 minutes to drive off the dissolved O_2 from the medium. Cool the tubes to 45°C before inoculation.

2. Aseptically inoculate the appropriately labeled tubes of thioglycollate with their respective test organisms by means of loop inoculations *to the depths of the media.*

3. Incubate the cultures for 24 to 48 hours at 37°C.

The appearance of the growth of organisms according to their gaseous requirements in thioglycollate medium is shown in **Figure 3**.

GasPak Anaerobic Technique
The GasPak system, shown in **Figure 4**, is a contemporary method for the exclusion of oxygen from a sealed jar used for incubation of anaerobic cultures in a nonreducing medium. This system uses a GasPak generator that consists of a foil package that generates hydrogen and carbon dioxide upon the addition of water. A palladium catalyst in the lid of the jar combines the evolved hydrogen with residual oxygen to form water, thereby creating a carbon dioxide environment within the jar that is conducive for anaerobic growth. The establishment of anaerobic conditions is verified by the color change of a methylene blue indicator strip in the jar. This blue indicator becomes colorless in the absence of oxygen.

1. With a glassware marking pencil, divide the bottom of each nutrient agar plate into two sections.

(a)   (b)   (c)   (d)   (e)

Figure 3 Bacterial growth patterns in thioglycollate broth tubes.
(a) Uninoculated control. (b,c) Uniform growth indicates facultative anaerobic bacteria. (d) Bubbles indicate gas-producing bacteria. (e) Bottom growth indicates anaerobic bacteria.

Figure 4 GasPak system

Screw clamp

Gasket

Palladium catalyst and holder

Hydrogen GasPak generator

Inverted inoculated plates

Anaerobic indicator strip (methylene blue)

5. Tear off the corner of the hydrogen and carbon dioxide gas generator and insert this inside the GasPak jar.

6. Place one set of plate cultures in an inverted position inside the GasPak chamber.

7. Expose the anaerobic indicator strip and place it inside the anaerobic jar so that the wick is visible from the outside.

8. With a pipette, add the required 10 ml of water to the gas generator and quickly seal the chamber with its lid.

9. Place the sealed jar in an incubator at 37°C for 24 to 48 hours. After several hours of incubation, observe the indicator strip for a color change to colorless, which is indicative of anaerobic conditions.

10. Incubate the duplicate set of plates in an inverted position for 24 to 48 hours at 37°C under aerobic conditions.

Procedure Lab Two

1. Observe the fluid thioglycollate cultures, GasPak system, and aerobically incubated plate cultures for the presence of growth. Record your results in the chart provided in the Lab Report.

2. Based on your observation, record the oxygen requirement classification of each test organism as anaerobe, facultative anaerobe, or aerobe.

2. Label each section on two plates with the name of the organism to be inoculated.

3. Repeat Step 2 to prepare a duplicate set of cultures.

4. Using aseptic technique, make a single-line streak inoculation of each test organism in its respectively labeled section on both sets of plates.

Observations and Results

Bacterial Species	Fluid Thioglycollate	GasPak Anaerobic Incubation	Aerobic Incubation	Oxygen Requirement Classification
M. luteus		—	+1	yes
B. cereus		—	+2	yes
E. coli		—	+2	yes
C. sporogenes		+1	—	no

Review Questions

1. Why can media such as brain heart infusion and thioglycollate be used for the cultivation of anaerobes?

2. What are the purposes of the indicator strip and the gas generator in the GasPak system?

3. Heroin addicts have a high incidence of *Clostridium tetani* infections. Discuss the reasons for the development of this type of infection in these IV drug users.

4. While you are working in your garden, a tine of the pitchfork accidentally produces a deep puncture wound in the calf of your leg. Discuss the type of infectious process you would be primarily concerned about and why.

5. The physician who treats your puncture wound opts to insert a drain before applying the dressing. What is the rationale for the insertion of the drain?

Photo Credit

Credits are listed in order of appearance.

Photo 1: Experiment performed and photographed by
L. Brent Selinger, Department of Biological Sciences,
University of Lethbridge, Pearson Education

Serial Dilution–Agar Plate Procedure to Quantitate Viable Cells

LEARNING OBJECTIVES

Once you have completed this experiment, you should understand

1. The diverse methods used to determine the number of cells in a bacterial culture.

2. How to determine quantitatively the number of viable cells in a bacterial culture.

(a) Petroff-Hausser counting chamber

Principle

Studies involving the analysis of materials such as food, water, milk, and, in some cases, air require quantitative enumeration of microorganisms in the substances. Many methods have been devised to accomplish this, including direct microscopic counts, use of an electronic cell counter such as the Coulter Counter®, chemical methods for estimating cell mass or cellular constituents, turbidimetric measurements for increases in cell mass, and the serial dilution–agar plate method.

Direct Microscopic Counts

Direct microscopic counts require the use of a specialized slide called the **Petroff-Hausser counting chamber,** in which an aliquot of a bacterial suspension is counted and the total number of cells is determined mathematically. The Petroff-Hausser counting chamber is a thick glass microscope slide with a chamber 0.02 mm (1/50 mm) deep in the center. The chamber contains an etched grid and has improved Neubauer rulings (1/400 square mm). The slide and the counting chamber are illustrated in **Figure 1**.

The rulings cover 9 mm². The boundary lines (Neubauer rulings) are the center lines of the groups of three. The center square millimeter is ruled into groups of 16 small squares, and each group is separated by triple lines, the middle one of which is the boundary. The ruled surface is 0.02 mm below the cover glass, which makes

(b) Petroff-Hausser counting chamber grid

Figure 1 The Petroff-Hausser chamber

the volume over a square millimeter 0.02 mm³ (cubic mm). All cells are counted in this square millimeter.

The number of bacterial cells counted is calculated as follows:

$$\text{number of cells per mm} = \text{number of cells counted} \times \text{dilution} \times 50{,}000$$

[The factor of 50,000 is used in order to determine the cell count for 1 ml: 1 ml = 1000 mm³ = (50 times the chamber depth of 0.02 mm) × 1000.] Although rapid, a direct count has the disadvantages that both living and dead cells are counted and that it is not sensitive to populations of fewer than 1 million cells.

Figure 2 Pour-plate technique

Breed smears are used mainly to quantitate bacterial cells in milk. Using stained smears confined to a 1-square-millimeter ruled area of the slide, the total population is determined mathematically. This method also fails to discriminate between viable and dead cells.

Electronic Cell Counters

The **Coulter Counter** is an example of an instrument capable of rapidly counting the number of cells suspended in a conducting fluid that passes through a minute orifice through which an electric current is flowing. Cells, which are nonconductors, increase the electrical resistance of the conducting fluid, and the resistance is electronically recorded, enumerating the number of organisms flowing through the orifice. In addition to its inability to distinguish between living and dead cells, the apparatus is also unable to differentiate inert particulate matter from cellular material.

Chemical Methods

While not considered means of direct quantitative analysis, chemical methods may be used to indirectly measure increases both in protein concentration and in DNA production. In addition, cell mass can be estimated by dry weight determination of a specific aliquot of the culture. Measurement of certain metabolic parameters may also be used to quantitate bacterial populations. The amount of oxygen consumed (oxygen uptake) is directly proportional to the increasing number of vigorously growing aerobic cells, and the rate of carbon dioxide production is related to increased growth of anaerobic organisms.

Spectrophotometric Analysis

Increased turbidity in a culture is another index of growth. With turbidimetric instruments, the amount of transmitted light decreases as the cell population increases, and the decrease in radiant energy is converted to electrical energy and indicated on a galvanometer. This method is rapid but limited because sensitivity is restricted to microbial suspensions of 10 million cells or greater.

Serial Dilution–Agar Plate Analysis

While all these methods may be used to enumerate the number of cells in a bacterial culture, the major disadvantage common to all is that the total count includes dead as well as living cells. Sanitary and medical microbiology at times require determination of viable cells. To accomplish this, the serial dilution–agar plate technique is used. Briefly, this method involves serial dilution of a bacterial suspension in sterile water blanks, which serve as a diluent of known volume. Once diluted, the suspensions are placed on suitable nutrient media. The **pour-plate technique,** illustrated in **Figure 2,** is the procedure usually employed. Molten agar, cooled to 45°C, is poured into a Petri dish containing a specified amount of the diluted sample. Following addition of the molten-then-cooled agar, the cover is replaced, and the plate is gently rotated in a circular motion to achieve uniform distribution of microorganisms. This procedure is repeated for all dilutions to be plated. Dilutions should be plated in duplicate for greater accuracy, incubated overnight, and counted on a **Quebec colony counter** either by hand or by an electronically modified version of this instrument. **Figure 3** is an illustration of this apparatus for counting colonies.

Figure 3 Quebec colony counter for the enumeration of bacterial colonies

Plates suitable for counting must contain not fewer than 30 nor more than 300 colonies. See **Figure 4**. The total count of the suspension is obtained by multiplying the number of cells per plate by the dilution factor, which is the reciprocal of the dilution.

Advantages of the serial dilution–agar plate technique are as follows:

1. Only viable cells are counted.

2. It allows isolation of discrete colonies that can be subcultured into pure cultures, which may then be easily studied and identified.

Disadvantages of this method are as follows:

1. Overnight incubation is necessary before colonies develop on the agar surface.

2. More glassware is used in this procedure.

3. The need for greater manipulation may result in erroneous counts due to errors in dilution or plating.

The following experiment uses the pour-plate technique for plating serially diluted culture samples.

CLINICAL APPLICATION

The Multiple Uses of Cell Counts

Determining how many cells are present in a sample is of particular importance in the food and dairy industries, which monitor the number and types of bacteria in their products. Elevated bacteria counts can indicate a sick animal, inadequate sanitation, or improper storage. Viable cell counts are also used in water treatment facilities as well as in wineries and breweries, where the number of yeast cells is monitored. In medical laboratories, sometimes the number of cells and growth rates are used to determine antimicrobial sensitivity as well as the course of infection.

AT THE BENCH

Materials
Culture
24- to 48-hour nutrient broth culture of *Escherichia coli.*

Media
Per designated student group: six 20-ml nutrient agar deep tubes and seven sterile 9-ml water blanks.

Equipment
Hot plate, waterbath, thermometer, test tube rack, Bunsen burner, sterile 1-ml serological pipettes, mechanical pipetting device, sterile Petri dishes, Quebec colony counter, manual hand counter, disinfectant solution in a 500-ml beaker, glassware marking pencil, turntable, bent glass rod, and beaker with 95% alcohol.

| 10^5 | 10^6 | 10^7 | 10^8 |

Figure 4 Agar plating method for viable cell counts using dilutions 1×10^5, 1×10^6, 1×10^7, and 1×10^8

Serial Dilution–Agar Plate Procedure to Quantitate Viable Cells

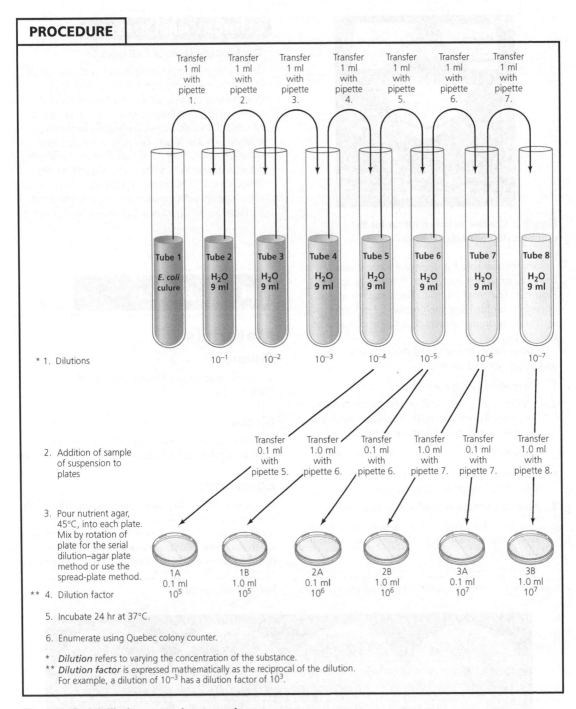

Figure 5 Serial dilution–agar plate procedure

Procedure Lab One

This procedure is illustrated in **Figure 5**. A photograph of the dilutions is shown in **Figure 6**.

1. Liquefy six agar deep tubes in an autoclave or by boiling. Cool the molten agar tubes and maintain in a water bath at 45°C.

2. Label the *E. coli* culture tube with the number 1 and the seven 9-ml water blanks as numbers 2 through 8. Place the labeled tubes in a test tube rack. Label the Petri dishes 1A, 1B, 2A, 2B, 3A, and 3B.

3. Mix the *E. coli* culture (Tube 1) by rolling the tube between the palms of your hands to ensure even dispersal of cells in the culture.

4. With a sterile pipette, aseptically transfer 1 ml from the bacterial suspension, Tube 1, to water blank Tube 2. Discard the pipette in the beaker of disinfectant. The culture has been diluted 10 times to 10^{-1}.

5. Mix Tube 2 and, with a fresh pipette, transfer 1 ml to Tube 3. Discard the pipette. The culture has been diluted 100 times to 10^{-2}.

6. Mix Tube 3 and, with a fresh pipette, transfer 1 ml to Tube 4. Discard the pipette. The culture has been diluted 1000 times to 10^{-3}.

7. Mix Tube 4 and, with a fresh pipette, transfer 1 ml to Tube 5. Discard the pipette. The culture has been diluted 10,000 times to 10^{-4}.

8. Mix Tube 5 and, with a fresh pipette, transfer 0.1 ml of this suspension to Plate 1A. Return the pipette to Tube 5 and transfer 1 ml to Tube 6. Discard the pipette. The culture has been diluted 100,000 times to 10^{-5}.

9. Mix Tube 6 and, with a fresh pipette, transfer 1 ml of this suspension to Plate 1B. Return the pipette to Tube 6 and transfer 0.1 ml to Plate

2A. Return the pipette to Tube 6 and transfer 1 ml to Tube 7. Discard the pipette. The culture has been diluted 1,000,000 times to 10^{-6}.

10. Mix Tube 7 and, with a fresh pipette, transfer 1 ml of this suspension to Plate 2B. Return the pipette to Tube 7 and transfer 0.1 ml to Plate 3A. Return the pipette to Tube 7 and transfer 1 ml to Tube 8. Discard the pipette. The culture has been diluted 10,000,000 times to 10^{-7}.

11. Mix Tube 8 and, with a fresh pipette, transfer 1 ml of this suspension to Plate 3B. Discard the pipette. The dilution procedure is now complete.

12. Check the temperature of the molten agar medium to be sure the temperature is 45°C. Remove a tube from the waterbath and wipe the outside surface dry with a paper towel. Using the pour-plate technique, pour the agar into Plate 1A as shown in Figure 2 and rotate the plate gently to ensure uniform distribution of the cells in the medium.

13. Repeat Step 12 for the addition of molten nutrient agar to Plates 1B, 2A, 2B, 3A, and 3B.

14. Once the agar has solidified, incubate the plates in an inverted position for 24 hours at 37°C.

Note: If desired, the spread-plate technique may be substituted for the agar pour-plate method described in this experiment. In this case, the dilutions may be placed on the surface of the hardened agar with a sterile pipette and distributed over the surface by means of a bent glass rod and turntable. Following incubation, cell counts may be made as described in this experiment. The resultant cell counts should be the same with either system. The main difference is that there will be no subsurface colonies in the spread-plate method.

10^{-1} 10^{-2} 10^{-3} 10^{-4} 10^{-5} 10^{-6}

Figure 6 Serial dilution of bacterial culture for quantitation of viable cell numbers

Procedure Lab Two

1. Using a Quebec colony counter and a mechanical hand counter, observe all colonies on plates. Statistically valid plate counts are only obtained from bacterial cell dilutions that yield between 30 and 300 colonies. Plates with more than 300 colonies cannot be counted and *400* are designated as **too numerous to count—TNTC**; plates with fewer than 30 colonies *20* are designated as **too few to count—TFTC**. Count only plates containing between 30 and 300 colonies. Remember to count all subsurface as well as surface colonies.

2. The number of organisms per ml of original culture is calculated by multiplying the number of colonies counted by the dilution factor:

   number of cells per ml =
   number of colonies × dilution factor

Examples:

a. Colonies per plate = 50

Dilution factor = $1 : 1 \times 10^6$ $(1 : 1,000,000)$

Volume of dilution added to plate = 1 ml

$50 \times 1,000,000 = 50,000,000$ or

(5×10^7) CFUs/ml

(colony-forming units)

b. Colonies per plate = 50

Dilution factor = $1 : 1 \times 10^5$ $(1 : 1,00,000)$

Volume of dilution added to plate = 0.1 ml

$50 \times 100,000 = 50,000,000$ (5×10^6)

cells/0.1 ml

$5,000,000 \times 10 = 50,000,000$

(5×10^7) CFUs/ml

3. Record your observations and calculated bacterial counts per ml of sample in the Lab Report.

4. Since the dilutions plated are replicates of each other, determine the average of the duplicate bacterial counts per ml of sample and record in the chart provided in the Lab Report.

Observations and Results

Plate	Dilution Factor	ml of Dilution Plated	Final Dilution on Plate	Number of Colonies	Bacterial Count per ml of Sample (CFU/ml)	Average Count per ml of Sample (CFU/ml)	
1A	10^5	.1	10^5	TMTC		———	TNTC
1B	10^5	1	10^5	TMTC		———	
2A	10^6	.1	10^8	TNTC		———	3.8×10^8
2B	10^6	1	10^6	TNTC		———	
3A	10^7	.1	10^7	128	1.28×10^9	———	1.9×10^9
3B	10^7	1	10^7	348	3.48×10^9	———	

Review Questions

1. What is the major disadvantage of microbial counts performed by methods other than the serial dilution–agar plate procedure?

2. Distinguish between dilution and dilution factor.

3. What are the advantages and disadvantages of the serial dilution–agar plate procedure?

4. If 0.1 ml of a 1×10^{-6} dilution plate contains 56 colonies, calculate the number of cells per ml of the original culture.

5. How would you record your observation of a plate containing 305 colonies? A plate with 15 colonies?

6. Explain the chemical methods for measuring cell growth.

7. Your instructor asks you to determine the number of organisms in a water sample. Observation of your dilution plates reveals the presence of spreading colonial forms on some of the culture plates. What is the rationale for the elimination of these plate counts from your experimental data?

Photo Credits

Credits are listed in order of appearance.

Photo 1:   Hausser Scientific

Photo 2:   L. Brent Selinger, Department of Biological Sciences, University of Lethbridge, Pearson Education

Photo 3:   Experiment performed and photographed by L. Brent Selinger, Department of Biological Sciences, University of Lethbridge, Pearson Education

Photo 4:   Experiment performed and photographed by L. Brent Selinger, Department of Biological Sciences, University of Lethbridge, Pearson Education

The Bacterial Growth Curve

Figure 1 **Population growth curve**

Principle

Bacterial population growth studies require inoculation of viable cells into a sterile broth medium and incubation of the culture under optimum temperature, pH, and gaseous conditions. Under these conditions, the cells will reproduce rapidly and the dynamics of the microbial growth can be charted in a population growth curve, which is constructed by plotting the increase in cell numbers versus time of incubation. The curve can be used to delineate stages of the growth cycle. It also facilitates measurement of cell numbers and the rate of growth of a particular organism under standardized conditions as expressed by its **generation time,** the time required for a microbial population to double.

The stages of a typical growth curve (**Figure 1**) are as follows:

1. **Lag phase:** During this stage the cells are adjusting to their new environment. Cellular metabolism is accelerated, resulting in rapid biosynthesis of cellular macromolecules, primarily enzymes, in preparation for the next phase of the cycle. Although the cells are increasing in size, there is no cell division and therefore no increase in numbers.

2. **Logarithmic (log) phase:** Under optimum nutritional and physical conditions, the physiologically robust cells reproduce at a uniform

and rapid rate by binary fission. Thus, there is a rapid exponential increase in population, which doubles regularly until a maximum number of cells is reached. The time required for the population to double is the generation time. The length of the log phase varies, depending on the organisms and the composition of the medium. The average may be estimated to last 6 to 12 hours.

3. **Stationary phase:** During this stage, the number of cells undergoing division is equal to the number of cells that are dying. Therefore there is no further increase in cell number, and the population is maintained at its maximum level for a period of time. The primary factors responsible for this phase are the depletion of some essential metabolites and the accumulation of toxic acidic or alkaline end products in the medium.

4. **Decline, or death, phase:** Because of the continuing depletion of nutrients and buildup of metabolic wastes, the microorganisms die at a rapid and uniform rate. The decrease in population closely parallels its increase during the log phase. Theoretically, the entire population should die during a time interval equal to that of the log phase. This does not occur, however, since a small number of highly resistant organisms persist for an indeterminate length of time.

From Experiment 21 of *Microbiology: A Laboratory Manual*, Tenth Edition. James G. Cappuccino, Natalie Sherman. Copyright © 2014 by Pearson Education, Inc. All rights reserved.

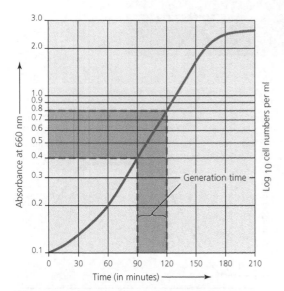

Figure 2 Indirect method of determining generation time

Construction of a complete bacterial growth curve requires that aliquots of a 24-hour shake-flask culture be measured for population size at intervals during the incubation period. Such a procedure does not lend itself to a regular laboratory session. Therefore, this experiment follows a modified procedure designed to demonstrate only the lag and log phases. The curve will be plotted on semilog paper by using two values for the measurement of growth. The direct method requires enumeration of viable cells in serially diluted samples of the test culture taken at 30-minute intervals. The indirect method uses spectrophotometric measurement of the developing turbidity at the same 30-minute intervals, as an index of increasing cellular mass.

You will determine generation time with indirect and direct methods by using data on the growth curve. Indirect determination is made by simple extrapolation from the log phase as illustrated in **Figure 2**. Select two points on the absorbance scale, such as 0.2 and 0.4, that represent a doubling of turbidity. Using a ruler, extrapolate by drawing a line between each of the selected absorbances on the ordinate (y-axis) and the plotted line of the growth curve. Then draw perpendicular lines from these endpoints on the plotted line of the growth curve to their respective time intervals on the abscissa (x-axis). With this information, determine the generation time (GT) as follows:

$$GT = t_{(A\ 0.4)} - t_{(A\ 0.2)}$$

$$GT = 90 \text{ minutes} - 60 \text{ minutes} = 30 \text{ minutes}$$

The generation time may be calculated directly using the log of cell numbers scale on a growth curve. The following example uses information from a hypothetical growth curve to calculate the generation time directly.

C_O = number of cells at time zero

C_E = number of cells at end of a specified time (t)

N = number of generations (doublings)

To describe logarithmic growth, the following equation is used:

$$N = (\log C_E - \log C_O)/\log 2$$

Using this formula, the logarithmic tables to the base 10, and the following supplied information, we may now solve for the generation time:

C_E = 52,000,000 cells	$\log C_E$ = 7.7218
C_O = 25,000 cells	$\log C_O$ = 4.4048
	$\log 2$ = 0.301

$$N = (7.7218 - 4.4048)/0.301 = 11 \text{ generations}$$

$$\text{generation time (GT)} = \frac{\text{the specified time } (t)}{\text{number of generations } (N)}$$

$$t = 180 \text{ minutes}$$

$$GT = 180/11 = 16 \text{ minutes}$$

CLINICAL APPLICATION

Using Growth Curves to Determine Antimicrobial Resistance

In medical laboratories, growth curves are being mathematically modeled to quickly determine antimicrobial susceptibility. By monitoring turbidity in a series of wells, each containing a test bacterium and a dilution of an antimicrobial agent, the entire growth curve of the bacterium can be determined from early measurements, greatly speeding up the testing process for drugs as well as assessing newly resistant bacteria.

AT THE BENCH

Materials
Cultures

5- to 10-hour (log phase) brain heart infusion broth culture of *Escherichia coli* with A of 0.08–0.10 at 600 nm.

Media

Per designated student group: 100 ml of brain heart infusion in a 250-ml Erlenmeyer flask; eighteen 99-ml sterile water blanks; and four 100-ml bottles of nutrient agar.

Equipment

37°C waterbath shaker incubator, Bausch & Lomb Spectronic 20 spectrophotometer, 13×100-mm cuvettes, Quebec colony counter, 24 sterile Petri dishes, 1-ml and 10-ml sterile pipettes, mechanical pipetting device, glassware marking pencil, 1000-ml beaker, and Bunsen burner.

Procedure Lab One

1. Separate the eighteen 99-ml sterile water blanks into six sets of three water blanks each. Label each set as to time of inoculation (t_0, t_{30}, t_{60}, t_{90}, t_{120}, t_{150}) and the dilution to be effected in each water blank (10^{-2}, 10^{-4}, 10^{-6}).

2. Label six sets of four Petri dishes as to time of inoculation and dilution to be plated (10^{-4}, 10^{-5}, 10^{-6}, 10^{-7}).

3. Liquefy the four bottles of nutrient agar in an autoclave. Cool and maintain at 45°C.

4. With a sterile pipette, add approximately 5 ml of the log phase *E. coli* culture to the flask containing 100 ml of brain heart infusion broth. The approximate initial A (t_0) should be 0.08 to 0.1 at 600 nm.

5. After the t_0 A has been determined, shake the culture flask and aseptically transfer 1 ml to the 99-ml water blank labeled t_0 10^{-2} and continue to dilute serially to 10^{-4} and 10^{-6}. *Note: A new pipette must be used for each subsequent dilution.*

6. Place the culture flask in a waterbath shaker set at 120 rpm at 37°C, and time for the required 30-minute intervals.

7. Shake the t_0 dilution bottle as illustrated in **Figure 3**. Plate the t_0 dilutions on the appropriately labeled t_0 plates as shown in **Figure 4**. Aseptically pour 15 ml of the molten agar into each plate and mix by gentle rotation.

Figure 3 Method for mixing sample in a dilution bottle

8. Thereafter, at each 30-minute interval, shake and aseptically transfer a 5-ml aliquot of the culture to a cuvette and determine its absorbance. Also, aseptically transfer a 1-ml aliquot of the culture into the 10^{-2} water blank of the set labeled with the appropriate time, complete the serial dilution, and plate in the respectively labeled Petri dishes. *Note: A new pipette must be used for each subsequent dilution.*

9. When the pour-plate cultures harden, incubate them in an inverted position for 24 hours at 37°C.

Procedure Lab Two

1. Perform cell counts on all plates. Cell counts are often referred to as colony-forming units (CFUs) because each single cell in the plate becomes visible as a colony, which can then be counted.

2. Record your results in the Lab Report.

The Bacterial Growth Curve

Figure 4 **Spectrophotometric and dilution-plating procedure for use in bacterial growth curves**

Name: _____

Date: _____ Section: _____

Observations and Results

1. Record the absorbances and corresponding cell counts in the chart below.

Incubation Time (minutes)	Absorbance at 600 nm	Plate Counts (CFU/ml)	Log of CFU/ml
0			
30			
60			
90			
120			
150			

2. On the semilog paper provided:

    a. Plot a curve relating the absorbances on the ordinate versus incubation time on the abscissa as shown in Figure 2.

    b. Plot a population curve with the log of the viable cells/ml on the ordinate and the incubation time on the abscissa. On both graphs, use a ruler to draw the best line connecting the plotted points. The straight-line portion of the curve represents the log phase.

3. Calculate the generation time for this culture by the direct method (using the mathematical formula) and by the indirect method (extrapolating from the A scale on the plotted curve). Show calculations, and record the generation time.

    a. Direct method:

    b. Indirect method:

Review Questions

1. Does the term *growth* convey the same meaning when applied to bacteria and to multicellular organisms? Explain.

2. Why do variations in generation time exist:

   a. Among different species of microorganisms?

   b. Within a single microbial species?

3. The generation time and growth rate of an organism grown in the laboratory can be easily determined by constructing a typical growth curve.

   a. Would you expect the growth rate of the infectious organisms found in an abscess that developed from a wound to mimic the growth curve obtained in the laboratory? Explain.

   b. Would you expect antibiotic therapy to be effective without any other concurrent treatment of the abscess?

4. Is generation time a useful parameter to indicate the types of media best suited to support the growth of a specific organism? Explain.

The Bacterial Growth Curve

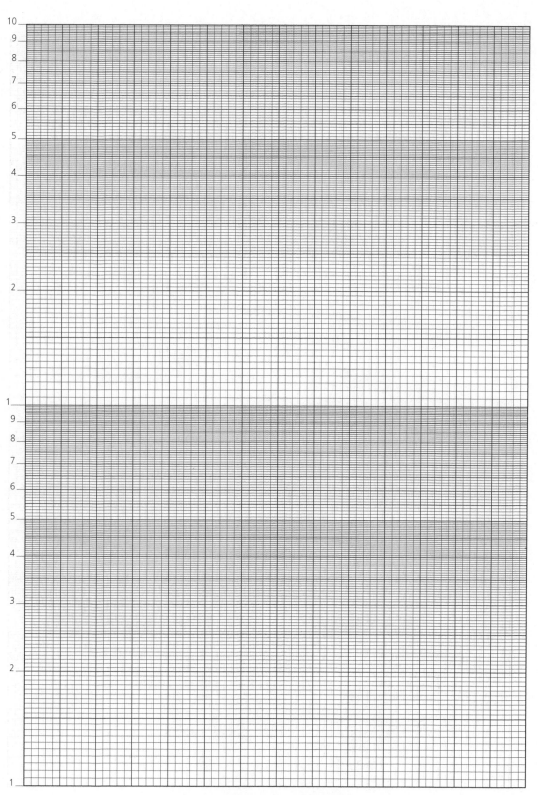

Absorbance versus Incubation Time

The Bacterial Growth Curve

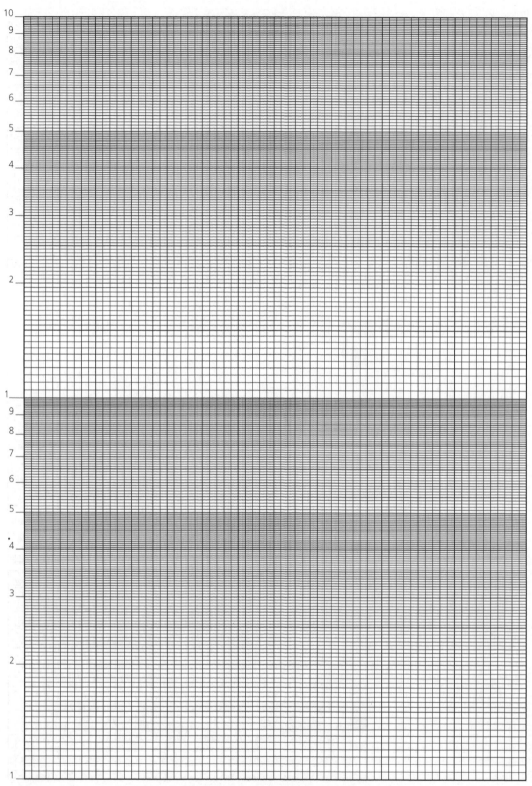

Colony-Forming Units (CFUs) versus Incubation Time

Photo Credit

Credits are listed in order of appearance.

Biochemical Activities of Microorganisms

LEARNING OBJECTIVES

When you have completed the experiments in this section, you should understand

1. The nature and activities of exoenzymes and endoenzymes.
2. Experimental procedures for differentiation of enteric microorganisms.
3. Biochemical test procedures for identification of microorganisms.

Introduction

Microorganisms must be separated and identified for a wide variety of reasons, such as

1. Determination of pathogens responsible for infectious diseases.
2. Selection and isolation of strains of fermentative microorganisms necessary for the industrial production of alcohols, solvents, vitamins, organic acids, antibiotics, and industrial enzymes.
3. Isolation and development of suitable microbial strains necessary for the manufacture and the enhancement of quality and flavor in certain food materials such as yogurt, cheeses, and other milk products.
4. Comparison of biochemical activities for taxonomic purposes.

To accomplish these tasks, the microbiologist is assisted by the fact that, just as human beings possess a characteristic and specific set of fingerprints, microorganisms all have their own identifying biochemical characteristics. These so-called biochemical fingerprints are the properties controlled by the cells' enzymatic activity, and they are responsible for bioenergetics, biosynthesis, and biodegradation.

The sum of all these chemical reactions is defined as **cellular metabolism,** and the biochemical transformations that occur both outside and inside the cell are governed by biological catalysts called **enzymes.**

Extracellular Enzymes (Exoenzymes)

Exoenzymes act on substances outside of the cell. Most high-molecular-weight substances are not able to pass through cell membranes, and therefore these raw materials—foodstuffs such as polysaccharides, lipids, and proteins—must be degraded to low-molecular-weight materials—nutrients—before they can be transported into the cell. Because of the reactions involved, exoenzymes are mainly **hydrolytic enzymes** that reduce high-molecular-weight materials into their building blocks by introducing water into the molecule. This liberates smaller molecules, which may then be transported into the cell and assimilated.

Intracellular Enzymes (Endoenzymes)

Endoenzymes function inside the cell and are mainly responsible for synthesis of new protoplasmic requirements and production of cellular energy from assimilated materials. The ability of cells to act on nutritional substrates permeating cell membranes indicates the presence of many endoenzymes capable of transforming the chemically specific substrates into essential materials.

Biochemical Activities of Microorganisms

Figure 1 Biochemical activities of microorganisms

This transformation is necessary for cellular survival and function, and it is the basis of cellular metabolism. As a result of these metabolic processes, metabolic products are formed and excreted by the cell into the environment. Assay of these end products not only aids in identification of specific enzyme systems but also serves to identify, separate, and classify microorganisms. **Figure 1** represents a simplified schema of experimental procedures used to acquaint students with the intracellular and extracellular enzymatic activities of microorganisms.

The experiments you will carry out in this section can be performed in either of two ways. A short version uses a limited number of organisms to illustrate the possible end product(s) that may result from enzyme action on a substrate. The organisms for this version are designated in the individual exercises.

The alternative, or long, version involves the use of 13 microorganisms. This version provides a complete overview of the biochemical fingerprints of the organisms and supplies the format for their separation and identification. If this alternative version is selected, the following organisms are recommended for use:

Escherichia coli

Enterobacter aerogenes

Klebsiella pneumoniae

Shigella dysenteriae

Salmonella typhimurium

Proteus vulgaris

Pseudomonas aeruginosa

Alcaligenes faecalis

Micrococcus luteus

Lactococcus lactis

Staphylococcus aureus

Bacillus cereus

Corynebacterium xerosis

Extracellular Enzymatic Activities of Microorganisms

LEARNING OBJECTIVES

Once you have completed this experiment, you should be able to

1. Understand the function of microbial extracellular enzymes.

2. Determine the ability of microorganisms to excrete hydrolytic extracellular enzymes capable of degrading the polysaccharide starch, the lipid tributyrin, and the proteins casein and gelatin.

Figure 1 Starch agar plate. Starch hydrolysis on left; no starch hydrolysis on right.

Principle

Because of their large sizes, high-molecular-weight nutrients such as polysaccharides, lipids, and proteins are not capable of permeating the cell membrane. These macromolecules must first be hydrolyzed by specific extracellular enzymes into their respective basic building blocks. These low-molecular-weight substances can then be transported into the cells and used for the synthesis of protoplasmic requirements and energy production. The following procedures are designed to investigate the exoenzymatic activities of different microorganisms.

Starch Hydrolysis

Starch is a high-molecular-weight, branching polymer composed of **glucose** molecules linked together by **glycosidic bonds.** The degradation of this macromolecule first requires the presence of the extracellular enzyme **amylase** for its hydrolysis into shorter polysaccharides, namely **dextrins,** and ultimately into **maltose** molecules. The final hydrolysis of this disaccharide, which is catalyzed by **maltase,** yields low-molecular-weight, soluble **glucose** molecules that can be transported into the cell and used for energy production through the process of glycolysis.

In this experimental procedure, starch agar is used to demonstrate the hydrolytic activities

of these exoenzymes. The medium is composed of nutrient agar supplemented with starch, which serves as the polysaccharide substrate. The detection of the hydrolytic activity following the growth period is made by performing the starch test to determine the presence or absence of starch in the medium. Starch in the presence of iodine will impart a blue-black color to the medium, indicating the absence of starch-splitting enzymes and representing a negative result. If the starch has been hydrolyzed, a clear zone of hydrolysis will surround the growth of the organism. This is a positive result. Positive and negative results are shown in **Figure 1.**

Lipid Hydrolysis

Lipids are high-molecular-weight compounds possessing large amounts of energy. The degradation of lipids such as **triglycerides** is accomplished by extracellular hydrolyzing enzymes, called **lipases** (esterases), that cleave the **ester bonds** in this molecule by the addition of water to form the building blocks **glycerol** (an alcohol) and **fatty acids.** **Figure 2** shows this reaction. Once assimilated into the cell, these basic components can be further metabolized through aerobic respiration to produce cellular energy, adenosine triphosphate (ATP). The

Figure 2 Lipid hydrolysis

components may also enter other metabolic pathways for the synthesis of other cellular protoplasmic requirements.

In this experimental procedure, tributyrin agar is used to demonstrate the hydrolytic activities of the exoenzyme lipase. The medium is composed of nutrient agar supplemented with the triglyceride tributyrin as the lipid substrate. Tributyrin forms an emulsion when dispersed in the agar, producing an opaque medium that is necessary for observing exoenzymatic activity.

Following inoculation and incubation of the agar plate cultures, organisms excreting lipase will show a zone of **lipolysis,** which is demonstrated by a clear area surrounding the bacterial growth. This loss of opacity is the result of the hydrolytic reaction yielding soluble glycerol and fatty acids and represents a positive reaction for lipid hydrolysis. In the absence of lipolytic enzymes, the medium retains its opacity. This is a negative reaction. Positive and negative results are shown in **Figure 3**.

Casein Hydrolysis

Casein, the major milk protein, is a macromolecule composed of **amino acid** subunits linked together by **peptide bonds** (CO—NH). Before their assimilation into the cell, proteins must undergo step-by-step degradation into **peptones**, **polypeptides**, **dipeptides,** and ultimately into their building blocks, **amino acids.** This process is called peptonization, or **proteolysis,** and it is mediated by extracellular enzymes called **proteases.** The function of these proteases is to cleave the peptide bond CO—NH by introducing water into the molecule. The reaction then liberates the amino acids, as illustrated in **Figure 4**.

The low-molecular-weight soluble amino acids can now be transported through the cell membrane into the intracellular amino acid pool for use in the synthesis of structural and functional cellular proteins.

Figure 3 Tributyrin agar plate. Lipid hydrolysis on left; no lipid hydrolysis on right.

Figure 4 Protein hydrolysis

In this experimental procedure, milk agar is used to demonstrate the hydrolytic activity of these exoenzymes. The medium is composed of nutrient agar supplemented with milk that contains the protein substrate casein. Similar to other proteins, milk protein is a colloidal suspension that gives the medium its color and opacity because it deflects light rays rather than transmitting them.

Following inoculation and incubation of the agar plate cultures, organisms secreting proteases will exhibit a zone of proteolysis, which is demonstrated by a clear area surrounding the bacterial growth. This loss of opacity is the result of a hydrolytic reaction yielding soluble, noncolloidal amino acids, and it represents a positive reaction. In the absence of protease activity, the medium surrounding the growth of the organism remains opaque, which is a negative reaction.

Gelatin Hydrolysis

Although the value of gelatin as a nutritional source is questionable (it is an incomplete protein, lacking the essential amino acid tryptophan), its value in identifying bacterial species is well established. Gelatin is a protein produced by hydrolysis of collagen, a major component of connective tissue and tendons in humans and other animals. Below temperatures of 25°C, gelatin will maintain its gel properties and exist as a solid; at temperatures above 25°C, gelatin is liquid. **Figure 5** shows gelatin hydrolysis.

Liquefaction is accomplished by some microorganisms capable of producing a proteolytic extracellular enzyme called **gelatinase,** which acts to hydrolyze this protein to **amino acids.** Once this degradation occurs, even very low temperatures of 4°C will not restore the gel characteristic.

In this experimental procedure, you will use nutrient gelatin deep tubes to demonstrate the hydrolytic activity of gelatinase. The medium consists of nutrient broth supplemented with 12% gelatin. This high gelatin concentration results in a stiff medium and also serves as the substrate for the activity of gelatinase.

Following inoculation and incubation for 48 hours, the cultures are placed in a refrigerator at 4°C for 30 minutes. Cultures that remain liquefied produce gelatinase and demonstrate *rapid* gelatin hydrolysis. Re-incubate all solidified cultures for an additional 5 days. Refrigerate for 30 minutes and observe for liquefaction. Cultures that remain liquefied are indicative of *slow* gelatin hydrolysis.

(a) Positive for gelatin liquefaction

(b) Negative for gelatin liquefaction

Figure 5 Nutrient gelatin hydrolysis

CLINICAL APPLICATION

Pathogens and Extracellular Enzymes

Bacteria use enzymes to alter their environments and to gain new sources of nutrients. When known bacterial pathogens are causing symptoms or damage not normally associated with that species, laboratories may test for newly acquired extracellular enzymes. Most known pathogens have been characterized by their abilities to digest proteins (fibronectin and collagen) as well as lipids and starches (glycolipids and glycoproteins).

AT THE BENCH

Materials

Cultures

24- to 48-hour trypticase soy broth cultures of *Escherichia coli, Bacillus cereus, Pseudomonas aeruginosa,* and *Staphylococcus aureus* for the short version. 24- to 48-hour brain heart infusion broth cultures of the 13 organisms for the long version.

Media

Short version: Two plates each of starch agar, tributyrin agar, and milk agar, and three nutrient gelatin deep tubes per designated student group. Long version: Four plates each of starch agar, tributyrin agar, and milk agar, and 14 nutrient gelatin deep tubes per designated student group.

Reagent

Gram's iodine solution.

Equipment

Bunsen burner, inoculating loop and needle, glassware marking pencil, test tube rack, and refrigerator.

Procedure Lab One

1. Prepare the starch agar, tributyrin agar, and milk agar plates for inoculation as follows:

   a. Short procedure: Using two plates per medium, divide the bottom of each Petri dish into two sections. Label the sections as *E. coli, B. cereus, P. aeruginosa,* and *S. aureus,* respectively.

   b. Long procedure: Repeat Step 1a, dividing three plate bottoms into three sections and one plate bottom into four sections for each of the required media, to accommodate the 13 test organisms.

2. Using aseptic technique, make a single-line streak inoculation of each test organism on the agar surface of its appropriately labeled section on the agar plates.

3. Using aseptic technique, inoculate each experimental organism in its appropriately labeled gelatin deep tube by means of a stab inoculation.

4. Incubate all plates in an inverted position for 24 to 48 hours at 37°C. Incubate the gelatin deep tube cultures for 48 hours. Re-incubate all negative cultures for an additional 5 days.

Procedure Lab Two
Starch Hydrolysis

1. Flood the starch agar plate cultures with Gram's iodine solution, allow the iodine to remain in contact with the medium for 30 seconds, and pour off the excess.

2. Examine the cultures for the presence or absence of a blue-black color surrounding the growth of each test organism. Record your results in the chart provided in the Lab Report.

3. Based on your observations, determine and record which organisms were capable of hydrolyzing the starch.

Lipid Hydrolysis

1. Examine the tributyrin agar plate cultures for the presence or absence of a clear area, or zone of lipolysis, surrounding the growth of

each of the organisms. Record your results in the chart provided in the Lab Report.

2. Based on your observations, determine and record which organisms were capable of hydrolyzing the lipid.

Casein Hydrolysis

1. Examine the milk agar plate cultures for the presence or absence of a clear area, or zone of proteolysis, surrounding the growth of each of the bacterial test organisms. Record your results in the chart provided in the Lab Report.

2. Based on your observations, determine and record which of the organisms were capable of hydrolyzing the milk protein casein.

Gelatin Hydrolysis

1. Place all gelatin deep tube cultures into a refrigerator at 4°C for 30 minutes.

2. Examine all the cultures to determine whether the medium is solid or liquid. Record your results in the chart provided in the Lab Report.

3. Based on your observations following the 2-day and 7-day incubation periods, determine and record in the Lab Report (a) which organisms were capable of hydrolyzing gelatin and (b) the rate of hydrolysis.

Observations and Results

Starch and Lipid Hydrolysis

Bacterial Species	STARCH HYDROLYSIS		LIPID HYDROLYSIS	
	Appearance of Medium	**Result (+) or (−)**	**Appearance of Medium**	**Result (+) or (−)**
E. coli				
E. aerogenes				
K. pneumoniae				
S. dysenteriae				
S. typhimurium				
P. vulgaris				
P. aeruginosa				
A. faecalis				
M. luteus				
L. lactis				
S. aureus				
B. cereus				
C. xerosis				

Casein and Gelatin Hydrolysis

| Bacterial Species | CASEIN HYDROLYSIS | | GELATIN HYDROLYSIS | | |
| | Appearance of Medium | Result (+) or (−) | Liquefaction (+) or (−) | | Rate of Hydrolysis (Slow or Rapid) |
			2 days	7 days	
E. coli					
E. aerogenes					
K. pneumoniae					
S. dysenteriae					
S. typhimurium					
P. vulgaris					
P. aeruginosa					
A. faecalis					
M. luteus					
L. lactis					
S. aureus					
B. cereus					
C. xerosis					

Review Questions

1. Why is the catalytic activity of enzymes essential to ensure and regulate cellular metabolism?

2. Why are microorganisms able to cause dairy products, such as milk, to sour or curdle?

3. Give a reason why it is necessary for polysaccharides, such as starch or cellulose, to be digested outside of the cell even though disaccharides, such as lactose or sucrose, are digestible inside the cell.

Photo Credits

Credits are listed in order of appearance.

Photo 1: David Alexander, University of Portland

Photo 2: James Cappuccino

Carbohydrate Fermentation

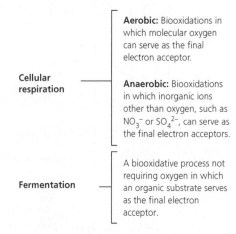

Figure 1 Biooxidative pathways

Principle

Most microorganisms obtain their energy through a series of orderly and integrated enzymatic reactions leading to the biooxidation of a substrate, frequently a carbohydrate. The major pathways by which this is accomplished are shown in **Figure 1**.

Organisms use carbohydrates differently depending on their enzyme complement. Some organisms are capable of fermenting sugars such as glucose anaerobically, while others use the aerobic pathway. Still others, facultative anaerobes, are enzymatically competent to use both aerobic and anaerobic pathways, and some organisms lack the ability to oxidize glucose by either. In this exercise the fermentative pathways are of prime concern.

In fermentation, substrates such as carbohydrates and alcohols undergo anaerobic dissimilation and produce an organic acid (for example, lactic, formic, or acetic acid) that may be accompanied by gases such as hydrogen or carbon dioxide. Facultative anaerobes are usually the so-called fermenters of carbohydrates. Fermentation is best described by considering the degradation of glucose by way of the **Embden-Meyerhof pathway,** also known as the **glycolytic pathway,** illustrated in **Figure 2**.

As the diagram shows, one mole of glucose is converted into two moles of pyruvic acid, which is the major intermediate compound produced by glucose degradation. Subsequent metabolism of

pyruvate is not the same for all organisms, and a variety of end products result that define their different fermentative capabilities. This can be seen in **Figure 3**.

Fermentative degradation under anaerobic conditions is carried out in a fermentation broth tube containing a Durham tube, an inverted inner vial for the detection of gas production as illustrated in **Figure 4**. A typical carbohydrate fermentation medium contains

1. Nutrient broth ingredients for the support of the growth of all organisms.

2. A specific carbohydrate that serves as the substrate for determining the organism's fermentative capabilities.

3. The pH indicator phenol red, which is red at a neutral pH (7) and changes to yellow at a slightly acidic pH of 6.8, indicating that slight amounts of acid will cause a color change.

The critical nature of the fermentation reaction and the activity of the indicator make it imperative that all cultures should be observed within 48 hours. Extended incubation may mask acid-producing reactions by production of alkali because of enzymatic action on substrates other than the carbohydrate.

Carbohydrate Fermentation

Figure 2 The Embden-Meyerhof pathway

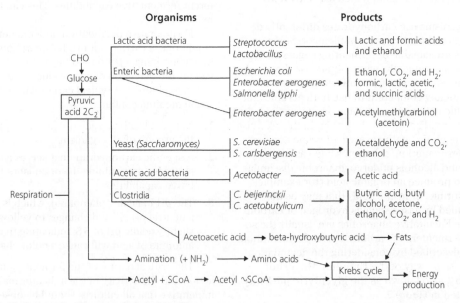

Figure 3 Variations in the use of pyruvic acid

Following incubation, carbohydrates that have been fermented with the production of acidic wastes will cause the phenol red (**Figure 5a**) to turn yellow, thereby indicating a positive reaction (**Figures 5b** and **c**). In some cases, acid production is accompanied by the evolution of a gas (CO_2) that will be visible as a bubble in the inverted tube (**Figure 5b**). Cultures that are not capable of fermenting a carbohydrate substrate will not change the

Carbohydrate Fermentation

Figure 4 **Detection of gas production**

Figure 5 **Carbohydrate fermentation test.**
(a) Uninoculated, **(b)** acid and gas, **(c)** acid, and
(d) negative.

indicator, and the tubes will appear red; there will not be a concomitant evolution of gas. This is a negative reaction (**Figure 5d**).

The lack of carbohydrate fermentation by some organisms should not be construed as absence of growth. The organisms use other nutrients in the medium as energy sources. Among these nutrients are peptones present in nutrient broth. Peptones can be degraded by microbial enzymes to amino acids that are in turn enzymatically converted by oxidative deamination to ketoamino acids. These are then metabolized through the Krebs cycle for energy production. These reactions liberate ammonia, which accumulates in the medium, forming ammonium hydroxide (NH_4OH) and producing an alkaline environment. When this occurs, the phenol red turns to a deep red in the now basic medium. This alternative pathway of aerobic respiration is illustrated in **Figure 6**.

CLINICAL APPLICATION

Using Fermentation Products to Identify Bacteria

The fermentation of carbohydrates assists in the identification of some bacteria by determining what nutrients they are using and what products they produce. The pattern of sugars fermented may be unique to a particular genus, species, or strain. Lactose fermentation is one test that distinguishes between enteric and non-enteric bacteria. Dextrose fermentation allows for the differentiation between the oxidase (+) *Vibrio* and *Pseudomonads* species in patients suffering from septicemia after eating contaminated fish.

AT THE BENCH

Materials
Cultures

24- to 48-hour Trypticase soy broth cultures of *Escherichia coli, Alcaligenes faecalis, Salmonella typhimurium,* and *Staphylococcus aureus* for the short version. 24- to 48-hour Trypticase soy broth cultures of the 13 organisms for the long version.

Media

Per designated student group: phenol red lactose, dextrose (glucose), and sucrose broths: 5 of each for the short version, 14 of each for the long version.

Equipment

Bunsen burner, inoculating loop, and glassware marking pencil.

Procedure Lab One

1. Using aseptic technique, inoculate each experimental organism into its appropriately labeled medium by means of loop inoculation. *Note: Take care during this step not to shake the fermentation tube;* shaking the tube may accidentally force a bubble of air into the inverted

Carbohydrate Fermentation

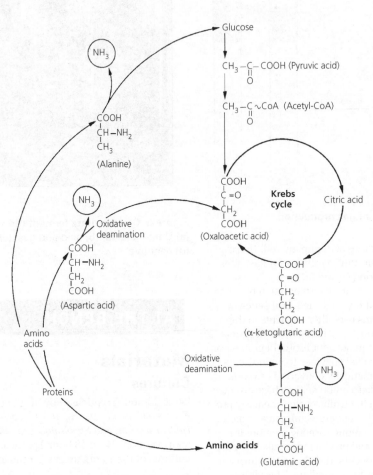

Figure 6 Proteins as energy sources for microbes

gas vial, displacing the medium and possibly rendering a false-positive result. The last tube will serve as a control.

2. Incubate all tubes for 24 hours at 37°C.

Procedure Lab Two

1. Examine all carbohydrate broth cultures for color and the presence or absence of a gas bubble. Record your results in the chart provided in the Lab Report.

2. Based on your observations, determine and record whether or not each organism was capable of fermenting the carbohydrate substrate with the production of acid or acid and gas.

Observations and Results

Bacterial Species	Lactose Observation (color of medium, bubble in fermentation tube)	Result (A), (A/G), or (−)	Dextrose Observation (color of medium, bubble in fermentation tube)	Result (A), (A/G), or (−)	Sucrose Observation (color of medium, bubble in fermentation tube)	Result (A), (A/G), or (−)
E. coli						
E. aerogenes						
K. pneumoniae						
S. dysenteriae						
S. typhimurium						
P. vulgaris						
P. aeruginosa						
A. faecalis						
M. luteus						
L. lactis						
S. aureus						
B. cereus						
C. xerosis						
Control						

Review Questions

1. Distinguish between respiration and fermentation.

2. Do all microorganisms use pyruvic acid in the same way? Explain.

3. Describe a pathway used for the degradation of carbohydrates by strict anaerobes.

4. From your experimental data, you know that *P. aeruginosa* did not utilize any of the carbohydrates in the test media. In view of this, how do these organisms generate energy to sustain their viability?

5. *Clostridium perfringens*, an obligate anaerobe, is capable of utilizing the carbohydrates released from injured tissues as an energy source. During the infectious process, large amounts of gas accumulate in the infected tissues. Would you expect this gas to be CO_2? Explain.

Photo Credit

Credits are listed in order of appearance.

Photo 1: James Cappuccino

Triple Sugar–Iron Agar Test

LEARNING OBJECTIVES

Once you have completed this experiment, you should understand a rapid screening procedure that will

1. Differentiate among members of the Enterobacteriaceae.

2. Distinguish between the Enterobacteriaceae and other groups of intestinal bacilli.

Principle

The **triple sugar–iron (TSI) agar test** is designed to differentiate among the different groups or genera of the Enterobacteriaceae, which are all gram-negative bacilli capable of fermenting glucose with the production of acid, and to distinguish the Enterobacteriaceae from other gram-negative intestinal bacilli. This differentiation is made on the basis of differences in carbohydrate fermentation patterns and hydrogen sulfide production by the various groups of intestinal organisms.

To facilitate observation of carbohydrate utilization patterns, the TSI agar slants contain lactose and sucrose in 1% concentrations and glucose (dextrose) in a concentration of 0.1%, which permits detection of the utilization of this substrate only. The acid-base indicator phenol red is also incorporated to detect carbohydrate fermentation that is indicated by a change in color of the medium from orange-red to yellow in the presence of acids. The slant is inoculated by means of a stab-and-streak procedure. This requires the insertion of a sterile, straight needle from the base of the slant into the butt. Upon withdrawal of the needle, the slanted surface of the medium is streaked. Following incubation, you will determine the fermentative activities of the organisms as described below.

1. **Alkaline slant (red) and acid butt (yellow) with or without gas production (breaks in the agar butt).** Only glucose fermentation has occurred. The organisms preferentially degrade glucose first. Since this substrate is present in minimal concentration, the small amount of acid produced on the slant surface is oxidized rapidly. The peptones in the medium are also used in the production of alkali. In the butt the acid reaction is maintained because of reduced oxygen tension and slower growth of the organisms.

2. **Acid slant (yellow) and acid butt (yellow) with or without gas production.** Lactose and/or sucrose fermentation has occurred. Since these substances are present in higher concentrations, they serve as substrates for continued fermentative activities with maintenance of an acid reaction in both slant and butt.

3. **Alkaline slant (red) and alkaline butt (red) or no change (orange-red) butt.** No carbohydrate fermentation has occurred. Instead, peptones are catabolized under anaerobic and/or aerobic conditions, resulting in an alkaline pH due to production of ammonia. If only aerobic degradation of peptones occurs, the alkaline reaction is evidenced only on the slant surface. If there is aerobic and anaerobic utilization of peptone, the alkaline reaction is present on the slant and the butt.

For you to obtain accurate results, it is absolutely essential to observe the cultures within 18 to 24 hours following incubation. Doing so will ensure that the carbohydrate substrates have not been depleted and that degradation of peptones yielding alkaline end products has not taken place.

The TSI agar medium also contains sodium thiosulfate, a substrate for hydrogen sulfide (H_2S) production, and ferrous sulfate for detection of this colorless end product. Following incubation, only cultures of organisms capable of producing H_2S will show an extensive blackening in the butt because of the precipitation of the insoluble ferrous sulfide.

Figure 1 is a schema for the differentiation of intestinal bacilli on the basis of the TSI agar reactions.

Triple Sugar–Iron Agar Test

Acid slant Acid butt No H₂S	Acid slant Acid butt H₂S produced	Alkaline slant Acid butt No H₂S	Alkaline slant Acid butt H₂S produced	Alkaline slant Alkaline or no change butt
Escherichia *Klebsiella* *Enterobacter*	*Citrobacter* *Arizona* Some *Proteus* spp.	*Shigella* Some *Proteus* spp.	Most *Salmonella* *Arizona* *Citrobacter*	*Alcaligenes* *Pseudomonas* *Acinetobacter*

Figure 1 TSI reactions for differentiation of enteric microorganisms

CLINICAL APPLICATION

Differentiating Between *Proteus* Species

The TSI test can differentiate enteric organisms based on their abilities to reduce sulfur and ferment carbohydrates. It can be used to separate the three species of *Proteus, P. vulgaris, P. mirabilis,* and *P. penneri,* all of which are human opportunistic pathogens. *P. mirabilis* causes urinary tract infections and is sensitive to treatment with ampicillin and cephalosporins. *P. vulgaris,* a less common cause of urinary tract infections, is not sensitive to these antibiotics and is found as a nosocomial infectious agent amongst immunocompromised patients.

AT THE BENCH

Materials

Cultures

24-hour Trypticase soy broth cultures of *Pseudomonas aeruginosa, Escherichia coli, Salmonella typhimurium, Shigella dysenteriae, Proteus vulgaris,* and *Alcaligenes faecalis* for the short version. 24-hour Trypticase soy broth cultures of the 13 organisms for the long version.

Media

Per designated student group: triple sugar–iron agar slants: 7 for the short version, 14 for the long version.

Equipment

Bunsen burner, inoculating needle, test tube rack, and glassware marking pencil.

Procedure Lab One

1. Using aseptic technique, inoculate each experimental organism into its appropriately labeled tube by means of a stab-and-streak

inoculation. *Note: Do not fully tighten screw cap.* The last tube will serve as a control.

2. Incubate for 18 to 24 hours at 37°C.

Procedure Lab Two

1. Examine the color of both the butt and slant of all agar slant cultures (**Figure 2**). Based on your observations, determine the type of reaction that has taken place (acid, alkaline, or none) and the carbohydrate that has been fermented (dextrose, lactose, and/or sucrose, all, or none) in each culture. Record your observations and results in the chart provided in the Lab Report.

2. Examine all cultures for the presence or absence of blackening within the medium. Based on your observations, determine whether or not each organism was capable of H₂S production. Record your observations and results in the chart provided in the Lab Report.

Figure 2 Reactions in triple sugar–iron agar.
(a) Uninoculated; **(b)** alkaline slant/acid butt, H₂S; **(c)** alkaline slant/acid butt; **(d)** acid slant/acid butt, gas; and **(e)** acid slant/acid butt.

Observations and Results

Bacterial Species	CARBOHYDRATE FERMENTATION			H₂S PRODUCTION		Gas
	Butt Color and Reaction	Slant Color and Reaction	Carbohydrate Fermented	Blackening	H₂S (+) or (−)	
E. coli	—	white		—	—	—
E. aerogenes	—	white		—	—	—
K. pneumoniae	—	white		—	—	
S. dysenteriae						
S. typhimurium	green	red	+	+	+	
P. vulgaris						
P. aeruginosa	—	red	+	—	—	
A. faecalis	orange	red	+	—	—	
M. luteus						
L. lactis	—	white		—	—	
S. aureus	—	white		—	—	
B. cereus						
C. xerosis						
Control						

Review Questions

1. What is the purpose of the TSI test?

2. Explain why the TSI medium contains a lower concentration of glucose than of lactose and sucrose.

3. Explain the purpose of the phenol red in the medium.

4. Explain the purpose of thiosulfate in the medium.

5. Explain why the test observations must be made between 18 and 24 hours after inoculation.

Photo Credit

Credits are listed in order of appearance.

Photo 1:   James Cappuccino

IMViC Test

Identification of enteric bacilli is of prime importance in controlling intestinal infections by preventing contamination of food and water supplies. The groups of bacteria that can be found in the intestinal tract of humans and lower mammals are classified as members of the family **Enterobacteriaceae.** They are short, gram-negative, non–spore-forming bacilli. Included in this family are:

1. **Pathogens** such as members of the genera *Salmonella* and *Shigella*.

2. **Occasional pathogens** such as members of the genera *Proteus* and *Klebsiella*.

3. **Normal intestinal flora** such as members of the genera *Escherichia* and *Enterobacter*, which are saprophytic inhabitants of the intestinal tract.

Differentiation of the principal groups of Enterobacteriaceae can be accomplished on the basis of their biochemical properties and enzymatic reactions in the presence of specific substrates. The **IMViC** series of tests (**indole, methyl red, Voges-Proskauer,** and **citrate utilization**) can be used.

Figure 11 shows the biochemical reactions that occur during the IMViC tests. It is designed to assist you in the execution and interpretation of each test.

The following experiments are designed for either a short or long version. The short version uses selected members of the enteric family. The long procedure makes use of bacterial species that do not belong solely to the Enterobacteriaceae. Nonenteric forms are included to acquaint you with the biochemical activities of other organisms grown in these media and to enable you to use these data for further comparisons of both types of bacteria. Selected organisms to be used in the long-version procedures are listed below. The enteric organisms are subdivided as lactose fermenters and non–lactose fermenters.

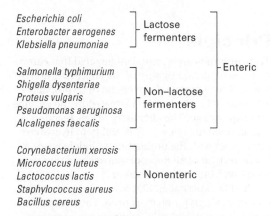

CLINICAL APPLICATION

Identification of Enteric Bacteria

The IMViC test is used to identify members of the Enterobacteriaceae, some of which are powerful pathogens such as members of the the genera *Shigella* and *Salmonella,* which cause intestinal infections. Identification of the causative agent may lead to the source of the infection, such as raw food (*Salmonella*) or fecal contamination of food (*Shigella*). This will aid in determining the possible number of individuals that have been exposed and who may require medical attention. This test uses the organisms' biochemical properties and enzymatic reactions on specific substrates as a means of identification.

From Experiment 25 of *Microbiology: A Laboratory Manual*, Tenth Edition. James G. Cappuccino, Natalie Sherman.

Once you have completed this test, you should be able to

1. Determine the ability of microorganisms to degrade the amino acid tryptophan.

Principle

Tryptophan is an essential amino acid that can undergo oxidation by way of the enzymatic activities of some bacteria. Conversion of tryptophan into metabolic products is mediated by the enzyme **tryptophanase.** The chemistry of this reaction is illustrated in **Figure 1.** This ability to hydrolyze tryptophan with the production of indole is not a characteristic of all microorganisms and therefore serves as a biochemical marker.

In this experiment, SIM agar, which contains the substrate tryptophan, is used. The presence of indole is detectable by adding Kovac's reagent, which produces a cherry red reagent layer. This color is produced by the reagent, which is composed of *p*-dimethylaminobenzaldehyde, butanol, and hydrochloric acid. Indole is extracted from the medium into the reagent layer by the acidified butyl alcohol component and forms a complex with the *p*-dimethylaminobenzaldehyde, yielding the

cherry red color. The chemistry of this reaction is illustrated in **Figure 2.**

Cultures producing a red reagent layer following addition of Kovac's reagent are indole-positive. The absence of red coloration demonstrates that the substrate tryptophan was not hydrolyzed and indicates an indole-negative reaction.

AT THE BENCH

Materials
Cultures

24- to 48-hour Trypticase soy broth cultures of *E. coli, P. vulgaris,* and *E. aerogenes* for the short version. 24- to 48-hour Trypticase soy broth cultures of the 13 organisms for the long version.

Media

SIM agar deep tubes per designated student group: 4 for the short version, 14 for the long version.

Reagent

Kovac's reagent.

Equipment

Bunsen burner, inoculating needle, test tube rack, and glassware marking pencil.

Figure 1 Enzymatic degradation of tryptophan

Tryptophan   Tryptophanase →   Indole   Pyruvic acid   Ammonia

Figure 2 Indole reaction with Kovac's reagent

p-dimethylaminobenzaldehyde   Indole   HCl Alcohol — Dehydration reduction →   Quinoidal red-violet compound

Figure 3 Indole production test.
(a) Uninoculated, **(b)** negative, and **(c)** positive.

Procedure Lab One

1. Using aseptic technique, inoculate each experimental organism into its appropriately labeled deep tube by means of a stab inoculation. The last tube will serve as a control.

2. Incubate tubes for 24 to 48 hours at 37°C.

Procedure Lab Two

1. Add 10 drops of Kovac's reagent to all deep tube cultures and agitate the cultures gently.

2. Examine the color of the reagent layer in each culture (refer to **Figure 3**). Record your results in the chart in the Lab Report.

3. Based on your observations, determine and record whether or not each organism was capable of hydrolyzing the tryptophan.

PART B   Methyl Red Test

LEARNING OBJECTIVES

Once you have completed this experiment, you should be able to

1. Determine the ability of microorganisms to ferment glucose with the production and stabilization of high concentrations of acid end products.

2. Differentiate between all glucose-fermenting enteric organisms, particularly *E. coli* and *E. aerogenes*.

Principle

The hexose monosaccharide **glucose** is the major substrate utilized by all enteric organisms for energy production. The end products of this process will vary depending on the specific enzymatic pathways present in the bacteria. In this test the pH indicator methyl red detects the presence of large concentrations of acid end products. Although most enteric microorganisms ferment glucose with the production of organic acids, this test is of value in the separation of *E. coli* and *E. aerogenes*.

Both of these organisms initially produce organic acid end products during the early incubation period. The low acidic pH (4) is stabilized and maintained by *E. coli* at the end of incubation. During the later incubation period, *E. aerogenes* enzymatically converts these acids to nonacidic end products such as 2,3-butanediol and acetoin (acetylmethylcarbinol), resulting in an elevated pH of approximately 6. The glucose fermentation reaction generated by *E. coli* is illustrated in **Figure 4**.

As shown, the methyl red indicator in the pH range of 4 will turn red, which is indicative of a positive test. At a pH of 6, still indicating the presence of acid but with a lower hydrogen ion concentration, the indicator turns yellow and is a negative test. Production and detection of the nonacidic end products from glucose fermentation by *E. aerogenes* is amplified in Part C of this exercise, the Voges-Proskauer test, which is performed simultaneously with the methyl red test.

AT THE BENCH

Materials

Cultures

24- to 48-hour Trypticase soy broth cultures of *E. coli*, *E. aerogenes*, and *K. pneumoniae* for the short version. 24- to 48-hour Trypticase soy broth cultures of the 13 organisms for the long version. In Lab Two, aliquots of these experimental cultures must be set aside for the Voges-Proskauer test.

Media

MR-VP broth per designated student group: 4 for the short version, 14 for the long version.

$$\text{Glucose} + H_2O \longrightarrow \begin{bmatrix} \text{Lactic acid} \\ \text{Acetic acid} \\ \text{Formic acid} \end{bmatrix} + CO_2 + H_2 \ (\text{pH 4.0}) \longrightarrow \text{Methyl red indicator turns red color}$$

Figure 4 Glucose fermentation reaction with methyl red pH reagent

(a)   (b)   (c)

Figure 5 Methyl red test. (a) Uninoculated, **(b)** positive, and **(c)** negative.

Reagent

Methyl red indicator.

Equipment

Bunsen burner, inoculating loop, test tubes, and glassware marking pencil.

Procedure Lab One

1. Using aseptic technique, inoculate each experimental organism into its appropriately labeled tube of medium by means of a loop inoculation. The last tube will serve as a control.

2. Incubate all cultures for 24 to 48 hours at 37°C.

Procedure Lab Two

1. Transfer approximately one-third of each culture into an empty test tube and set these tubes aside for the Voges-Proskauer test.

2. Add five drops of the methyl red indicator to the remaining aliquot of each culture.

3. Examine the color of all cultures (refer to **Figure 5**). Record the results in the chart in the Lab Report.

4. Based on your observations, determine and record whether or not each organism was capable of fermenting glucose with the production and maintenance of a high concentration of acid.

LEARNING OBJECTIVE

Once you have completed this experiment, you should be able to

1. Differentiate further among enteric organisms such as *E. coli*, *E. aerogenes*, and *K. pneumoniae*.

Principle

The Voges-Proskauer test determines the capability of some organisms to produce nonacidic or neutral end products, such as acetylmethylcarbinol, from the organic acids that result from glucose metabolism. This glucose fermentation, which is characteristic of *E. aerogenes*, is illustrated in **Figure 6**.

The reagent used in this test, Barritt's reagent, consists of a mixture of alcoholic α-naphthol and 40% potassium hydroxide solution. Detection of acetylmethylcarbinol requires this end product to be oxidized to a diacetyl compound. This reaction will occur in the presence of the α-naphthol catalyst and a guanidine group that is present in the peptone of the MR-VP medium. As a result, a pink complex is formed, imparting a rose color to the medium. The chemistry of this reaction is illustrated in **Figure 7**.

Development of a deep rose color in the culture 15 minutes following the addition of Barritt's reagent is indicative of the presence of acetylmethylcarbinol and represents a positive result. The absence of rose coloration is a negative result.

Glucose + O_2 ⟶ Acetic acid ⟶ $\left[\begin{array}{c}\text{2,3-butanediol}\\\text{acetylmethylcarbinol}\end{array}\right]$ + CO_2 + H_2 (pH 6.0)

Figure 6 Glucose fermentation by *E. aerogenes*

Acetylmethyl-carbinol   α-naphthol $\xrightarrow[\text{Oxidation}]{\text{40\% KOH}}$ Diacetyl   Guanidine group of peptone   ⟶ Pink complex

Figure 7 Acetylmethylcarbinol reaction with Barritt's reagent

(a)   (b)   (c)

Figure 8 Voges-Proskauer test.
(a) Uninoculated, (b) negative, and (c) positive.

AT THE BENCH

Materials

Cultures

24- to 48-hour Trypticase soy broth cultures of *E. coli*, *E. aerogenes*, and *K. pneumoniae* for the short version. 24- to 48-hour Trypticase soy broth cultures of the 13 organisms for the long version. *Note: Aliquots of these experimental cultures must be set aside from the methyl red test.*

Reagent

Barritt's reagents A and B.

Equipment

Bunsen burner, inoculating loop, and glassware marking pencil.

Procedure Lab One

Refer to the methyl red test in Part B of this exercise.

Procedure Lab Two

1. To the aliquots of each broth culture separated during the methyl red test, add 10 drops of Barritt's reagent A and shake the cultures. Immediately add 10 drops of Barritt's reagent B and shake. Reshake the cultures every 3 to 4 minutes.

2. Examine the color of the cultures 15 minutes after the addition of Barritt's reagent. Refer to **Figure 8**. Record your results in the Lab Report.

3. Based on your observations, determine and record whether or not each organism was capable of fermenting glucose with ultimate production of acetylmethylcarbinol.

PART D Citrate Utilization Test

LEARNING OBJECTIVE

Once you have completed this experiment, you should be able to

1. Differentiate among enteric organisms on the basis of their ability to ferment citrate as a sole source of carbon.

1.

Citrate → (Citrase) → Oxaloacetic acid → Pyruvic acid + Acetic acid + Excess carbon dioxide

2. $CO_2 + 2Na^+ + H_2O \longrightarrow Na_2CO_3 \longrightarrow$ Alkaline pH $\longrightarrow$ Color change from green to blue

Figure 9 Enzymatic degradation of citrate

Principle

In the absence of fermentable glucose or lactose, some microorganisms are capable of using **citrate** as a carbon source for their energy. This ability depends on the presence of a **citrate permease** that facilitates the transport of citrate in the cell. Citrate is the first major intermediate in the Krebs cycle and is produced by the condensation of active acetyl with oxaloacetic acid. Citrate is acted on by the enzyme **citrase,** which produces oxaloacetic acid and acetate. These products are then enzymatically converted to pyruvic acid and carbon dioxide. During this reaction the medium becomes alkaline—the carbon dioxide that is generated combines with sodium and water to form sodium carbonate, an alkaline product. The presence of sodium carbonate changes the bromthymol blue indicator incorporated into the medium from green to deep Prussian blue. The chemistry of this reaction is illustrated in **Figure 9**.

Following incubation, citrate-positive cultures are identified by the presence of growth on the surface of the slant, which is accompanied by blue coloration. Citrate-negative cultures will show no growth, and the medium will remain green.

AT THE BENCH

Materials

Cultures

24- to 48-hour Trypticase soy broth cultures of *E. coli, E. aerogenes*, and *K. pneumoniae* for the short version. 24- to 48-hour Trypticase soy broth cultures of the 13 organisms for the long version.

Media

Simmons citrate agar slants per designated student group: 4 for the short version, 14 for the long version.

Equipment

Bunsen burner, inoculating needle, test tube rack, and glassware marking pencil.

Procedure Lab One

1. Using aseptic technique, inoculate each organism into its appropriately labeled tube by means of streak inoculation. The last tube will serve as a control.

2. Incubate all cultures for 24 to 48 hours at 37°C.

(a)   (b)

Figure 10 Citrate utilization test. (a) Tube is negative, showing no growth on slant surface. **(b)** Tube is positive, showing growth on slant surface.

Procedure Lab Two

1. Examine all agar slant cultures for the presence or absence of growth and coloration of the medium. Refer to **Figure 10**. Record your results in the chart in the Lab Report.

2. Based on your observations, determine and record whether or not each organism was capable of using citrate as its sole source of carbon.

Figure 11 Summary of iMViC reactions

Observations and Results

PART A: Indole Production Test

Bacterial Species	Color of Reagent Layer	Tryptophan Hydrolysis (+) or (−)
E. coli		
E. aerogenes		
K. pneumoniae		
S. dysenteriae		
S. typhimurium		
P. vulgaris		
P. aeruginosa		
A. faecalis		
M. luteus		
L. lactis		
S. aureus		
B. cereus		
C. xerosis		
Control		

PARTS B, C: Methyl Red Test and Voges-Proskauer Test

Bacterial Species	METHYL RED TEST		VOGES-PROSKAUER TEST	
	Color of Medium	(+) or (−)	Color of Medium	(+) or (−)
E. coli				
E. aerogenes				
K. pneumoniae				
S. dysenteriae				
S. typhimurium				
P. vulgaris				
P. aeruginosa				
A. faecalis				
M. luteus				
L. lactis				
S. aureus				
B. cereus				
C. xerosis				
Control				

PART D: Citrate Utilization Test

Bacterial Species	Presence or Absence of Growth (+) or (−)	Color of Medium	Citrate Utilization (+) or (−)
E. coli			
E. aerogenes			
K. pneumoniae			
S. dysenteriae			
S. typhimurium			
P. vulgaris			
P. aeruginosa			
A. faecalis			
M. luteus			
L. lactis			
S. aureus			
B. cereus			
C. xerosis			
Control			

Review Questions

1. Discuss the medical significance of the IMViC series of tests.

2. Explain the chemical mechanism for detecting indole in a bacterial culture.

3. Account for the development of alkalinity in cultures capable of using citrate as their sole carbon source.

4. In the carbohydrate fermentation test, we found that both *E. coli* and *E. aerogenes* produced the end products acid and gas. Account for the fact that *E. coli* is methyl red–positive and *E. aerogenes* is methyl red–negative.

5. The end products of tryptophan degradation are indole and pyruvic acid. Why do we test for the presence of indole rather than pyruvic acid as the indicator of tryptophanase activity?

6. Simmons citrate medium contains primarily inorganic ammonium, potassium, and sodium salts, plus organic citrate. What is the rationale for using a medium with this type of composition for the performance of the citrate utilization test?

Photo Credits

Credits are listed in order of appearance.

Photo 1: James Cappuccino

Photo 2: James Cappuccino

Photo 3: James Cappuccino

Photo 4: James Cappuccino

Hydrogen Sulfide Test

Principle

There are two major fermentative pathways by which some microorganisms are able to produce hydrogen sulfide (H_2S).

Pathway 1: Gaseous H_2S may be produced by the reduction (hydrogenation) of organic sulfur present in the amino acid cysteine, which is a component of peptones contained in the medium. These peptones are degraded by microbial enzymes to amino acids, including the sulfur-containing amino acid cysteine. This amino acid in the presence of a **cysteine desulfurase** loses the sulfur atom, which is then reduced by the addition of hydrogen from water to form bubbles of hydrogen sulfide gas ($H_2S\uparrow$) as illustrated:

$$
\begin{array}{ccc}
CH_2 - SH & & CH_3 \\
| & \xrightarrow[\textbf{desulfurase}]{\textbf{Cysteine}} & | \\
CH - NH_2 & & C = O + H_2S\uparrow + NH_3 \\
| & & | \\
COOH & & COOH \\
\textbf{Cysteine} & & \textbf{Pyruvic}\ \ \textbf{Hydrogen}\ \ \textbf{Ammonia} \\
& & \textbf{acid}\quad \textbf{sulfide} \\
& & \quad\quad\ \ \textbf{gas}
\end{array}
$$

Pathway 2: Gaseous H_2S may also be produced by the reduction of inorganic sulfur compounds such as the thiosulfates ($S_2O_3^{2-}$), sulfates (SO_4^{2-}), or sulfites (SO_3^{2-}). The medium contains sodium thiosulfate, which certain microorganisms are capable of reducing to sulfite with the liberation of hydrogen sulfide. The sulfur atoms act as hydrogen acceptors during oxidation of the inorganic compound as illustrated in the following:

$$2S_2O_3^{2-} + 4H^+ + 4e^- \xrightarrow[\textbf{reductase}]{\textbf{Thiosulfate}} 2SO_3^{2-} + 2H_2S\uparrow$$

Thiosulfate   **Sulfite**   **Hydrogen Sulfide gas**

In this experiment the SIM medium contains peptone and sodium thiosulfate as the sulfur substrates; ferrous sulfate ($FeSO_4$), which behaves as the H_2S indicator; and sufficient agar to make the medium semisolid and thus enhance anaerobic respiration. Regardless of which pathway is used, the hydrogen sulfide gas is colorless and therefore not visible. Ferrous ammonium sulfate in the medium serves as an indicator by combining with the gas, forming an insoluble black ferrous sulfide precipitate that is seen along the line of the stab inoculation and is indicative of H_2S production. Absence of the precipitate is evidence of a negative reaction. The overall reactions for both pathways and their interpretation are illustrated in **Figure 1**.

Motility

SIM agar may also be used to detect motile organisms. Motility is recognized when culture growth (turbidity) of flagellated organisms is not restricted to the line of inoculation. Growth of nonmotile organisms is confined to the line of inoculation.

From Experiment 26 of *Microbiology: A Laboratory Manual*, Tenth Edition. James G. Cappuccino, Natalie Sherman. Copyright © 2014 by Pearson Education, Inc. All rights reserved.

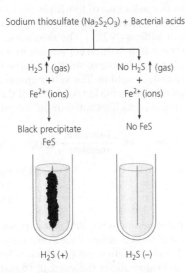

$$CH_2-SH \quad\quad CH_3$$
$$| \quad\quad\quad\quad\quad |$$
$$CH-NH_2 \xrightarrow[\text{desulfurase}]{\text{Cysteine}} C=O \;+\; NH_3 \;+\; H_2S \uparrow$$
$$| \quad\quad\quad\quad\quad |$$
$$COOH \quad\quad COOH$$

Cysteine   Pyruvic   Ammonia   **H₂S gas**
            acid   (colorless)

Sodium thiosulfate ($Na_2S_2O_3$) + Bacterial acids

$H_2S \uparrow$ (gas)	No $H_2S \uparrow$ (gas)
+	+
Fe^{2+} (ions)	Fe^{2+} (ions)
Black precipitate FeS	No FeS

H₂S (+)   H₂S (−)

Figure 1 Detection of hydrogen sulfide

Figure 2 Hydrogen sulfide production test.
(a) Negative, **(b)** positive with motility, and **(c)** positive with no motility.

CLINICAL APPLICATION

Identifying Intestinal Pathogens

While generally considered a self-limiting symptom, diarrhea due to *Proteus* is initially difficult to differentiate from early stages of the more severe bloody diarrhea (dysentery) associated with some *Shigella* or *Salmonella* species. Bacteria belonging to the genera *Salmonella* and *Proteus* enzymatically metabolize inorganic sulfur compounds and sulfur-containing amino acids, producing H₂S. The hydrogen sulfide test is one way to separate and identify *Shigella dysentariae*, which does not produce H₂S, from *Proteus* and *Salmonellla*.

AT THE BENCH

Materials

Cultures

24- to 48-hour Trypticase soy broth cultures of *Enterobacter aerogenes, Shigella dysenteriae, Proteus vulgaris,* and *Salmonella typhimurium* for the short version. 24- to 48-hour Trypticase soy broth cultures of the 13 organisms for the long version.

Media

SIM agar deep tubes per designated student group: 5 for the short version, 14 for the long version.

Equipment

Bunsen burner, inoculating needle, test tube rack, and glassware marking pencil.

Procedure Lab One

1. Aseptically inoculate each experimental organism into its appropriately labeled tube by means of stab inoculation. The last tube will serve as a control.

2. Incubate all cultures for 24 to 48 hours at 37°C.

Procedure Lab Two

1. Examine all SIM cultures for the presence or absence of black coloration along the line of the stab inoculation. Refer to **Figure 2**, and record your results in the chart provided in the Lab Report.

2. Based on your observations, determine and record whether or not each organism was capable of producing hydrogen sulfide.

3. Observe all cultures for the presence (+) or absence (−) of motility. Record your results in the chart in the Lab Report.

Observations and Results

Bacterial Species	Color of Medium	H₂S Production (+) or (−)	Motility (+) or (−)
E. coli			
E. aerogenes			
K. pneumoniae			
S. dysenteriae			
S. typhimurium			
P. vulgaris			
P. aeruginosa			
A. faecalis			
M. luteus			
L. lactis			
S. aureus			
B. cereus			
C. xerosis			
Control			

Review Questions

1. Distinguish between the types of substrates available to cells for H_2S production.

2. Explain how SIM medium is used to detect motility.

3. Explain the function of the ferrous ammonium sulfate in SIM agar.

4. Why is *P. vulgaris* H$_2$S-positive and *E. aerogenes* H$_2$S-negative?

5. A stool specimen of a patient with severe diarrhea was cultured in a series of specialized media for isolation of enteric organisms. The cultures yielded three isolates that were species of *Salmonella*, *Shigella*, and *Escherichia*. Explain why the H$_2$S production test would be diagnostically significant.

Photo Credit

Urease Test

Principle

Urease, which is produced by some microorganisms, is an enzyme that is especially helpful in the identification of *Proteus vulgaris*. Although other organisms may produce urease, their action on the substrate urea tends to be slower than that seen with *Proteus* species. Therefore, this test serves to rapidly distinguish members of this genus from other non–lactose-fermenting enteric microorganisms.

Urease is a hydrolytic enzyme that attacks the nitrogen and carbon bond in amide compounds such as urea and forms the alkaline end product ammonia. This chemical reaction is illustrated in **Figure 1**.

The presence of urease is detectable when the organisms are grown in a urea broth medium containing the pH indicator phenol red. As the substrate urea is split into its products, the presence of ammonia creates an alkaline environment that causes the phenol red to turn to a deep pink. This is a positive reaction for the presence of urease. Failure of a deep pink color to develop is evidence of a negative reaction.

$$
\underset{\text{Urea}}{\underset{\text{O}}{\overset{H_2N \quad NH_2}{\underset{\|}{\overset{\diagdown \diagup}{C}}}}} \quad + \quad 2H_2O \quad \xrightarrow{\textbf{Urease}} \quad \underset{\substack{\text{Carbon} \\ \text{dioxide}}}{CO_2} \quad + \quad \underset{\text{Water}}{H_2O} \quad + \quad \underset{\text{Ammonia}}{2NH_3}
$$

Figure 1 Enzymatic degradation of urea

AT THE BENCH

Materials

Cultures

24- to 48-hour Trypticase soy broth cultures of *Escherichia coli*, *Proteus vulgaris*, *Klebsiella pneumoniae*, and *Salmonella typhimurium* for the short version. 24- to 48-hour Trypticase soy broth cultures of the 13 organisms for the long version.

Media

Urea broth per designated student group: 5 for the short version, 14 for the long version.

Equipment

Bunsen burner, inoculating loop, test tube rack, and glassware marking pencil.

Procedure Lab One

1. Using aseptic technique, inoculate each experimental organism into its appropriately labeled tube by means of loop inoculation. The last tube will serve as a control.

2. Incubate cultures 24 to 48 hours at 37°C.

(a)   (b)

Figure 2 Urease test. (a) Negative and **(b)** positive.

Procedure Lab Two

1. Examine all urea broth cultures for color (refer to **Figure 2**). Record your results in the chart in the Lab Report.

2. Based on your observations, determine and record whether or not each organism was capable of hydrolyzing the substrate urea.

Observations and Results

Bacterial Species	Color of Medium	Urea Hydrolysis (+) or (−)
E. coli		
E. aerogenes		
K. pneumoniae		
S. dysenteriae		
S. typhimurium		
P. vulgaris		
P. aeruginosa		
A. faecalis		
M. luteus		
L. lactis		
S. aureus		
B. cereus		
C. xerosis		
Control		

Review Questions

1. Explain the mechanism of urease activity.

2. Explain the function of phenol red in the urea broth medium.

3. Explain how the urease test is useful for identifying members of the genus *Proteus*.

4. A swollen can of chicken soup is examined by the public health laboratory and found to contain large numbers of gram-negative, H_2S-positive bacilli. Which biochemical tests would you perform to identify the genus of the contaminant? Justify your test choices.

Photo Credit

Credits are listed in order of appearance.

Photo 1:   James Cappuccino

Litmus Milk Reactions

Principle

The major milk substrates capable of transformation are the milk sugar lactose and the milk proteins casein, lactalbumin, and lactoglobulin. To distinguish among the metabolic changes produced in milk, a pH indicator, the oxidation-reduction indicator litmus, is incorporated into the medium. Litmus milk now forms an excellent differential medium in which microorganisms can metabolize milk substrates depending on their enzymatic complement. A variety of different biochemical changes result, as follows:

Litmus milk
- Lactose fermentation
- Gas production
- Litmus reduction
- Curd formation
- Proteolysis
- Alkaline reaction

Lactose Fermentation

Organisms capable of using **lactose** as a carbon source for energy production utilize the inducible enzyme **β-galactosidase** and degrade lactose as follows:

The presence of **lactic acid** is easily detected because litmus is purple at a neutral pH and turns pink when the medium is acidified to an approximate pH of 4.

Gas Formation

The end products of the microbial fermentation of lactose are likely to include the **gases $CO_2\uparrow$ + $H_2\uparrow$**. The presence of gas may be seen as separations of the curd or by the development of tracks or fissures within the curd as gas rises to the surface.

Litmus Reduction

Fermentation is an anaerobic process involving biooxidations that occur in the absence of molecular oxygen. These oxidations may be visualized as the removal of hydrogen (dehydrogenation) from a substrate. Since hydrogen ions cannot exist in the free state, there must be an immediate and concomitant electron acceptor available to bind these hydrogen ions, or else oxidation-reduction reactions are not possible and cells cannot manufacture energy. In the litmus milk test, **litmus** acts as such an acceptor. While in the oxidized state, the litmus is purple; when it accepts hydrogen from a substrate, it will become reduced and turn white or milk-colored. This oxidation of lactose, which produces lactic acid, butyric acid, $CO_2\uparrow$, and $H_2\uparrow$, is as follows:

Lactose → Glucose → Pyruvic acid →
- Lactic acid
- Butyric acid
- CO_2 + H_2

The excess hydrogen is now accepted by the hydrogen acceptor litmus, which turns white and is said to be reduced.

Curd Formation

The biochemical activities of different microorganisms grown in litmus milk may result in the production of two distinct types of curds (clots). Curds are designated as either acid or rennet,

From Experiment 28 of *Microbiology: A Laboratory Manual*, Tenth Edition. James G. Cappuccino, Natalie Sherman.
Copyright © 2014 by Pearson Education, Inc. All rights reserved.

depending on the biochemical mechanism responsible for their formation.

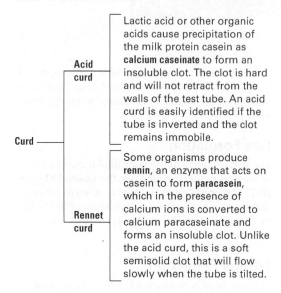

Curd
- Acid curd — Lactic acid or other organic acids cause precipitation of the milk protein casein as **calcium caseinate** to form an insoluble clot. The clot is hard and will not retract from the walls of the test tube. An acid curd is easily identified if the tube is inverted and the clot remains immobile.
- Rennet curd — Some organisms produce **rennin**, an enzyme that acts on casein to form **paracasein**, which in the presence of calcium ions is converted to calcium paracaseinate and forms an insoluble clot. Unlike the acid curd, this is a soft semisolid clot that will flow slowly when the tube is tilted.

Proteolysis (Peptonization)

The inability of some microorganisms to obtain their energy by way of lactose fermentation means they must use other nutritional sources such as proteins for this purpose. By means of proteolytic enzymes, these organisms hydrolyze the milk proteins, primarily casein, into their basic building blocks, namely amino acids. This digestion of proteins is accompanied by the evolution of large quantities of ammonia, resulting in an alkaline pH in the medium. The litmus turns deep purple in the upper portion of the tube, while the medium begins to lose body and produces a translucent, brown, wheylike appearance as the protein is hydrolyzed to amino acids.

Alkaline Reaction

An alkaline reaction is evident when the color of the medium remains unchanged or changes to a deeper blue. This reaction is indicative of the partial degradation of **casein** into **shorter polypeptide chains,** with the simultaneous release of alkaline end products that are responsible for the observable color change.

Figure 1 and **2** show the possible litmus milk reactions and their appearance following the appropriate incubation of the cultures.

Figure 1 Litmus milk reactions. (a) Uninoculated, **(b)** acid, **(c)** acid with reduction and curd, **(d)** alkaline, and **(e)** proteolysis.

CLINICAL APPLICATION

Differentiating Enterobacteriaceae and *Clostridium*.

The litmus milk test differentiates members of the Enterobacteriaceaeae from other gram-negative bacilli based on the enterics' ability to reduce litmus. It is also used to differentiate members within the genus *Clostridium*. Watery diarrhea caused by *C. perfringes* (contaminated food) is generally considered self-limiting. But diarrhea caused by *C. difficle* may be associated with antibiotic use that has removed the normal flora of the colon.

AT THE BENCH

Materials
Cultures

24- to 48-hour Trypticase soy broth cultures of *Escherichia coli, Alcaligenes faecalis, Lactococcus lactis,* and *Pseudomonas aeruginosa* for the short version. 24- to 48-hour Trypticase soy broth cultures of the 13 organisms for the long version.

Litmus Milk Reactions

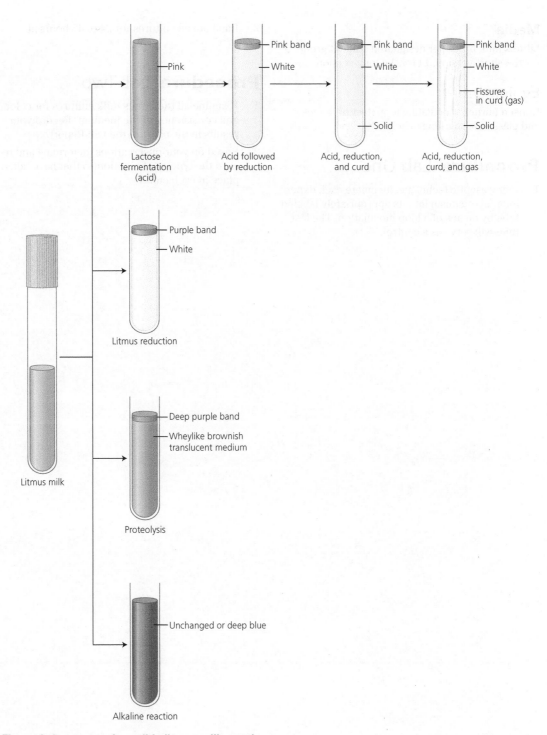

Figure 2 **Summary of possible litmus milk reactions**

Media

Litmus milk broth per designated student group: 5 for the short version, 14 for the long version.

Equipment

Bunsen burner, inoculating loop, test tube rack, and glassware marking pencil.

Procedure Lab One

1. Using aseptic technique, inoculate each experimental organism into its appropriately labeled tube by means of a loop inoculation. The last tube will serve as a control.

2. Incubate all cultures for 24 to 48 hours at 37°C.

Procedure Lab Two

1. Examine all the litmus milk cultures for color and consistency of the medium. Record your results in the chart in the Lab Report.

2. Based on your observations, determine and record the type(s) of reaction(s) that have taken place in each culture.

Observations and Results

Bacterial Species	Appearance of Medium	Litmus Milk Reactions
E. coli	pink/white bottom	
E. aerogenes	purple/pink	
K. pneumoniae	pink	
~~S. dysenteriae~~		
S. typhimurium	dark top then white	
P. vulgaris		
P. aeruginosa	clear/white/pink	
A. faecalis	dark purple	Alkaline
~~M. luteus~~		
L. lactis	clear/yellow/white	
S. aureus	purple then pink	
~~B. cereus~~		
~~C. xerosis~~		
Control		

Review Questions

1. Distinguish between acid and rennet curds.

2. Describe the litmus milk reactions that may occur when proteins are metabolized as an energy source.

3. Explain how the litmus in the litmus milk acts as a redox indicator.

4. Can a litmus milk culture show a pink band at the top and a brownish translucent layer at the bottom? Explain.

5. Explain why litmus milk is considered a good differential medium.

Photo Credit

Credits are listed in order of appearance.

Photo 1: James Cappuccino

Nitrate Reduction Test

Principle

The reduction of nitrates by some aerobic and facultative anaerobic microorganisms occurs in the absence of molecular oxygen, an anaerobic process. In these organisms anaerobic respiration is an oxidative process whereby the cell uses inorganic substances such as nitrates (NO_3^-) or sulfates (SO_4^{2-}) to supply oxygen that is subsequently utilized as a final hydrogen acceptor during energy formation. The biochemical transformation may be visualized as follows:

Partial Reduction

$$NO_3^- + 2H^+ + 2e^- \xrightarrow{\text{Nitrate reductase}} NO_2^- + H_2O$$

| Nitrate | Hydrogen electrons | | Nitrite | Water |

Some organisms possess the enzymatic capacity to act further on nitrites to reduce them to ammonia (NH_3^+) or molecular nitrogen (N_2). These reactions may be described as follows:

Complete Reduction

$$NO_2^- \longrightarrow NH_3^+$$

Nitrite   Ammonia

or

$$2NO_3^- + 12H^+ + 10e^- \longrightarrow N_2 + 6H_2O$$

Nitrate   Molecular nitrogen

Nitrate reduction can be determined by cultivating organisms in a nitrate broth medium. The medium is basically a nutrient broth supplemented with 0.1% potassium nitrate (KNO_3) as the nitrate substrate. In addition, the medium is made into a semisolid by the addition of 0.1% agar. The semisolidity impedes the diffusion of oxygen into the medium, thereby favoring the anaerobic requirement necessary for nitrate reduction.

Following incubation of the cultures, an organism's ability to reduce nitrates to nitrites is determined by the addition of two reagents: Solution A, which is sulfanilic acid, followed by Solution B, which is α-naphthylamine. *Note: This should not be confused with Barritt's reagent.* Following reduction, the addition of Solutions A and B will produce an immediate cherry red color.

$$NO_3^- \xrightarrow{\text{Nitrate reductase}} NO_2^- \text{ (Red color on addition of Solutions A and B)}$$

Cultures not producing a color change suggest one of two possibilities: (1) nitrates were not reduced by the organism, or (2) the organism possessed such potent **nitrate reductase** enzymes that nitrates were rapidly reduced beyond nitrites to ammonia or even molecular nitrogen. To determine whether or not nitrates were reduced past the nitrite stage, a small amount of zinc powder is added to the basically colorless cultures already containing Solutions A and B. Zinc reduces nitrates to nitrites. The development of red color therefore verifies that nitrates were not reduced to nitrites by the organism. If nitrates were not reduced, a negative nitrate reduction reaction has occurred. If the addition of zinc does not produce a color change, the nitrates in the medium were reduced beyond nitrites to ammonia or nitrogen gas. This is a positive reaction, as shown in **Figure 1**. Results of nitrate reduction tests are shown in **Figure 2**.

From Experiment 29 of *Microbiology: A Laboratory Manual*, Tenth Edition. James G. Cappuccino, Natalie Sherman. Copyright © 2014 by Pearson Education, Inc. All rights reserved.

Nitrate Reduction Test

Sulfanilic acid (colorless) + α-naphthylamine (colorless) + Nitrous acid → Sulfobenzene azo-α-naphthylamine (red) + Water

Figure 1 Formation of colored complex indicative of NO_3^- reduction

(a) (b) (c) (d)

Figure 2 Nitrate reduction tests. (a) Uninoculated, **(b)** positive with Solutions A + B, **(c)** positive with Solutions A + B + zinc powder, and **(d)** negative with Solutions A + B + zinc powder.

CLINICAL APPLICATION

Differentiating *Mycobacterium tuberculosis* from Non-tubercle *Mycobacterium*

This test is used to identify intestinal bacteria that are able to reduce nitrates to nitrites. When presented with a patient that exhibits the symptoms of tuberculosis and is positive for tubercles on an x-ray, a sputum sample will be tested for *Mycobacterium*. To distinguish between *Mycobacterium tuberculosis* and other *Mycobacterium* species a nitrate reduction test will be used since *M. tuberculosis* is the only *Mycobacterium* species with this capacity.

AT THE BENCH

Materials

Cultures

24- to 48-hour Trypticase soy broth cultures of *Escherichia coli*, *Alcaligenes faecalis*, and

Pseudomonas aeruginosa for the short version. 24- to 48-hour Trypticase soy broth cultures of the 13 organisms for the long version.

Media

Trypticase nitrate broth per designated student group: 4 for the short version, 14 for the long version.

Reagents

Solution A (sulfanilic acid), Solution B (α-naphthylamine), and zinc powder.

Equipment

Bunsen burner, inoculating loop, test tube rack, and glassware marking pencil.

Procedure Lab One

1. Using aseptic technique, inoculate each experimental organism into its appropriately labeled tube by means of a loop inoculation. The last tube will serve as a control.

2. Incubate all cultures for 24 to 48 hours at 37°C.

Procedure Lab Two

1. Add five drops of Solution A and then five drops of Solution B to all nitrate broth cultures. Observe and record in the Lab Report chart whether or not a red coloration develops in each of the cultures.

2. Add a minute quantity of zinc to the cultures in which no red color developed. Observe and record whether or not red coloration develops in each of the cultures.

3. On the basis of your observations, determine and record in the Lab Report chart whether or not each organism was capable of nitrate reduction. Identify the end product (NO_2^- or NH_3^+/N_2), if any, that is present.

Observations and Results

Bacterial Species	Red Coloration with Solutions A and B (+) or (−)	Red Coloration with Zinc (+) or (−)	Nitrate Reductions (+) or (−)	End Products
E. coli				
E. aerogenes				
K. pneumoniae				
S. dysenteriae				
S. typhimurium				
P. vulgaris				
P. aeruginosa				
A. faecalis				
M. luteus				
L. lactis				
S. aureus				
B. cereus				
C. xerosis				
Control				

Review Questions

1. Explain the function of the 0.1% agar in the nitrate medium.

2. Explain the functions of Solutions A and B.

3. If a culture does not undergo a color change on the addition of Solutions A and B, explain how you would interpret this result.

4. Explain why the development of a red color on the addition of zinc is a negative test.

5. Discuss the relationship between an organism's ability to reduce nitrate past the nitrite stage and that organism's proteolytic activity.

Photo Credit

Credits are listed in order of appearance.

Photo 1:   James Cappuccino

Catalase Test

LEARNING OBJECTIVE

Once you have completed this experiment, you should be able to

1. Determine the ability of some microorganisms to degrade hydrogen peroxide by producing the enzyme catalase.

Principle

During aerobic respiration, microorganisms produce hydrogen peroxide and, in some cases, an extremely toxic superoxide. Accumulation of these substances will result in death of the organism unless they can be enzymatically degraded. These substances are produced when aerobes, facultative anaerobes, and microaerophiles use the aerobic respiratory pathway, in which oxygen is the final electron acceptor, during degradation of carbohydrates for energy production. Organisms capable of producing **catalase** rapidly degrade hydrogen peroxide as illustrated:

$$2H_2O_2 \xrightarrow{\text{Catalase}} 2H_2O + O_2 \uparrow$$

Hydrogen peroxide ⟶ Water Free oxygen

Aerobic organisms that lack catalase can degrade especially toxic superoxides using the enzyme **superoxide dismutase;** the end product of a superoxide dismutase is H_2O_2, but this is less toxic to the bacterial cells than are the superoxides.

The inability of strict anaerobes to synthesize catalase, peroxidase, or superoxide dismutase may explain why oxygen is poisonous to these microorganisms. In the absence of these enzymes, the toxic concentration of H_2O_2 cannot be degraded when these organisms are cultivated in the presence of oxygen.

Catalase production can be determined by adding the substrate H_2O_2 to an appropriately incubated Trypticase soy agar slant culture. If catalase is present, the chemical reaction mentioned is indicated by bubbles of free oxygen gas ($O_2 \uparrow$). This is a positive catalase test; the absence of bubble formation is a negative catalase test. **Figure 1** shows the results of the catalase test using (a) the tube method, (b) the plate method, and (c) slide method.

CLINICAL APPLICATION

Differentiation of *Staphylococci, Streptococci,* and Enterobacteriaceae

The catalase test is used for the biochemical differentiation of catalase-positive *Staphylococci* and catalase-negative *Streptococci*, as well as members of the Enterobacteriaceae. With the increasing worry about methicillin-resistant strains of *Staphylococcus* in hospital settings, the catalase test is a quick and easy way to differentiate *S. aureus*, which may be MRSA, from other *Staphylococcus* species that have exhibited lower incidences of methicillin-resistance.

AT THE BENCH

Materials

Cultures

24- to 48-hour Trypticase soy broth cultures of *Staphylococcus aureus, Micrococcus luteus*, and *Lactococcus lactis* for the short version. 24- to 48-hour Trypticase soy broth cultures of the 13 organisms for the long version.

Media

Trypticase soy agar slants per designated student group: 4 for the short version, 14 for the long version.

Reagent

3% hydrogen peroxide.

Equipment

Tube method: Bunsen burner, inoculating loop, test tube rack, and glassware marking pencil.

From Experiment 30 of *Microbiology: A Laboratory Manual*, Tenth Edition. James G. Cappuccino, Natalie Sherman.

(b) Plate method

(a) Tube method

(c) Slide method

Figure 1 Catalase test. Negative results are shown on the left and positive results on the right in the **(a)** tube method and **(b)** plate method. Negative results are shown on the top and positive results on the bottom in the **(c)** slide method.

Slide method: Bunsen burner, inoculating loop, glassware marking pencil, glass microscope slides (4 for the short version, 14 for the long version), Petri dish and cover.

Procedure Lab One
Tube Method

1. Using aseptic technique, inoculate each experimental organism into its appropriately labeled tube by means of a streak inoculation. The last tube will serve as a control.
2. Incubate all cultures for 24 to 48 hours at 37°C.

Procedure Lab Two
Tube method

1. Allow three or four drops of the 3% hydrogen peroxide to flow over the entire surface of each slant culture.

2. Examine each culture for the presence or absence of bubbling or foaming. Record your results in the chart in the Lab Report.
3. Based on your observations, determine and record whether or not each organism was capable of catalase activity.

Slide Method

1. Label slides with the names of the organisms.
2. Using a sterile loop, collect a small sample of the first organism from the culture tube and transfer it to the appropriately labeled slide.
3. Place the slide in the Petri dish.
4. Place one drop of 3% hydrogen peroxide on the sample. Do not mix. Place the cover on the Petri dish to contain any aerosols.
5. Observe for immediate presence of bubble formation. Record your results in the chart in the Lab Report.
6. Repeat Steps 2 through 5 for the remaining test organisms.

Observations and Results

Bacterial Species	PRESENCE OR ABSENCE OF BUBBLING		CATALASE PRODUCTION (+) OR (−)	
	Tube	Slide	Tube	Slide
E. coli				
E. aerogenes				
K. pneumoniae				
S. dysenteriae				
S. typhimurium				
P. vulgaris				
P. aeruginosa				
A. faecalis				
M. luteus				
L. lactis				
S. aureus				
B. cereus				
C. xerosis				
Control				

Review Questions

1. Explain the toxic effect of O_2 on strict anaerobes.

2. Illustrate the chemical reaction involved in the degradation of hydrogen peroxide in the presence of catalase.

3. Would catalase be classified as an endoenzyme or an exoenzyme?
   Explain.

4. Account for the ability of streptococci to tolerate O_2 in the absence
   of catalase activity.

Photo Credits

Credits are listed in order of appearance.

Photo 1: David Alexander, University of Portland

Photo 2: Brenda Grafton Wellmeyer Department of
Biology, Lone Star College North Harris

Oxidase Test

LEARNING OBJECTIVE

Once you have completed this experiment, you should be able to

1. Perform an experimental procedure that is designed to distinguish among groups of bacteria on the basis of cytochrome oxidase activity.

CLINICAL APPLICATION

Test to Distinguish Family Enterobacteriaceae from non-Enterobacteriaceae

The Enterobacteriaceae are cytochrome oxidase–negative, while the genera *Neisseria* and *Pseudomonas* are cytochrome oxidase–positive. The oxidase test is an important tool in the identification of *Neisseria meningitis*, the causative agent of bacterial meningitis, which has a significant morbidity and mortality rate. In addition, yeast of medical importance such as *Candida* can be separated from *Saccharomyces* and *Torulopsis* by this test.

Principle

Oxidase enzymes play a vital role in the operation of the electron transport system during aerobic respiration. **Cytochrome oxidase** catalyzes the oxidation of a reduced cytochrome by molecular oxygen (O_2), resulting in the formation of H_2O or H_2O_2. Aerobic bacteria, as well as some facultative anaerobes and microaerophiles, exhibit oxidase activity. The oxidase test aids in differentiation among members of the genera *Neisseria* and *Pseudomonas*, which are oxidase-positive, and Enterobacteriaceae, which are oxidase-negative.

The ability of bacteria to produce cytochrome oxidase can be determined by the addition of the test reagent *p*-aminodimethylaniline oxalate to colonies grown on a plate medium. This light pink reagent serves as an artificial substrate, donating electrons and thereby becoming oxidized to a blackish compound in the presence of the oxidase and free oxygen. Following the addition of the test reagent, the development of pink, then maroon, and finally dark purple coloration on the surface of the colonies is indicative of cytochrome oxidase production and represents a positive test. No color change, or a light pink coloration on the colonies, is indicative of the absence of oxidase activity and is a negative test. The filter paper method may also be used and is described in this experiment.

AT THE BENCH

Materials

Cultures

24- to 48-hour Trypticase soy broth cultures of *Escherichia coli*, *Pseudomonas aeruginosa*, and *Alcaligenes faecalis* for the short version. 24- to 48-hour Trypticase soy broth cultures of the 13 organisms for the long version.

Media

Trypticase soy agar plates per designated student group: one for the short version, four for the long version.

Reagent

p-Aminodimethylaniline oxalate (Difco 0329-13-9).

Equipment

Plate method: Bunsen burner, inoculating loop, and glassware marking pencil.

Filter paper method: All of the above and filter paper (one for short version, four for long version).

Procedure Lab One
Plate Method

1. Prepare the Trypticase soy agar plate(s) for inoculation as follows:

   a. Short procedure: With a glassware marking pencil, divide the bottom of a Petri dish into three sections and label each section with the name of the test organism to be inoculated.

   b. Long procedure: Repeat Step 1a, dividing three plates into three sections and one plate into four sections to accommodate the 13 test organisms.

2. Using aseptic technique, make a single-line streak inoculation of each test organism on the agar surface of its appropriate section of the plate(s).

3. Incubate the plate(s) in an inverted position for 24 to 48 hours at 37°C.

Procedure Lab Two
Plate Method

1. Add two or three drops of the *p*-aminodimethylaniline oxalate to the surface of the growth of each test organism.

2. Observe the growth for the presence or absence of a color change from pink, to maroon, and finally to purple. Positive test (+), color change in 10–30 seconds; negative test (−), no color change, or light pink color. Refer to **Figure 1**. Record the results on the chart in the Lab Report.

3. Based on your observations, determine and record whether or not each organism was capable of producing cytochrome oxidase.

Figure 1 Oxidase test. Negative test, on left, results in no color change, and positive test, on right, results in a color change to purple.

Filter Paper Method

1. Prepare Petri dishes as described in Lab One Steps 1a and 1b.

2. Place filter paper in Petri dish.

3. With a sterile loop, obtain a heavy loopful of the first test organism and gently smear it on the filter paper.

4. Drop one or two drops of *p*-aminodimethylaniline oxalate reagent on the test organism.

5. Observe the organism for the appearance of a purple color within 30 seconds of contact with the oxidase reagent, indicating a positive test.

6. Repeat Steps 3 to 5 for the remaining test organisms.

7. Record your results in the chart in the Lab Report.

Observations and Results

Bacterial Species	COLOR OF COLONIES		OXIDASE PRODUCTION (+) OR (−)	
	Plate	**Filter paper**	**Plate**	**Filter paper**
E. coli				
E. aerogenes				
K. pneumoniae				
S. dysenteriae				
S. typhimurium				
P. vulgaris				
P. aeruginosa				
A. faecalis				
M. luteus				
L. lactis				
S. aureus				
B. cereus				
C. xerosis				
Control				

Review Questions

1. What is the function of cytochrome oxidase?

2. Why are strict aerobes oxidase-positive?

3. The oxidase test is used to differentiate among which groups of bacteria?

4. What is the function of the test reagent in this procedure?

5. Your instructor asks you to isolate and identify the organisms in an unknown culture. You find that the culture contains two gram-negative bacilli that produce swarming colonies. What biochemical test would you use to identify the bacilli? Justify your answer.

Photo Credit

Credits are listed in order of appearance.
Photo 1: David Alexander, University of Porltand

Utilization of Amino Acids

The study of the metabolism of amino acids began in the early part of the twentieth century. Some investigators found that the enteric microorganisms, such as *Proteus* and the so-called Providence species, were able to deaminate a variety of amino acids that provided a vehicle for distinguishing these microorganisms from other members of the large family of the Enterobacteriaceae. It was determined that 11 of the 22 amino acids were deaminated by amino acid oxidases, and it was phenylalanine deaminase that produced the most rapid enzymatic activity. Thus, phenylalanine deaminase became the most widely studied deaminase used to differentiate enteric organisms.

Likewise, some organisms were found to be capable of decarboxylating amino acids, providing a way to differentiate between the enteric genera and species. For instance, lysine decarboxylase is capable of differentiating between *Salmonella* and *Citrobacter*. Ornithine decarboxylase separates *Enterobacter* from *Klebsiella*. Decarboxylase enzymes are numerous, and each is specific for a particular substrate.

It is now evident that decarboxylases and deaminases play a vital role in the utilization of amino acids and the metabolism of nitrogen compounds.

PART A   Decarboxylase Test

LEARNING OBJECTIVE

Once you have completed this experiment, you should be able to

1. Identify and differentiate organisms based on their ability to enzymatically degrade amino acid substrates.

Principle

Every biologically active protein is composed of the 20 essential amino acids. Structurally, amino acids are composed of an alpha carbon (—C—), an amino group (—NH$_2$), a carboxyl group (—COOH), and a hydrogen atom (—H). Also attached to the alpha carbon is a side group or an atom designated by an (—R), which differs in each of the amino acids.

$$NH_2 - \overset{\overset{R}{|}}{\underset{\underset{H}{|}}{C}} - COOH$$

Decarboxylation is a process whereby some microorganisms that possess decarboxylase enzymes are capable of removing the carboxyl group to yield end products consisting of an **amine** or **diamine** plus **carbon dioxide.** Decarboxylated amino acids play an essential role in cellular metabolism since the amines produced may serve as end products for the synthesis of other molecules required by the cell. Decarboxylase enzymes are designated as adaptive (or induced) enzymes and are produced in the presence of specific amino acid substrates upon which they act. These amino acid substrates must possess at least one chemical group other than an amine (—NH$_2$) or a carboxyl group (—COOH). In the process of decarboxylation, organisms are cultivated in an acid environment and in the presence of a specific substrate. The decarboxylation end product (amines) results in a shift to a more alkaline pH.

In the clinical or diagnostic microbiology laboratory, three decarboxylase enzymes are used to differentiate members of the Enterobacteriaceae: lysine, ornithine, and arginine. Decarboxylase activity is determined by cultivating the organism in a nutrient medium containing glucose, the specific amino acid substrate, and bromthymol blue (the pH indicator). If decarboxylation occurs, the pH of the medium becomes alkaline despite the fermentation of glucose since the end products (amines or diamines) are alkaline. The function of the glucose in the medium is to ensure good microbial growth and thus more reliable results in the presence of the pH indicator. The presence of each decarboxylase enzyme can be tested for by supplementing decarboxylase broth with the specific

From Experiment 32 of *Microbiology: A Laboratory Manual*, Tenth Edition. James G. Cappuccino, Natalie Sherman.

$$NH_2-\underset{\underset{H}{|}}{\overset{\overset{H}{|}}{C}}-\underset{\underset{H}{|}}{\overset{\overset{H}{|}}{C}}-\underset{\underset{H}{|}}{\overset{\overset{H}{|}}{C}}-\underset{\underset{H}{|}}{\overset{\overset{H}{|}}{C}}-\underset{\underset{H}{|}}{\overset{\overset{NH_2}{|}}{C}}-COOH \xrightarrow[\text{decarboxylase}]{\text{Lysine}} NH_2-\underset{\underset{H}{|}}{\overset{\overset{H}{|}}{C}}-\underset{\underset{H}{|}}{\overset{\overset{H}{|}}{C}}-\underset{\underset{H}{|}}{\overset{\overset{H}{|}}{C}}-\underset{\underset{H}{|}}{\overset{\overset{H}{|}}{C}}-\underset{\underset{H}{|}}{\overset{\overset{NH_2}{|}}{C}}-H + CO_2$$

Lysine

Cadaverine   Carbon dioxide

Figure 1 Degradation of lysine

amino acid substrate, namely lysine, arginine, and ornithine. For example, **lysine decarboxylase** degrades L-lysine, forming the diamine end product **cadaverine** plus **carbon dioxide** as illustrated in **Figure 1**.

In the experiment that follows, the decarboxylation of L-lysine will be studied. It should be noted that decarboxylation reactions occur under anaerobic conditions that are satisfied by sealing the culture tubes with sterile mineral oil. In the sealed tubes, all of the unbound oxygen is utilized during the organisms' initial growth phase, and the pH of the medium becomes alkaline as carbon dioxide (CO_2) is produced in the culture tube. A pH indicator such as bromcresol purple is usually incorporated into the medium for the easy detection of pH changes. The production of acid end products will cause the bromcresol purple to change color from purple to yellow, indicating that acid has formed, the medium has been acidified, and the decarboxylase enzymes have been activated. The activated enzyme responds with the production of the alkalinizing diamine (cadaverine) and carbon dioxide, which will produce a final color change from yellow back to purple, thereby indicating that L-lysine has been decarboxylated. The development of a turbid purple color verifies a positive test for amino acid decarboxylation. The absence of a purple color indicates a negative result.

CLINICAL APPLICATION

Distinguishing between *Enterobacter* Species

The decarboxylase test identifies bacteria based on the production of ammonia from the amino acids lysine, ornithine, and arginine. The decarboxylase test can be used to differentiate the causative agent in many nosocomial infections of immunocompromised patients. The bacterium *Enterobacter aerogenes* is lysine decarboxylase positive while other *Enterobacter* species are negative. It is used primarily to identify bacteria within the Enterobacteriaceae family.

AT THE BENCH

Materials
Cultures

24-hour nutrient broth cultures of *Proteus vulgaris*, *Escherichia coli*, and *Citrobacter freundii* for the short version. 24- to 48-hour nutrient broth cultures of the 13 organisms for the long version.

Media

Per designated student group: three tubes of Moeller's decarboxylase broth supplemented with L-lysine (10 gm/l) (labeled LD+), three tubes of Moeller's decarboxylase broth without lysine (labeled LD−).

Equipment

Bunsen burner, glassware marking pencil, inoculating loop and needle, sterile Pasteur pipettes, rubber bulbs, test tube rack, and sterile mineral oil.

Procedure Lab One

1. With a glassware marking pencil, label three tubes of the LD+ medium with the name of the organism to be inoculated. Similarly label three tubes of LD− medium. The use of (LD−) control tubes is essential since some bacterial strains are capable of turning substrate-free media positive. *Note: Control tubes should remain yellow after incubation, denoting that only glucose was fermented.* The presence of a positive control tube invalidates the test, and no interpretation is possible.

2. Using aseptic technique, inoculate each experimental organism into its appropriately labeled tube using a loop inoculation.

3. Place a rubber bulb onto a sterile Pasteur pipette and overlay the surface of the inoculated

Figure 2 Decarboxylase test. (a) Uninoculated, **(b)** negative, and **(c)** positive.

culture tubes with 1 ml of sterile mineral oil. Hold the tubes in a slanted position while adding the mineral oil. *Note: Do not let the tip of the pipette touch the inoculated medium or the sides of the test tube walls.*

4. Repeat the above procedure for the remaining test cultures.

5. Incubate all tubes at 37°C for 24 to 48 hours.

Procedure Lab Two

1. Examine each culture tube for the presence of a color change. Refer to **Figure 2**.

2. Based on your observations, determine whether or not each organism was capable of performing decarboxylation of lysine.

3. Record your results in the chart in the Lab Report.

PART B   Phenylalanine Deaminase Test

LEARNING OBJECTIVE

Once you have completed this experiment, you should be able to

1. Demonstrate the ability of some organisms to remove the amino group ($-NH_2$) from amino acids.

Principle

Microorganisms that contain deaminase enzymes are capable of removing the amino group ($-NH_2$) from amino acids and other NH_2-containing chemical compounds. During this process the amino acid, under the auspices of its specific deaminase, will produce keto acids and ammonia as end products. In the experiment to follow, the amino acid phenylalanine will be deaminated by **phenylalanine deaminase** and converted to the **keto acid phenylpyruvic acid** and **ammonia.** The organisms are cultured on a medium incorporating phenylalanine as the substrate. This chemical reaction is illustrated in **Figure 3**.

If the organism possesses phenylalanine deaminase, phenylpyruvic acid will be released into the medium and can be detected by the addition of a 10 to 12% ferric chloride solution to the surface of the medium. If a green color develops, the enzymatic deamination of the substrate has occurred and is indicative of a positive result. The absence of any color change indicates a negative result. The resultant green color produced upon the addition of ferric chloride ($FeCl_3$) is due to the formation of a keto acid (phenylpyruvic acid). It has been shown that α- and β-keto acids give a positive color reaction with either alcoholic or aqueous solutions of $FeCl_3$. Phenylpyruvic acid is an α-keto acid. The results should be read immediately following the addition of the reagent since the color produced fades quickly. When not in use, the ferric chloride reagent should be refrigerated and kept in a dark bottle to avoid exposure to light. The stability of this reagent varies and should be checked weekly with known positive cultures.

CLINICAL APPLICATION

Differentiating Intestinal Bacteria

The phenylalanine deaminase test uses the differential medium phenylalanine agar to detect bacteria containing the enzyme phenylalanine deaminase, and is used to differentiate the genera *Proteus, Morganella,* and *Providencia* from other gram-negative intestinal bacilli. These genera of enteric and environmental bacteria are known to cause UTIs and gastroenteritis. It is clinically important to distinguish them from other enteric bacteria due to their high level of antibiotic resistance.

Utilization of Amino Acids

$$\text{Phenylalanine} \xrightarrow[\text{deaminase}]{\text{Phenylalanine}} \text{Phenylpyruvic acid} + NH_3$$

Phenylalanine — $CH_2 - CH - COOH$ with NH_2

Phenylpyruvic acid — $CH_2 - C - COOH$ with O

Ammonia — NH_3

Figure 3 Deamination of phenylalanine

AT THE BENCH

Materials

Cultures

24-hour nutrient broth cultures of *Escherichia coli* and *Proteus vulgaris* for the short version. 24-hour nutrient broth cultures of the 13 organisms for the long version.

Media

Two phenylalanine agar slants.

Reagents

10 to 12% ferric chloride solution.

Equipment

Bunsen burner, glassware marking pencil, Pasteur pipettes, rubber bulbs, test tube racks, and inoculating loop.

Procedure Lab One

1. Using aseptic technique, inoculate each experimental organism into its appropriately labeled tube using a streak inoculation.
2. Incubate cultures at 37°C for 24 to 48 hours.

Procedure Lab Two

1. Add 5 to 10 drops of the ferric chloride solution to each agar slant and mix gently. Ferric chloride is a chelating agent and binds to the phenylpyruvic acid to produce a green color on the slant (**Figure 4**).

(a)   (b)   (c)

Figure 4 Phenylalanine deaminase test.
(a) Uninoculated, (b) negative, and (c) positive.

2. Based on your observations, determine whether or not each organism was capable of amino acid deamination. *Note: Results should be read immediately following the addition of ferric chloride because the green color fades rapidly.*
3. Record your results in the Lab Report.

Observations and Results

Parts A, B: Decarboxylase Test and Phenylalanine Deaminase Test

Bacterial Species	DECARBOXYLASE TEST				PHENYLALANINE DEAMINASE TEST	
	Color of Medium		Lysine Decarboxylase (+) or (−)		Color after FeCl₃	Deamination (+) or (−)
	LD+	LD−	LD+	LD−		
E. coli						
E. aerogense						
K. pneumoniae						
S. dysenteriae						
S. typhimurium						
P. vulgaris						
P. aeruginosa						
A. faecalis						
M. luteus						
L. lactis						
S. aureus						
B. cereus						
C. xerosis						
C. freundii						
Control						

Review Questions

1. A negative decarboxylase test is indicated by the production of a yellow color in the medium. Explain the reason for the development of this color.

2. Explain why deaminase activity must be determined immediately following the addition of ferric chloride.

3. What is the function of ferric chloride in the detection of deaminase activity?

4. Explain why the anaerobic environment is essential for decarboxylation of the substrate to occur.

5. Following a normal delivery, a nurse observes that the urine of the infant has a peculiar odor resembling that of burnt sugar or maple syrup. Subsequent examination by the pediatrician reveals that this child has maple syrup urine disease.

   a. What is this disease?

   b. How is it treated?

Photo Credits

Credits are listed in order of appearance.
Photo 1:   Experiment performed and photographed by L. Brent Selinger, Department of Biological Sciences, University of Lethbridge, Pearson Education

Photo 2:   Experiment performed and photographed by L. Brent Selinger, Department of Biological Sciences, University of Lethbridge, Pearson Education

Genus Identification of Unknown Bacterial Cultures

Principle

Identification of unknown bacterial cultures is one of the major responsibilities of the microbiologist. Samples of blood, tissue, food, water, and cosmetics are examined daily in laboratories throughout the world for the presence of contaminants. In addition, industrial organizations are constantly screening materials to isolate new antibiotic-producing organisms or organisms that will increase the yield of marketable products such as vitamins, solvents, and enzymes. Once isolated, these unknown organisms must be identified and classified.

The science of classification is called **taxonomy** and deals with the separation of living organisms into interrelated groups. *Bergey's Manual* has been the official, internationally accepted reference for bacterial classification since 1923. The current edition, *Bergey's Manual of Systematic Bacteriology*, arranges related bacteria into 33 groups called sections rather than into the classical taxonomic groupings of phylum, class, order, and family. The interrelationship of the organisms in each section is based on characteristics such as morphology, staining reactions, nutrition, cultural characteristics, physiology, cellular chemistry, and biochemical test results for specific metabolic end products.

At this point you have developed sufficient knowledge of staining methods, isolation techniques, microbial nutrition, biochemical activities, and characteristics of microorganisms to be able to work independently in attempting to identify the genus of an unknown culture. Characteristics of the major organisms that have been used in experiments thus far are given in Table 1. You are to use this table for the identification of the unknown cultures. The observations and results obtained following the experimental procedures are the basis of this identification. *However, you should note that your biochemical results may not be identical to those shown in Table 1; they may vary because of variations in bacterial strains (subgroups of a species).* Therefore, it becomes imperative to recall the specific biochemical tests that differentiate among the different genera of the test organisms.

The rationale for the performance of this exercise later in the semester is twofold. First, you will have acquired expanded knowledge of microbial activities and will be more proficient in laboratory skills. Second, and more important, you will be more cognizant of and more critical in your approach to species identification using dichotomous keys supplemented with *Bergey's Manual*.

CLINICAL APPLICATION

Application of Learned Assays to Identify an Unknown Bacterial Pathogen

The role of the clinical laboratory in a hospital is to quickly and efficiently identify the causative agent of a patient's infection. This will entail choosing the correct assays and performing them in the correct order to logically identify the genus and species of the agent.

From Experiment 33 of *Microbiology: A Laboratory Manual*, Tenth Edition. James G. Cappuccino, Natalie Sherman.

Genus Identification of Unknown Bacterial Cultures

TABLE 1	Cultural and Biochemical Characteristics of Unknown Organisms																	
				FERMENTATION														
ORGANISM	GRAM STAIN	AGAR SLANT CULTURAL CHARACTERISTICS	LITMUS MILK REACTION	LACTOSE	DEXTROSE	SUCROSE	H_2S PRODUCTION	NO_3 REDUCTION	INDOLE PRODUCTION	MR REACTION	VP REACTION	CITRATE USE	UREASE ACTIVITY	CATALASE ACTIVITY	OXIDASE ACTIVITY	GELATIN LIQUEFACTION	STARCH HYDROLYSIS	LIPID HYDROLYSIS
Escherichia coli	Rod −	White, moist, glistening growth	Acid, curd ±, gas ±, reduction ±	AG	AG	A±	−	+	+	+	−	−	−	+	−	−	−	−
Enterobacter aerogenes	Rod −	Abundant, thick, white, glistening growth	Acid	AG	AG	AG±	−	+	−	−	+	+	·−	+	−	−	−	−
Klebsiella pneumoniae	Rod −	Slimy, white, somewhat translucent, raised growth	Acid, gas, curd ±	AG	AG	AG	−	+	−	±	±	+	+	+	−	−	−	−
Shigella dysenteriae	Rod −	Thin, even, grayish growth	Alkaline	−	A	A±	−	+	±	+	−	−	−	+	−	−	−	−
Salmonella typhimurium	Rod −	Thin, even, grayish growth	Alkaline	−	AG±	A±	+	+	−	+	−	+	−	+	−	−	−	−
Proteus vulgaris	Rod −	Thin, blue-gray, spreading growth	Alkaline	−	AG	AG±	+	+	+	+	−	±	+	+	−	+	−	−
Pseudomonas aeruginosa	Rod −	Abundant, thin, white growth, with medium turning green	Rapid peptonization	−	−	−	−	+	−	−	−	+	−	+	+	+ Rapid	−	+
Alcaligenes faecalis	Rod* −	Thin, white, spreading, viscous growth	Alkaline	−	−	−	−	−	−	−	−	±	−	+	+	−	−	−
Staphylococcus aureus	Cocci +	Abundant, opaque, golden growth	Acid reduction ±	A	A	A	−	+	−	+	±	−	−	+	−	+	−	+
Lactococcus lactis	Cocci +	Thin, even growth	Acid, rapid reduction with curd	A	A	A	−	−	−	+	−	−	−	−	−	−	−	−
Micrococcus luteus	Cocci +	Soft, smooth, yellow growth	Alkaline	−	−	−	−	±	−	−	−	−	+	+	−	+ Slow	−	−
Corynebacterium xerosis	Rod +	Grayish, granular, limited growth	Alkaline	−	A±	A±	−	+	−	−	−	−	−	+	−	−	−	−
Bacillus cereus	Rod +	Abundant, opaque, white waxy growth	Peptonization	−	A	A	−	+	−	−	±	−	−	+	−	+ Rapid	+	±

Note: AG = Acid and gas; ± = Variable reaction; Rod* = Coccobacillus

Materials

Cultures

Number-coded 24- to 48-hour Trypticase soy agar slant cultures of the 13 bacterial species will be provided with one unknown pure culture.

Media

Two Trypticase soy agar slants, and one each of the following per student: phenol red sucrose broth, phenol red lactose broth, phenol red dextrose broth, SIM agar deep tube, MR-VP broth, tryptic nitrate broth, Simmons citrate agar slant, urea broth, litmus milk, Trypticase soy agar plate, nutrient gelatin deep tube, starch agar plate, and tributyrin agar plate.

Reagents

Crystal violet; Gram's iodine; 95% ethyl alcohol; safranin; methyl red; 3% hydrogen peroxide; Barritt's reagent, Solutions A and B; Kovac's reagent; zinc powder; and p-aminodimethylaniline oxalate.

Equipment

Bunsen burner, inoculating loop and needle, staining tray, immersion oil, lens paper, bibulous paper, microscope, and glassware marking pencil.

Procedure Lab One

1. Perform a Gram stain of the unknown organism. Observe and record in the Lab Report chart the reaction and the morphology and arrangement of the cells.

2. Using aseptic inoculating technique, inoculate two Trypticase soy agar slants by means of a streak inoculation. Following incubation, you will use one slant culture to determine the cultural characteristics of the unknown microorganism. You will use the second as a stock subculture should it be necessary to repeat any of the tests.

3. Exercising care in aseptic technique so as not to contaminate cultures and thereby obtain spurious results, inoculate the media for the following biochemical tests:

Medium	Test
a. Phenol red lactose brothb b. Phenol red dextrose broth c. Phenol red sucrose broth	Carbohydrate fermentationc
d. Litmus milk	Litmus milk reactions
e. SIM medium	Indole production H_2S production
f. Tryptic nitrate broth	Nitrate reduction
g. MR-VP broth	Methyl red test Voges-Proskauer test
h. Simmons citrate agar slant	Citrate utilization
i. Urea broth	Urease activity
j. Trypticase soy agar slant	Catalase activity
k. Starch agar plate	Starch hydrolysis
l. Tributyrin agar plate	Lipid hydrolysis
m. Nutrient gelatin deep tube	Gelatin liquefaction
n. Trypticase soy agar plate	Oxidase test

4. Incubate all cultures for 24 to 72 hours at 37°C.

Procedure Lab Two

1. Examine a Trypticase soy agar slant culture and determine the cultural characteristics of your unknown organism. Record your results in the Lab Report.

2. Perform biochemical tests on the remaining cultures, making reference to the specific laboratory exercise for each test. Record your observations and results.

3. Based on your results, identify the genus and species of the unknown organism. *Note: Results may vary depending on the strains of each species used and the length of time the organism has been maintained in stock culture. The observed results may not be identical to the expected results. Therefore choose the organism that best fits the results summarized in Table 1.*

Name: _____

Date: _____ Section: _____

Observations and Results

Description of Unknown's Characteristics	Student	
	Culture no. _____	
	Organism _____	
Experimental Procedure	**Observations**	**Results**
Gram stain		
Acid-fast stain		
Shape and arrangement		
Cultural characteristics		
Litmus milk reactions		
Carbohydrate fermentations: Lactose		
Dextrose		
Sucrose		
H_2S production		
Nitrate reduction		
Indole production		
Methyl red test		
Voges-Proskauer test		
Citrate utilization		
Urease activity		
Catalase activity		
Starch hydrolysis		
Lipid hydrolysis		
Gelatin liquefaction		
Oxidase test		

Photo Credits

Credits are listed in order of appearance.

Photo 1:   David Alexander, University of Portland

Photo 2:   James Cappuccino

Photo 3:   Experiment performed and photographed by
L. Brent Selinger, Department of Biological Sciences,
University of Lethbridge, Pearson Education

Photo 4:   James Cappuccino

Photo 5:   James Cappuccino

Photo 6:   James Cappuccino

Photo 7:   James Cappuccino

Photo 8:   James Cappuccino

Photo 9:   James Cappuccino

Photo 10:   James Cappuccino

Photo 11:   James Cappuccino

Photo 12:   James Cappuccino

Photo 13:   James Cappuccino

Photo 14:   David Alexander, University of Portland

Photo 15:   Brenda Grafton Wellmeyer Department of
Biology, Lone Star College North Harris

Photo 16:   David Alexander, University of Porltand

Photo 17:   Experiment performed and photographed
by L. Brent Selinger, Department of Biological Sciences,
University of Lethbridge, Pearson Education

Photo 18:   Experiment performed and photographed
by L. Brent Selinger, Department of Biological Sciences,
University of Lethbridge, Pearson Education

The Protozoa

LEARNING OBJECTIVES

Once you have completed the experiments in this section, you should be

1. Familiar with the distinguishing characteristics of protozoans.
2. Able to identify free-living and parasitic protozoans in microscopic views.

Introduction

The protozoa are a large and diverse group of unicellular, eukaryotic organisms. Most are free-living, but some are parasites. Their major distinguishing characteristics are

1. The absence of a cell wall; some, however, possess a flexible layer, a pellicle, or a rigid shell of inorganic materials outside of the cell membrane.

2. The ability during their entire life cycle or part of it to move by locomotor organelles or by a gliding mechanism.

3. Heterotrophic nutrition whereby the free-living forms ingest particulates such as bacteria, yeast, and algae, while the parasitic forms derive nutrients from the body fluids of their hosts.

4. Primarily asexual means of reproduction, although sexual modes occur in some groups.

Protozoan taxonomy is being continually updated as new technology enables classification based on molecular characteristics. To ease our discussion of protozoans, we follow a more traditional taxonomic scheme, dividing them into four groups based on means of locomotion.

1. **Sarcodina:** Motility results from the streaming of ectoplasm, producing protoplasmic projections called pseudopods (false feet).

Prototypic amoebas include the free-living *Amoeba proteus* and the parasite *Entamoeba histolytica*.

2. **Mastigophora:** Locomotion is effected by one or more whiplike, thin structures called flagella. Free-living members include the genera *Cercomonas*, *Heteronema*, and *Euglena*, which are photosynthetic protists that may be classified as flagellated algae. The parasitic forms include *Trichomonas vaginalis*, *Giardia intestinalis* (formerly called *Giardia lamblia*), and the *Trypanosoma* species.

3. **Ciliophora:** Locomotion is carried out by means of short hairlike projections called cilia, whose synchronous beating propels the organisms. The characteristic example of free-living members of this group is *Paramecium caudatum*, and the parasitic example is *Balantidium coli*.

4. **Sporozoa:** Unlike other members of this phylum, sporozoa do not have locomotor organelles in their mature stage; however, immature forms exhibit some type of movement. All the members of this group are parasites. The most significant members belong to the genus *Plasmodium*, the malarial parasites of animals and humans.

From Part 6 of *Microbiology: A Laboratory Manual*, Tenth Edition. James G. Cappuccino, Natalie Sherman.

Free-Living Protozoa

Principle

There are more than 20,000 known species of free-living protozoa. It is not within the scope of this manual to present an in-depth study of this large and diverse population. Therefore in this procedure you will use Table 1 and **Figures 1** and **Figure 2** to become familiar with the general structural characteristics of representative protozoa, and you will identify these in a sample of pond water.

CLINICAL APPLICATION

Wet Mounts for Diagnosis

Wet mount slides, often utilizing stains, are routinely used in the examination of stool samples for infectious protozoans such as *Entamoeba histolytica*. This organism causes amoebic dysentery and has been known to lead to severe liver damage. Although most infections are asymptomatic, carriers can still spread the disease. Diagnosis may require examination of several slide preparations.

AT THE BENCH

Materials

Cultures

Stagnant pond water and prepared slides of amoebas, paramecia, euglenas, and stentors.

Reagent

Methyl cellulose.

Equipment

Microscope, glass slides, coverslips, and Pasteur pipettes.

Procedure

1. Obtain a drop of pond water from the bottom of the culture and place it in the center of a clean slide.

2. Add a drop of methyl cellulose to the culture to slow down the movement of the protozoa.

3. Apply a coverslip in the following manner to prevent formation of air bubbles:

   a. Place one edge of the coverslip against the outer edge of the drop of culture.

   b. After the drop of culture spreads along the inner aspect of the edge of the coverslip, gently lower the coverslip onto the slide.

4. Examine your slide preparation under scanning, low-power, and high-power objectives with diminished light, and observe for the different protozoa present. Record your results in the Lab Report.

From Experiment 34 of *Microbiology: A Laboratory Manual*, Tenth Edition. James G. Cappuccino, Natalie Sherman. Copyright © 2014 by Pearson Education, Inc. All rights reserved.

TABLE 1 Structural Characteristics of Free-Living Protozoa

Sarcodina

Amoeba

- Pseudopod
- Ectoplasm
- Contractile vacuole
- Endoplasm
- Food vacuole
- Nucleus

1. **Pseudopods:** Protoplasmic projections that function for locomotion
2. **Ectoplasm:** Outer layer of cytoplasm; clear in appearance
3. **Endoplasm:** Inner cytoplasmic region; granular in appearance
4. **Nucleus:** One present
5. **Food vacuoles:** Contain engulfed food undergoing digestion
6. **Contractile vacuole:** Large, clear circular structure that regulates internal water pressure

Mastigophora

- Flagellum
- Mouth
- Eye spot
- Chloroplast
- Pellicle
- Nucleus

Euglena   *Cercomonas*   *Heteronema*

1. **Flagella:** One to several long whiplike structures that function for locomotion
2. **Pellicle:** Elastic layer outside of cell membrane
3. **Mouth:** Present but indistinct
4. **Chloroplast:** Organelles containing chlorophyll; present in photosynthetic forms only
5. **Eye spot:** Light-sensitive pigmented spot
6. **Nucleus:** One present

Ciliophora

- Cilia
- Pellicle
- Food vacuole
- Oral groove
- Micronucleus
- Macronucleus
- Contractile vacuole

Paramecium   *Stentor*   *Vorticella*

1. **Cilia:** Numerous, short, hairlike structures that function for locomotion
2. **Pellicle:** Outermost flexible layer
3. **Contractile vacuole** with radiating canals; regulates osmotic pressure
4. **Oral groove:** Indentation that leads to the mouth and gullet
5. **Food vacuoles:** Sites of digestion of ingested food
6. **Macronucleus:** A large nucleus that functions to control the cell's activities; one to several may be present
7. **Micronucleus:** A small nucleus that functions in conjugation, a mode of sexual reproduction

Figure 1 Amoeba

(a) *Euglena viridis*

(b) *Paramecium caudatum*

Figure 2 Euglena and Paramecium

Name: _____

Date: _____ Section: _____

Observations and Results

1. In the space provided, draw a representative sketch of several of the observed protozoa in stagnant pond water, indicate the magnifications used, and label their structural components. Identify each organism according to its class based on its mode of locomotion and its genus.

Magnification: _____ _____

Organelles of locomotion: _____ _____

Class: _____ _____

Genus: _____ _____

Magnification: _____ _____

Organelles of locomotion: _____ _____

Class: _____ _____

Genus: _____ _____

2. Draw representative sketches, indicate magnification, and label the structural components. Identify each organism according to its class based on locomotion and genus.

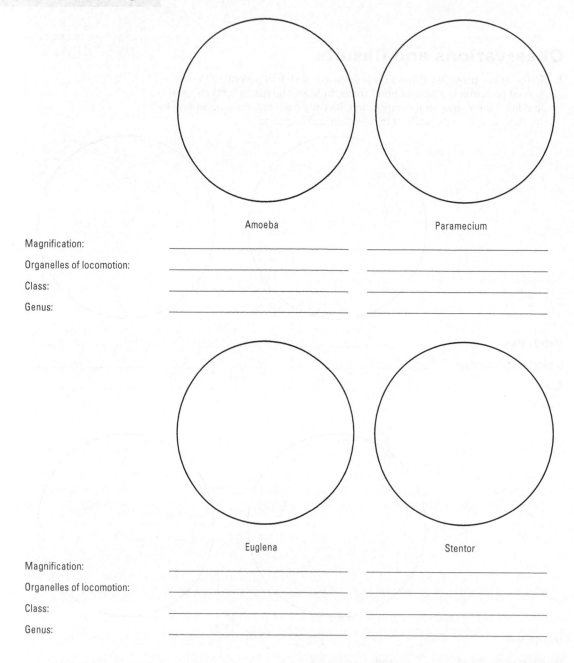

Amoeba

Paramecium

Magnification: _____   _____

Organelles of locomotion: _____   _____

Class: _____   _____

Genus: _____   _____

Euglena

Stentor

Magnification: _____   _____

Organelles of locomotion: _____   _____

Class: _____   _____

Genus: _____   _____

Review Questions

1. What are the distinguishing characteristics of the free-living members of Sarcodina, Mastigophora, and Ciliophora?

2. Identify and give the function of the following:
   a. Pseudopods:

   b. Contractile vacuole:

   c. Eye spot:

   d. Micronucleus:

   e. Pellicle:

   f. Oral groove:

3. People with AIDS are vulnerable to toxoplasmosis caused by the protozoan *Toxoplasma gondii*, resulting in infection of lungs, liver, heart, and brain, and often leading to death. About 25% of the world's population is infected, usually without developing symptoms. Why then are people with AIDS so susceptible to this disease?

Photo Credits

Credits are listed in order of appearance.

Photo 1: Eric V. Grave Photo Researchers, Inc.

Photo 2: Biophoto Associates Photo Researchers, Inc.

Photo 3: M.I. Walker Photo Researchers, Inc.

Parasitic Protozoa

Principle

Unlike the life cycles of the free-living forms, the life cycles of parasitic protozoa vary greatly in complexity. Knowledge of the various developmental stages in these life cycles is essential in the diagnosis, clinical management, and chemotherapy of parasitic infections.

Parasites with the simplest or most direct life cycles not requiring an intermediate host are the following:

1. *Entamoeba histolytica:* A pseudopodian parasite of the class Sarcodina that causes amebic dysentery. Infective, resistant cysts are released from the lumen of the intestine through the feces and are deposited in water, in soil, or on vegetation. On ingestion, the mature quadrinucleated cyst wall disintegrates and the nuclei divide, producing eight active trophozoites (metabolically active cells) that move to the colon, where they establish infection.

2. *Balantidium coli:* The ciliated parasitic protozoan exhibits a life cycle similar to that of *E. histolytica* except that no multiplication occurs within the cyst. This organism resides primarily in the lumen and submucosa of the large intestine. It causes intestinal ulceration and alternating constipation and diarrhea.

3. *Giardia intestinalis:* The intestinal mastigophoric flagellate exhibits a life cycle comparable to those of the above parasites. This organism is responsible for the induction of abdominal discomfort and severe diarrhea. Diagnosis is made by finding cysts in the formed stool and both cysts and trophozoites in the diarrhetic stool.

The mastigophoric hemoflagellate responsible for various forms of African sleeping sickness has a more complex life cycle. The *Trypanosoma* must have two hosts to complete its cyclic development: a vertebrate and an invertebrate, blood-sucking insect host. Humans are the definitive hosts harboring the sexually mature forms; the tsetse fly (*Glossina*) and the reduviid bug are the invertebrate hosts in which the developmental forms occur.

Table 1 illustrates the morphological characteristics of prototypic members of the parasitic protozoa except the Sporozoa.

Protozoa demonstrating the greatest degree of cyclic complexity are found in the class Sporozoa. They are composed of exclusively obligate parasitic forms, such as members of the genus *Plasmodium,* and are responsible for malaria in both humans and animals. The life cycle requires two hosts, a human being and the female *Anopheles* mosquito. It is significant to note that in this life cycle, the mosquito, and not the human, is the definitive host harboring the sexually mature parasite.

Malaria is initiated when a person is bitten by an infected mosquito, during which time infective sexually mature sporozoites are injected with the insect's saliva. These parasites pass rapidly from the blood into the liver, where they infect the parenchymal cells. This is the **pre-erythrocytic stage.** The parasites develop asexually within the liver cells by a process called **schizogony,** producing **merozoites.** This cycle may be repeated or the merozoites that are released from the ruptured liver cells may now infect red blood cells

TABLE 1	Characteristics of Representative Parasitic Protozoa				
CLASS, ORGANISM, AND INFECTION	STRUCTURAL CHARACTERISTICS	LOCOMOTOR ORGANELLES	SITE OF INFECTION	ISOLATION OF PARASITIC FORM	
SARCODINA *Entamoeba histolytica* Infection: Amebic dysentery Peripheral chromatin Central karyosome Uniform cytoplasm Red blood cell Nuclei Chromatoid body Early　　Late	**Trophozoite:** Shape: Variable Nucleus: Discrete nuclear membrane with central karyosome and peripheral chromatin granules Cytoplasm: Clear, red blood cells may be present **Cyst:** Shape: Round to oval with thick wall Nuclei: 1–4 present; mature cyst is quadrinucleated Chromatoid bodies: Sausage-shaped with rounded ends, present in young cysts only	Pseudopods None	Large intestine by ingestion of mature cysts	Diarrhetic stool Formed stool	
MASTIGOPHORA *Trypanosoma gambiense* Infection: African sleeping sickness Flagellum Undulating membrane Nucleus Volutin granules Kinetoplast	**Trophozoite:** Shape: Crescent Nucleus: Large, central, and polymorphic Cytoplasm: Granular **Cyst:** None	Single flagellum along undulating membrane	Peripheral blood-stream by means of tsetse fly vector	Peripheral blood	

and initiate the **erythrocytic stage.** During this asexual development, the parasite undergoes a series of morphological changes that are of diagnostic value. These forms are designated as **signet rings, trophozoites, schizonts, segmenters, merozoites,** and **gametocytes.** The merozoites are capable of reinfecting other blood cells or liver cells. Ingestion of the **microgametocytes** ($\male$) and **macrogametocytes** ($\female$) by another mosquito during a blood meal initiates the sexual cycle called **sporogamy.** Male and female gametes give rise to a zygote in the insect's gut. The zygote is then transformed into an **ookinete** that burrows through the gut wall to form an **oocyst** in which the sexually mature **sporozoites** develop, thereby completing the life cycle.

In this experiment, you will study the parasitic protozoa by using prepared slides and the diagnostic characteristics shown in **Figure 1** and Table 1. The purpose of the experiment is to help you understand life cycles of parasitic protozoa.

TABLE 1	Characteristics of Representative Parasitic Protozoa (continued)			
CLASS, ORGANISM, AND INFECTION	**STRUCTURAL CHARACTERISTICS**	**LOCOMOTOR ORGANELLES**	**SITE OF INFECTION**	**ISOLATION OF PARASITIC FORM**
MASTIGOPHORA *Giardia intestinalis* Infection: Dysentery — Nucleus — Karyosome — Median bodies — Axonemes — Nuclei — Median bodies — Retracted protoplasm — Axonemes	**Trophozoite:** Shape: Pear-shaped with concave sucking disc Nuclei: 2 bilaterally located with central karyosome and no peripheral chromatin Cytoplasm: Uniform and clear **Cyst:** Shape: Oval to ellipsoidal Nuclei: 2–4 present and protoplasm retracted from cyst wall Axostyle Parabasal body	4 pairs of flagella 4 pairs of flagella within cyst	Small intestine through ingestion of cysts	Diarrhetic stool Formed stool
CILIOPHORA *Balantidium coli* Infection: Dysentery — Cytostome — Cilia — Micronucleus — Macronucleus — Cyst wall — Macronucleus	**Trophozoite:** Shape: Oval Nuclei: Kidney-shaped macronucleus and a micronucleus Cytoplasm: Vacuolated **Cyst:** Shape: Round and thick-walled Nuclei: 1 macronucleus and a micronucleus that is not visible	Cilia Cilia within cyst	Large intestine by the ingestion of cysts	Diarrhetic stool Formed stool

CLINICAL APPLICATION

Understanding Parasitic Protozoa

Parasitic protozoa can exist extracellularly or intracellularly and possess diverse morphologies. They rapidly reproduce, asexually or sexually, with short generation times. They are highly organ, tissue, or cell specific. Examples are *Plasmodium* species, which colonize red blood cells (malaria); *Trichomonas*, which colonize the urinary tract (vaginal infections); and *Entamoeba*, which colonizes the large intestine (severe diarrhea).

AT THE BENCH

Materials
Prepared Slides

Entamoeba histolytica trophozoite and cyst, *Giardia intestinalis* trophozoite and cyst (formerly *G. lamblia*), *Balantidium coli* trophozoite and cyst, *Trypanosoma gambiense*, and *Plasmodium vivax* in human blood smears.

Parasitic Protozoa

Figure 1 Life cycle of *Plasmodium vivax*

Equipment

Microscope, immersion oil, and lens paper.

Procedure

1. Examine all available slides under the oil-immersion objective. Use Table 1, Figure 1, and the photographs in **Figure 2** through **Figure 6** to identify the distinguishing microscopic characteristics of each parasite studied.

2. Record your observations in the Lab Report.

(a) *Entamoeba histolytica* (650×)

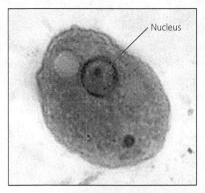

(b) A trophozoite of *Entamoeba histolytica* (2000×)

Figure 2 *Entamoeba histolytica*. Causative agent of amebic dysentery.

(a) Red blood cells infected by the ring stage (signet ring) (850×)

(b) Late schizont (segmenter) stage (1100×)

Figure 3 *Plasmodium vivax*. Causative agent of malaria.

Figure 4 *Trypanosoma gambiense.* Causative agent of African sleeping sickness (1300×).

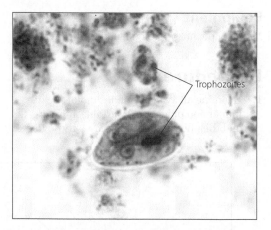

Figure 6 *Giardia intestinalis.* Causative agent of gastrointestinal diarrhea.

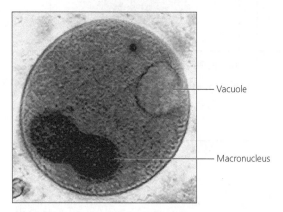

Figure 5 A cyst of the ciliated protozoan *Balantidium coli.* The cysts are spherical and lack surface cilia.

Observations and Results

Draw representative sketches of the parasitic organisms that you studied, and label the distinguishing structural characteristics you were able to observe.

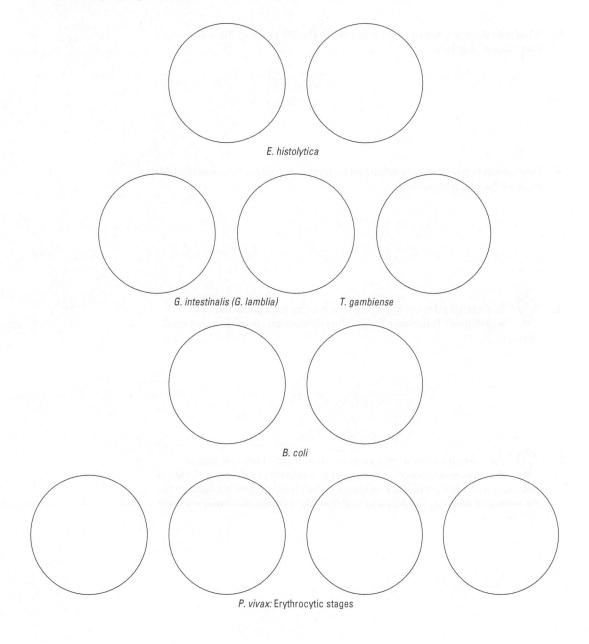

E. histolytica

G. intestinalis (G. lamblia)   *T. gambiense*

B. coli

P. vivax: Erythrocytic stages

Review Questions

1. Describe the developmental stages of the malarial parasite during sporog-amy and schizogony.

2. What role does the invertebrate host play in the life cycle of the try-panosomes? Explain.

3. Distinguish between the pre-erythrocytic and erythrocytic stages in the life cycle of the malarial parasite.

4. In malarial infections, the sexually mature parasite is found in which host? Is this true for all other protozoan parasitic infections? Explain.

5. On returning from a trip overseas, an individual with persistent diarrhea is diagnosed as having an *E. histolytica* infection. Fecal examination reveals the presence of blood in the stool, suggesting damage to the intestinal mucosa. Explain why and how the mucosa was compromised by this parasite.

Illustration Credits

All illustrations by Precision Graphics unless otherwise noted.

1:   From Harold S. Brown, *Basic Clinical Parasitology*, 4th
ed. New York: Appleton-Century-Crofts, 1975.

Photo Credits

Credits are listed in order of appearance.

Photo 1:   Centers for Disease Control and Prevention

Photo 2:   Centers for Disease Control and Prevention

Photo 3:   Biophoto Associates Photo Researchers, Inc.

Photo 4:   Eric V. Grave Photo Researchers, Inc.

Photo 5:   Marilise Brittes Rott

Photo 6:   Centers for Disease Control and Prevention

The Fungi

LEARNING OBJECTIVES

When you have completed the experiments in this section, you should be familiar with

1. The macroscopic and microscopic structures of yeast and molds.
2. The basic mycological culturing and staining procedures.
3. The ability to identify selected common fungal organisms.

Introduction

The branch of microbiology that deals with the study of fungi (yeasts and molds) is called **mycology.** True fungi are separated into the following four groups on the basis of their sexual modes of reproduction:

1. **Zygomycetes:** Bread and terrestrial molds. Reproductive spores are external and uncovered. Sexual spores are zygospores, and asexual spores are sporangiospores.

2. **Ascomycetes:** Yeasts and molds. Sexual spores, called ascospores, are produced in a saclike structure called an ascus. Conidia are asexual spores produced on a conidiophore.

3. **Basidiomycetes:** Fleshy fungi, toadstools, mushrooms, puffballs, and bracket fungi. Reproductive spores, basidiospores, are separate from specialized stalks called basidia.

4. **Deuteromycetes:** Also called **Fungi Imperfecti** because no sexual reproductive phase has been observed.

The major characteristics of these four groups of fungi are shown in Table 1.

Nutritionally, the fungi are heterotrophic, eukaryotic microorganisms that are enzymatically capable of metabolizing a wide variety of organic substrates. Fungi can have beneficial or detrimental effects on humans. Those that inhabit the soil play a vital role in decomposing dead plant and animal tissues, thereby maintaining a fertile soil environment. The fermentative fungi are of industrial importance in producing beer and wine, bakery products, cheeses, industrial enzymes, and antibiotics. The detrimental activities of some fungi include spoilage of foods by rots, mildews, and rusts found on fruit, vegetables, and grains. Some species are capable of producing toxins (for example, aflatoxin) and hallucinogens. A few fungal species are of medical significance because of their capacities to produce diseases in humans. Many of the pathogenic fungi are deuteromycetes and can be divided into two groups based on site of infection. The **superficial mycoses** cause infections of the skin, hair, and nails (for example, ringworm infections). The **systemic mycoses** cause infections of the subcutaneous and deeper tissues such as those of the lungs, genital areas, and nervous system.

TABLE 1	Major Characteristics of the Four Groups of Fungi			
	GROUP			
CHARACTERISTICS	ZYGOMYCETES	ASCOMYCETES	BASIDIOMYCETES	DEUTEROMYCETES
Mycelium	Nonseptate	Septate	Septate	Septate
Asexual spores	Found in sporangium; sporangiospores (nonmotile)	Formed on tip of conidiophore; conidia (nonmotile)	Same as the ascomycetes	Same as the ascomycetes
Sexual spores	Zygospores (motile), found in terrestrial forms; oospores, found in aquatic forms	Ascospores, contained in a saclike structure called the ascus	Basidiospores, carried on the outer surface of a club-shaped cell called the basidium	Fungi Imperfecti—no sexual reproductive phase observed; some members of the ascomycetes and basidiomycetes are Fungi Imperfecti
Common species	Bread molds, mildews, potato blight, *Rhizopus* species	Cup fungi, ergot, Dutch elm, yeast species	Smuts, rusts, puffballs, toadstools, mushrooms	*Aspergillus, Candida, Trichophyton, Cryptococcus, Blastomyces, Histoplasma, Microsporum,* and *Sporothrix*

Cultivation and Morphology of Molds

Molds are the major fungal organisms that can be seen by the naked eye. We have all seen them growing on foods such as bread or citrus fruit as a cottony, fuzzy, black, green, or orange growth, or as a mushroom with a visible cap attached to a stalk, depending on the mold. Examination with a simple hand lens shows that these organisms are composed of an intertwining branching mat called a **mycelium.** The filaments that make up this mycelial mat are called **hyphae.** Most of the mat grows on or in the surface of the nutrient medium so that it can extract nutrients; the mat is therefore called **vegetative mycelium.** Some of the mycelium mat rises upward from the mat and is referred to as **aerial mycelium.** Specialized hyphae are produced from the aerial mycelium and give rise to spores that are the reproductive elements of the mold. **Figures 1, 2, 5,** and **6** show the reproductive structures of some fungi.

The cultivation, growth, and observation of molds require techniques that differ from those used for bacteria. Mold cultivation requires the use of a selective medium such as Sabouraud agar or potato dextrose agar. These media favor mold growth because their low acidity (pH 4.5 to 5.6) discourages the growth of bacteria, which favor a neutral (pH 7.0) environment. The temperature requirements of molds are also different from those of bacteria, in that molds grow best at room temperature (25°C). In addition, molds grow at a much slower rate than bacteria do, requiring several days to weeks before visible colonies appear on a solid agar surface. Colony growth is shown in **Figures 3** and **4.**

PART A   Slide Culture Technique

LEARNING OBJECTIVES

When you have completed this experiment you should be

1. Acquainted with mold cultivation on glass slides.
2. Able to visualize and identify the structural components of molds.

Principle

Because the structural components of molds are very delicate, even simple handling with an inoculating loop may result in mechanical disruption of their components. The following slide culture

Spores Sporangiospores Conidia Oidia Chlamydospore Ascospores Basidiospores

Vegetative hyphae Sporangiophore Conidiophore Oidiophore Spores forming in hyphae Ascus Basidium

Figure 1 Spore and sporangia types

From Experiment 36 of *Microbiology: A Laboratory Manual*, Tenth Edition. James G. Cappuccino, Natalie Sherman. Copyright © 2014 by Pearson Education, Inc. All rights reserved.

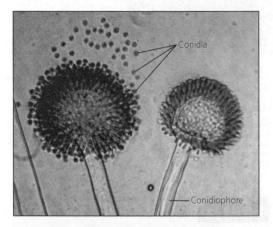

Figure 2 Conidiophore and conidia of mold
Aspergillus niger

Figure 3 Colony of *Penicillium chrysogenum*

**Figure 4 Colony of *Aspergillus niger* on a
Sabouraud agar plate**

Figure 5 Mucor mucedo

Figure 6 Rhizopus stolonifer

technique is used to avoid such disruption. A deep
concave slide containing a suitable nutrient medium with an acidic pH, such as Sabouraud agar, is
covered by a removable coverslip. Mold spores are
deposited in the surface of the agar and incubated
in a moist chamber at room temperature. Direct microscopic observation is then possible without fear
of disruption or damage to anatomical components.
Molds can be identified as to spore type and shape,
type of sporangia, and type of mycelium, as shown
in Figure 1 and Table 1.

CLINICAL APPLICATION

Cultivation of Fungi on Glass Slides

Since sporangia may be damaged during transfer to
a glass slide, the slide culture technique prevents
the disturbance and damage of the sporangia and
other spore structures required for fungi identification. Intact samples can be used to distinguish a
fungi like *Aspergillus niger,* which causes the most
common fungal infection of the ear, from *Aspergillus
flavus,* a fungal pathogen that may result in disseminating infection of the lungs.

AT THE BENCH

Materials

Cultures

7- to 10-day Sabouraud agar cultures of *camembert.*
Penicillium ~~chrysogenum~~ (formerly called
P. notatum) and *Aspergillus niger*, ~~*Mucor*~~
~~*mucedo*~~, and *Rhizopus stolonifer*.
2

Media

Per student group: one Sabouraud agar deep tube.

Equipment

Bunsen burner, waterbath, four concave glass slides,
four coverslips, petroleum jelly, sterile Pasteur
pipettes, toothpicks, four sterile Petri dishes, filter
paper, forceps, inoculating loop and needle, four sterile U-shaped bent glass rods, thermometer, dissecting
microscope, and beaker with 95% ethyl alcohol.

Procedure Lab One

1. Melt the deep tube of Sabouraud agar in a boiling water bath and cool to 45°C.

2. Place a piece of filter paper in the bottom of
   each Petri dish, insert a sterile bent glass rod
   into each dish, and replace the covers.

3. Using forceps, dip the concave slides and
   coverslips in a beaker of 95% ethyl alcohol,
   pass through Bunsen burner flame, remove
   from flame, and hold until all the alcohol has
   burned off the slides and coverslips.

4. Cool slides and coverslips. Place a slide, concave side up, with a coverslip to one side of
   the concavity, on the glass rod inside each
   Petri dish.

5. With a toothpick, add petroleum jelly to three
   sides surrounding the concavity of each slide.
   The fourth side will serve as a vent for air.

6. With a sterile Pasteur pipette, add one or two
   drops of cooled Sabouraud agar to the concavity of each slide.

7. Place a coverslip over the concave portion of
   each slide so that it is completely sealed.

8. With forceps, stand each slide upright inside
   its respective Petri dish until the agar solidifies, as illustrated below:

9. When agar is fully hardened, slide coverslips
   downward with forceps, and with a sterile
   needle inoculate each prepared slide with the
   spores from the test cultures.

10. Push the coverslips to their original positions,
    thereby sealing off the slide.

11. With a Pasteur pipette, moisten the filter paper
    with sterile water to provide a moist atmo-
    sphere. Remoisten filter paper when necessary
    during the incubation period.

12. Place the slide on the U-shaped bent rod,
    replace Petri dish cover, and label with the
    names of the organism and your initials.

13. Incubate the preparations for 7 days at 25°C.

Procedure Lab Two

1. Examine each mycological slide preparation
   under the low and high power of a dissecting microscope. Identify the mycelial mat,
   vegetative and reproductive hyphae, and
   spores. Use Table 1 to aid with your identification of mold structures.

2. Record your observations in the Lab Report.

PART B   Mold Cultivation on Solid Surfaces

LEARNING OBJECTIVES

*When you have completed this experiment,
you should be*

1. Acquainted with the technique of mold
   cultivation on agar plates.

2. Able to observe and identify colonial
   characteristics such as growth rate, texture,
   pigmentation on the surface and reverse
   side, and folds or ridges on the surface.

Principle

Cultivating molds on solid surfaces allows you to observe the variations in gross colonial morphology among different genera of molds. These variations in colonial appearance play a major role in the identification of the filamentous fungi. Most microbiologists are familiar with the gross appearance of multicellular fungi, but even to the untrained, the macroscopic differences in colonial growths are obvious and recognizable. For example, most people have seen rotting citrus fruits (lemons and oranges) produce a blue-green velvety growth characteristic of *Penicillium* species. It is also common for stale cheese to show a grayish-white furry growth of *Mucor* species, and the black stalklike appearance of *Rhizopus* molds growing on bread is familiar to many.

In this part of the experiment, you will be able to visualize the gross appearance of the colonial growth of four different molds.

CLINICAL APPLICATION

Isolation of Fungi on Solid Media

Before a fungal species may be identified or studied it must first be isolated. Similar to using an agar plate for isolating a distinct bacterial species, agar plating may be used as a growth medium for the isolation of fungi spores. Once spores have been isolated from individual sporangia, subculturing on solid agar or slides will allow for characterization and genetic studies of the fungus.

AT THE BENCH

Materials

Cultures

7- to 10-day Sabouraud agar cultures of *Aspergillus niger, Penicillium chrysogenum* (formerly called *P. notatum*), *Mucor mucedo*, and *Rhizopus stolonifer.*

Media

Per designated student group: three Sabouraud agar plates and one potato dextrose agar plate.

Equipment

Bunsen burner, four test tubes containing 2 ml of sterile saline, dissecting microscope, and an inoculating loop.

Procedure Lab One

1. Label the three Sabouraud agar plates as *Aspergillus niger, Penicillium chrysogenum,* and *Mucor mucedo,* and label the fourth plate containing potato dextrose agar as *Rhizopus stolonifer.*

2. Prepare a saline suspension of each mold culture. Label each of the four tubes of saline with the name of the organism. Using a sterile inoculating loop, scrape two loopfuls of mold culture into the corresponding tube of 2 ml of sterile saline and mix well by tapping the tube with your finger.

3. Using aseptic technique, inoculate each of the plates by placing a single loopful of mold suspension in the center of its respective agar plate. *Note: Do not spread the inoculum and do not shake or jostle the plates.*

4. Incubate all plates at room temperature, 25°C, for 7 to 10 days. *Note: Do not invert the plates.*

Procedure Lab Two

1. Examine each mold plate under the low and high power of a dissecting microscope. Refer to Table 1 for your identification of mold structures. *Note: Do not remove Petri dish covers.*

2. Record your observations in the Lab Report.

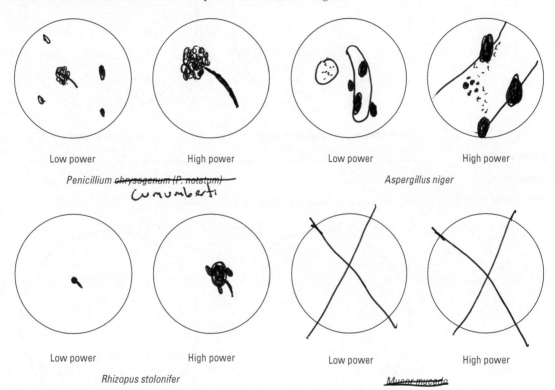

Observations and Results

PART A: Slide Culture Technique

Draw a representative microscopic field under low-power and high-power magnification and label the structural components of each test organism.

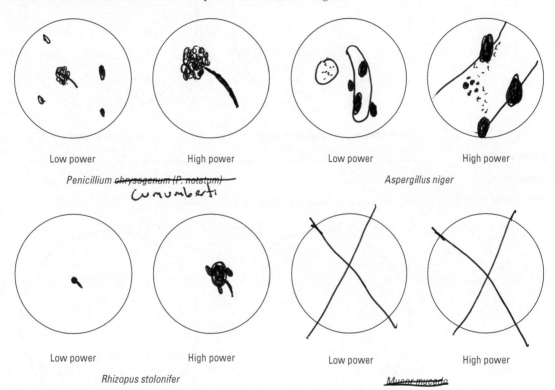

| Low power | High power | Low power | High power |

Penicillium chrysogenum (P. notatum)
Cucumberti

Aspergillus niger

| Low power | High power | Low power | High power |

Rhizopus stolonifer

Mucor mucedo

PART B: Mold Cultivation on Solid Surfaces

Draw sketches of the mold colonies under low power, indicating the extent of growth (diameter in mm), pigmentation, and the presence or absence of aerial hyphae. Refer to Table 1 to aid with your identification of mold structures.

Penicillium chrysogenum (P. notatum)

Aspergillus niger

Colony diameter (mm): _____   _____

Pigmentation: _____   _____

Aerial hyphae (+ or −): _____   _____

Rhizopus stolonifer

Mucor mucedo

Colony diameter (mm): _____   _____

Pigmentation: _____   _____

Aerial hyphae (+ or −): _____   _____

Review Questions

1. Cite some beneficial and harmful aspects of molds.

2. What is the advantage of using Sabouraud agar?

3. In the slide culture technique, what is the purpose of the following?
   a. Moistened filter paper in the Petri dish:

   b. A U-shaped glass rod in the Petri dish:

4. 💡 What is the advantage of the slide culture technique over that of a simple loop inoculation onto an agar plate (as in Part B)?

5. Why would it be advantageous to observe mold colonies on an agar plate?

6. 💡 Since dimorphism is a property of fungi, how do you account for the fact that molds grow preferentially *in vitro* rather than *in vivo*?

Photo Credits

Credits are listed in order of appearance.

Photo 1: Jared Martin, Center for Indoor Air Research, Texas Tech University Health Science Center, Lubbock, Texas

Photo 2: Leonard Lessun FBP, Photo Researchers, Inc.

Photo 3: James Cappuccino

Photo 4: Perennou Nuridsany Photo Researchers, Inc.

Photo 5: Biophoto Associates Photo Researchers, Inc.

Yeast Morphology, Cultural Characteristics, and Reproduction

Principle

Yeasts are nonfilamentous unicellular fungi. Yeast cultures resemble bacteria when grown on the surface of artificial laboratory media; however, they are 5 to 10 times larger than bacteria. Yeast colonies are illustrated in **Figure 1**. Microscopically, yeast cells may be ellipsoidal, spherical, or in some cases, cylindrical (**Figure 2**). Unlike molds, yeast do not have aerial hyphae and supporting sporangia.

Yeast reproduce asexually by **budding** or by **fission.** In budding, an outgrowth from the parent cell (a **bud**) pinches off, producing a daughter cell (**Figures 3a** and **4**). Fission occurs in certain species of yeast, such as those in the genus *Schizosaccharomyces*. During fission, the parent cell elongates, its nucleus divides, and it splits evenly into two daughter cells.

Some yeast may also undergo sexual reproduction when two sexual spores conjugate, giving rise to a zygote, or diploid cell. The nucleus of this cell divides by meiosis, producing four new haploid nuclei (sexual spores), called **ascospores,** contained within a structure called the **ascus** (**Figure 3b**). When the ascus ruptures, the ascospores are released and conjugate, starting the cycle again.

Yeasts are important for many reasons. *Saccharomyces cerevisiae* is referred to as baker's yeast and is used as the leavening agent in dough. Two major strains of yeast, *Saccharomyces carlsbergensis* and *Saccharomyces cerevisiae*, are used for brewing. The wine industry relies on wild yeast (present on the grape) for the fermentation of grape juice, which is supplemented with *Saccharomyces ellipsoideus* to begin the fermentation. Also, the high vitamin content of yeasts makes them particularly valuable as food supplements. As useful as some yeasts are, there are a few species that can create problems in the food industry or are harmful to humans. Undesired

(a) *Saccharomyces cerevisiae*   (b) *Candida albicans*   (c) *Rhodotorula rubra*

Figure 1 Colonies of yeast cells

Figure 2 Yeast Cells. *Schizosaccharomyces octosporus.*

Figure 4 Asexual yeast reproduction by budding. *Saccharomyces cerevisiae.*

(a) Asexual reproductive yeast structures

(b) Sexual reproductive yeast structures

Figure 3 Reproductive structures of yeast

yeast must be excluded from the manufacture of fruit juices, such as grape juice or apple cider, to prevent the fermentation of fruit sugars to alcohol. The contamination of soft cheese by some forms of yeast will destroy the product. Finally, some yeast such as *Candida albicans* are pathogenic and responsible for urinary tract and vaginal infections known as **moniliasis** and infections of the mouth called **thrush.**

The cultural characteristics, the type of reproduction, and the fermentative activities used to identify the different genera of yeast will all be studied in this experiment.

CLINICAL APPLICATION

Opportunistic Yeast

The yeast *Candida albicans* can cause infections of the mucus membranes lining the mouth, commonly called thrush, or the linings of the female urogenital tracts, called vulvovaginitis or, more commonly, "yeast infection." The yeast *Cryptococcus neoformans* can cause a pulmonary infection that can lead to meningitis. These yeast are considered to be opportunistic pathogens because they may cause serious or life-threatening infections in immunocompromised patients, such as people with cancer or AIDS.

AT THE BENCH

Materials
Cultures

7-day Sabouraud agar cultures of *Saccharomyces cerevisiae, Candida albicans, Rhodotorula rubra, Selenotila intestinalis,* and *Schizosaccharomyces octosporus.*

Media

Per designated student group: five tubes each of bromcresol purple glucose broth, bromcresol purple maltose broth, bromcresol purple lactose broth, and bromcresol purple sucrose broth, each containing a Durham tube; two glucose-acetate agar plates; and five test tubes (13×100 mm) containing 2 ml of sterile saline.

Reagents

Water-iodine solution, lactophenol–cotton-blue solution.

Equipment

Bunsen burner, inoculating loop and needle, 10 glass slides, 10 coverslips, 5 sterile Pasteur pipettes, glassware marking pencil, and microscope.

Procedure Lab One

Morphological Characteristics

Prepare a wet mount of each yeast culture in the following manner:

1. Suspend a loopful of yeast culture in a few drops of lactophenol–cotton-blue solution on a microscope slide and cover with a coverslip.

2. Examine all yeast wet-mount slide preparations under low and high power, noting the shape and the presence or absence of budding. Record your observations in the Lab Report.

Fermentation Studies

1. With a sterile loop, inoculate each experimental organism into appropriately labeled tubes of bromcresol purple glucose, maltose, lactose, and sucrose fermentation broths.

2. Incubate all cultures at 25°C for 4 to 5 days.

Sexual Reproduction

1. With a glassware marking pencil, divide the bottom of a glucose-acetate agar plate into three sections, and divide another glucose-acetate agar plate in half.

2. Label each section with the name of a test organism.

3. Label each tube of sterile saline with the name of a test organism.

4. With a sterile inoculating loop, suspend a heavy loopful of each test organism into its appropriately labeled tube of saline. Tap the tube with your finger to obtain a uniform cell suspension.

5. With a sterile Pasteur pipette, inoculate one drop of each test organism onto the surface of the appropriately labeled section on an agar plate. *Note: Allow the inoculum to diffuse into the agar for a few minutes. Do not swirl or rotate the plates.*

6. Incubate all plates at 25°C for 7 days. *Note: Visit the laboratory, if possible, during the incubation period and note when sporulation begins.*

Procedure Lab Two

Fermentation Studies

1. Examine all fermentation tubes for the presence of growth (turbidity), the presence or absence of acid (change in the color of medium), and the presence or absence of gas (bubble in Durham tube).

2. Record your results in the chart provided in the Lab Report.

Procedure Lab Three

Sexual Reproduction

1. Examine the glucose-acetate agar plates for the presence or absence of sporulation.

2. Prepare a water-iodine wet mount using a loopful of culture from each respective section on the glucose-acetate agar plate.

3. Observe the cells using the high-dry objective and record your observations in the Lab Report.

Observations and Results

Morphological Characteristics

Draw a representative field for each organism in the chart below. Note the shape and presence or absence of budding (+ or −).

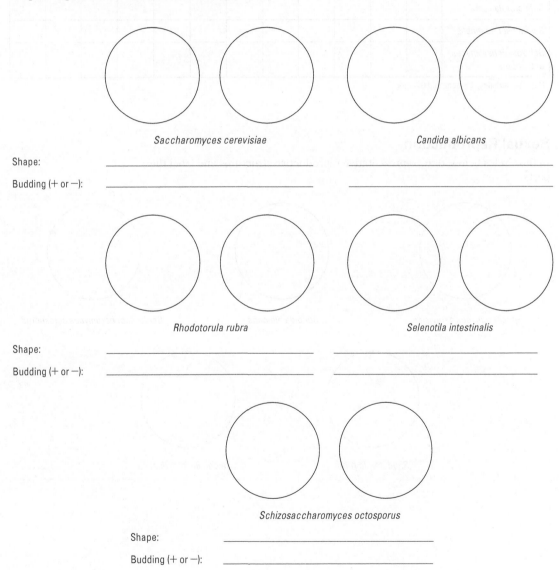

Saccharomyces cerevisiae

Candida albicans

Shape: _____   _____

Budding (+ or −): _____   _____

Rhodotorula rubra

Selenotila intestinalis

Shape: _____   _____

Budding (+ or −): _____   _____

Schizosaccharomyces octosporus

Shape: _____

Budding (+ or −): _____

Yeast Morphology, Cultural Characteristics, and Reproduction

Fermentation Studies

Use a plus (+) or minus (−) in the chart below to record your results.

Organism	GLUCOSE T	A	G	MALTOSE T	A	G	LACTOSE T	A	G	SUCROSE T	A	G
Saccharomyces cerevisiae												
Candida albicans												
Rhodotorula rubra												
Selenotila intestinalis												
Schizosaccharomyces octosporus												

Note: T = turbidity, A = acid, and G = gas

Sexual Reproduction

In the circles below, draw representative reproductive structures and label the parts.

Saccharomyces cerevisiae   *Candida albicans*   *Schizosaccharomyces octosporus*

Rhodotorula rubra   *Selenotila intestinalis*

Review Questions

1. Indicate the significance of the following structures in the reproductive activities of yeast cells.

   a. Buds

   b. Ascus

   c. Ascospores

2. Why are yeast cells classified as fungi, and how do they differ from other fungi?

3. Why is yeast of industrial importance?

4. Why are yeasts significant from a medical perspective?

5. Why is it necessary to pasteurize fruit juices?

6. A female patient develops candidiasis (moniliasis) following prolonged antibiotic therapy for a bladder infection caused by *Pseudomonas aeruginosa*. How can you account for the development of this concurrent vaginal infection?

7. With regard to the fermentation of wine, what kind of wine would be produced if you washed the grapes prior to crushing them?

Photo Credits

Credits are listed in order of appearance.

Photo 1: James Cappuccino

Photo 2: Biophoto Associates Photo Researchers, Inc.

Photo 3: John Durham Science Photo Library, Photo Researchers, Inc.

Photo 4: Nhu Nguyen

Photo 5: L. Brent Selinger, Department of Biological Sciences, University of Lethbridge, Pearson Education

Identification of Unknown Fungi

LEARNING OBJECTIVE

When you have completed this experiment, you should be able to

1. Identify a fungal unknown based on colonial morphology and microscopic appearance.

CLINICAL APPLICATION

Identification of Fungal Infection

When presented with a patient with symptoms that suggest an intestinal fungal infection or Crohn's Disease complications, isolation and identification of a fungal pathogen is required before the correct treatment may be prescribed. Using culturing techniques, an isolate of the fungi can be identified by mycelium morphology and genetic markers.

Principle

In this experiment, you will be provided with a number-coded pure culture of a representative fungal organism for cultivation and subsequent identification. Use Table 1 to aid in identification of the unknown culture.

(Text continues)

TABLE 1	Identification of Fungi	
DIAGRAM	**COLONIAL MORPHOLOGY**	**MICROSCOPIC APPEARANCE**
Molds Sporangium Columella Collarette Sporangiophore Stolon Mycelium Rhizoid *Rhizopus:* Black bread mold; common laboratory contaminant	Rapidly growing white-colored fungus swarms over entire plate; aerial mycelium cottony and fuzzy	Spores are oval, colorless, or brown; nonseptate mycelium gives rise to straight sporangiophores that terminate with black sporangium containing a columella; rootlike hyphae (rhizoids) penetrate the medium
Sporangium Columella Sporangiophore Mycelium *Mucor:* Food contaminant	Resembles the colonies of *Rhizopus* except that it lacks rhizoids and collarettes. Sporangiophore arises directly from mycelial mat. Note: Branching sporangiophores may occur with *Mucor.*	Spores are oval; nonseptate mycelium gives rise to single sporangiophores with globular sporangium containing a columella; there are no rhizoids

➜

From Experiment 38 of *Microbiology: A Laboratory Manual*, Tenth Edition. James G. Cappuccino, Natalie Sherman. Copyright © 2014 by Pearson Education, Inc. All rights reserved.

TABLE 1	Identification of Fungi (continued)	
DIAGRAM	**COLONIAL MORPHOLOGY**	**MICROSCOPIC APPEARANCE**
Molds (continued) — Conidia — Conidiophore — Mycelium *Alternaria:* Normally found on plant material; also found in house dust	Grayish-green or black colonies with gray edges rapidly swarming over entire plate; aerial mycelium not very dense, appears grayish to white	Multicelled spores (conidia) are pear-shaped and attached to single conidiophores arising from a septate mycelium
— Conidia — Conidiophore *Fusarium:* Found in soil; also likely in eye infections	Woolly, white, fuzzy colonies changing color to pink, purple, or yellow	Spores (conidia) are oval or crescent-shaped and attached to conidiophores arising from a septate mycelium; some spores are single cells, some are multicelled
— Conidia — Sterigma — Vesicle — Conidiophore — Mycelium *Aspergillus:* Plant and animal pathogens; some species used industrially	White colonies become greenish-blue, black, or brown as culture matures	Single-celled spores (conidia) in chains developing at the end of the sterigma arising from the terminal bulb of the conidiophore, the vesicle; long conidiophores arise from a septate mycelium
— Conidia — Sterigma — Metula — Conidiophore — Mycelium *Penicillium:* Antibiotic-producing citrus fruit contaminant; soil inhabitant	Mature cultures usually greenish or blue-green	Single-celled spores (conidia) in chains develop at the end of the sterigma arising from the metula of the conidiophore; branching conidiophores arise from a septate mycelium

Identification of Unknown Fungi

DIAGRAM	COLONIAL MORPHOLOGY	MICROSCOPIC APPEARANCE
TABLE 1 (continued)		
Molds (continued) — Conidia — Conidiophore — Septate mycelium *Cladosporium:* Dead and decaying plants	Small, heaped colonies are greenish-black and powdery	Spores (conidia) develop at the end of complex conidiophores arising from a septate mycelium that is usually brownish
— Conidia — Conidiophore — Mycelium *Cephalosporium:* Antibiotic production	Rapidly growing compact and moist colonies becoming cottony with aerial hyphae that are gray or rose-colored	Single-celled conical or elliptical spores (conidia) held together in clusters at the tips of the conidiophores by a mucoid substance; erect, unbranched conidiophores arise from a septate mycelium
Yeast — Bud *Torula:* Cheese and food contaminant	Colonies are pink, moist, with unbroken, even edges	Cells are oval, colorless, and reproduce by budding
— Chlamydoconidium — Pseudomycelium — Blastospores *Candida:* Human pathogen	Colonies are small, round, moist, and colorless, with unbroken, even edges	Yeastlike fungus produces pseudomycelium

AT THE BENCH

Materials

Cultures

Number-coded, 7-day Sabouraud broth spore suspensions of *Aspergillus, Mucor, Penicillium, Alternaria, Rhizopus, Cladosporium, Cephalosporium, Fusarium, Torula,* and *Candida.*

Media

One Sabouraud agar plate per student.

Reagent

Lactophenol–cotton-blue solution.

Equipment

Bunsen burner, dissecting microscope, hand lens, sterile cotton swabs, glass slides, coverslips, inoculating loop, and glassware marking pencil.

Procedure Lab One

1. With a sterile inoculating loop, inoculate an appropriately labeled Sabouraud agar plate with one of the provided unknown cultures by placing one loopful in the center of the plate. *Note: Do not spread culture.*

2. Incubate the plates in a noninverted position for 1 week at 25°C in a moist incubator.

Procedure Lab Two

1. Observe mold cultures with a hand lens, noting and recording their colonial morphologies.

2. Prepare a wet mount by suspending some of the culture in a few drops of lactophenol–cotton-blue solution. Be gentle to avoid damaging the fungal structures.

3. Examine the preparation under high-power and low-power magnifications with the aid of a dissecting microscope and record your observations in the Lab Report.

Observations and Results

1. Draw representative microscopic fields of your culture below.
2. Using Table 1, identify your unknown fungal organism.

   a. Color pigmentation

   b. Diameter (mm)

   c. Texture (cottony, smooth, etc.)

   d. Margin (entire, undulating, lobular, etc.)

   e. Aerial hyphae (septate, nonseptate)

Diagram of microscopic appearance:

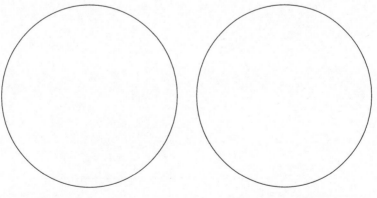

Low-power magnification   High-power magnification

Number assigned to
unknown culture: _____

Genus of fungal unknown: _____

Photo Credits

The Viruses

Once you have completed the experiments in this section, you should know

1. The chemical structures, morphologies, and replicative activities of bacterial viruses (bacteriophages).
2. How to perform a phage dilution procedure for the cultivation and enumeration of bacterial viruses.
3. How to isolate bacteriophages from sewage.

Introduction

Viruses are noncellular biological entities composed solely of a single type of nucleic acid surrounded by a protein coat called the capsid. Because of their limited and simplistic structures, viruses can be chemically defined as **nucleoproteins.** They are devoid of the sophisticated enzymatic and biosynthetic machinery essential for independent activities of cellular life. This lack of metabolic machinery mandates that they exist as parasites, and they cannot be cultivated outside of a susceptible living cell. Viruses are differentiated from cellular forms of life on the following bases:

1. They are ultramicroscopic and can only be visualized with the electron microscope.
2. They are filterable: They are able to pass through bacteria-retaining filters.
3. They do not increase in size.
4. They must replicate within a susceptible cell.
5. Replication occurs because the viral nucleic acid subverts the synthetic machinery of the host cell (namely, common host cell components and enzyme systems involved in decomposition, synthesis, and bioenergetics) for the purpose of producing new viral components.

6. Viruses are designated either RNA or DNA viruses because they contain one of the nucleic acids but never both.

Much of our knowledge of the mechanism of animal viral infection and replication has been based on our understanding of infection in bacteria by bacterial viruses, called the **bacteriophages,** or **phages.** The bacteriophages were first described in 1915 almost simultaneously by Twort and d'Herelle. The name *bacteriophage,* which in Greek means "to eat bacteria," was coined by d'Herelle because of the destruction through lysis of the infected cell. Bacteriophages exhibit notable variability in their sizes, shapes, and complexities of structure. The T-even (T2, T4, and T6) phages illustrated in **Figure 1** demonstrate the greatest morphological complexity.

Phage replication depends on the ability of the phage particle to infect a suitable bacterial host cell. Infection consists of the following sequential events:

1. **Adsorption:** Tail fibers of the phage particle bind to receptor sites on the host's cell wall.
2. **Penetration** (infection): Spiral protein sheath retracts, and an enzyme, early muramidase, perforates the bacterial cell wall, enabling the phage nucleic acid to pass through the hollow core into the host cell's

The Viruses

The functions of these structural components are as follows:

Component	Function
Capsid (protein coat)	Protection of nucleic acid from destruction by DNases
Nucleic acid core	Phage genome carrying genetic information necessary for replication of new phage particles
Spiral protein sheath	Retracts so that nucleic acid can pass from capsid into host cell's cytoplasm
End plate and **tail fibers**	Attachment of phage to specific receptor sites on a susceptible host's cell wall

Figure 1 Bacteriophage: Structural components and their functions

cytoplasm. The empty protein shell remains attached to the cell wall and is called the protein ghost.

3. **Replication:** The phage genome subverts the cell's synthetic machinery, which is then used for the production of new phage components.

4. **Maturation:** During this period, the new phage components are assembled and form complete, mature virulent phage particles.

5. **Release:** Late muramidase (lysozyme) lyses the cell wall, liberating infectious phage particles that are now capable of infecting new susceptible host cells, thereby starting the cycle over again.

Virulent phage particles that infect susceptible host cells always initiate the **lytic cycle** as described above. Other phage particles, called **temperate phages** [that is, **lambda (λ) phages**], incorporate their nucleic acid into the host's chromosome. Lysis of the host cell does not occur until it is induced by exogenous physical agents such as ultraviolet or ionizing radiation or

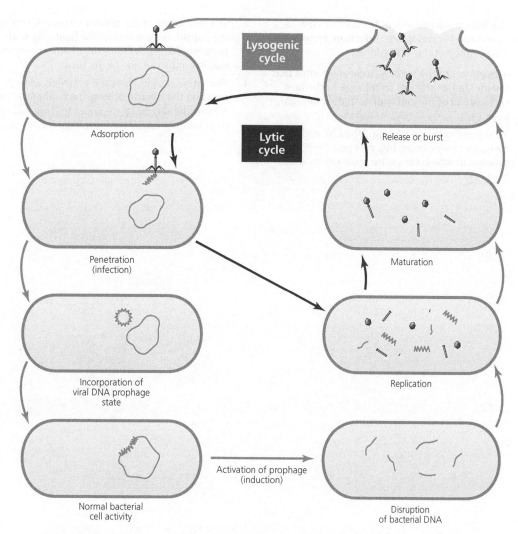

Figure 2 **The lytic and lysogenic life cycles of a bacteriophage**

chemical mutagenic agents. Bacterial cells containing the incorporated phage nucleic acid, the **prophage,** are called **lysogenic cells.** Lysogenic cells appear and function as normal cells, and they reproduce by fission. When induced by physical or chemical agents, these cells will release a virulent prophage from the host's genome, which then initiates the lytic cycle. **Figure 2** illustrates the lytic and lysogenic life cycles of a bacteriophage.

Animal viruses differ structurally from bacteriophages in that they lack the spiral protein sheath, end plate, and tail fibers. Their shapes may be helical or cuboidal (icosahedral, containing 20 triangular facets). Some animal viruses are designated as naked viruses because they are composed solely of nucleocapsids. In others, referred to as enveloped viruses, the nucleocapsid is surrounded by a lipid bilayer that may have glycoproteins associated with it.

The infectious process of the animal virus is very similar to bacteriophage infection. However, there are some notable differences:

1. Adsorption of the virus is to receptor sites that are located on the cell membrane of the host cell instead of the cell wall as in the bacterial host.

2. Viral penetration is accomplished by endocytosis, an energy-requiring, receptor-mediated process in which the entire virus enters the host cell.

3. The uncoating of the animal virus, removal of the capsid, occurs within the host cell; with bacteriophage infection, the phage capsid remains on the outside of the host.

4. The latent period, the time between adsorption and the release of virulent viral particles, is considerably longer—hours to days rather than minutes as in bacteriophage infection.

Cultivation and Enumeration of Bacteriophages

Figure 1 Plaque-forming units (PFUs)

Principle

This exercise demonstrates the ability of viruses to replicate inside a susceptible host cell. For this purpose, you will be provided with a virulent phage and a susceptible host cell culture. This technique also enables you to enumerate phage particles on the basis of plaque formation in a solid agar medium. **Plaques** are clear areas in an agar medium previously seeded with a diluted phage sample and a host cell culture. Each plaque represents the lysis of a phage-infected bacterial cell.

The procedure requires the use of a double-layered culture technique in which the hard agar serves as a base layer, and a mixture of phage and host cells in a soft agar forms the upper overlay. Susceptible *Escherichia coli* cells multiply rapidly and produce a lawn of confluent growth on the medium. When one phage particle adsorbs to a susceptible cell, penetrates the cell, replicates, and goes on to lyse other host cells, the destroyed cells produce a single plaque in the bacterial lawn (see **Figure 1**). Each plaque can be designated as a **plaque-forming unit (PFU)** and used to quantitate the number of infective phage particles in the culture.

The number of phage particles contained in the original stock phage culture is determined by counting the number of plaques formed on the seeded agar plate and multiplying this by the dilution factor. For a valid phage count, the number of plaques per plate should not exceed 300 nor be less than 30.

Example: 200 PFUs are counted in a 10^{-6} dilution.

$$(200) \times (10^6) = 200 \times 10^6 \ \text{ or } \ 2 \times 10^8$$
PFUs per ml of stock phage culture

Plates showing greater than 300 PFUs are **too numerous to count (TNTC)**; plates showing fewer than 30 PFUs are **too few to count (TFTC)**.

Identification of Pathogenic Bacteria

Bacterial viruses (bacteriophages) are very common in all natural environments and are directly related to the number of bacteria present. They are most prevalent in soil, intestines of animals, sewage, and seawater. These viral particles have played an important role in the development of all types of viruses. Since many phages are specific about which bacteria they attack, a process called phage typing is used in clinical and diagnostic laboratories for the identification of pathogenic bacteria.

AT THE BENCH

Materials

Cultures

24-hour nutrient broth cultures of *Escherichia coli B* and T2 coliphage.

Media

Five each of the following per designated student group: tryptone agar plates and tryptone soft agar, 2 ml per tube; and nine tryptone broth tubes, 9 ml per tube.

Equipment

Bunsen burner, waterbath, thermometer, 1-ml sterile pipettes, sterile Pasteur pipettes, mechanical pipetting device, test tube rack, and glassware marking pencil.

Procedure Lab One

To perform the dilution procedure as illustrated in **Figure 2**, do the following:

1. Label all dilution tubes and media as follows:

    a. Five tryptone soft agar tubes: 10^{-5}, 10^{-6}, 10^{-7}, 10^{-8}, 10^{-9}.

    b. Five tryptone hard agar plates: 10^{-5}, 10^{-6}, 10^{-7}, 10^{-8}, 10^{-9}.

    c. Nine tryptone broth tubes: 10^{-1} through 10^{-9}.

2. Place the five labeled soft tryptone agar tubes into a waterbath. Water should be of a depth just slightly above that of the agar in the tubes. Bring the waterbath to 100°C to melt the agar. Cool and maintain the melted agar at 45°C.

3. With 1-ml pipettes, aseptically perform a 10-fold serial dilution of the provided phage culture using the nine 9-ml tubes of tryptone.

4. To the tryptone soft agar tube labeled 10^{-5}, aseptically add two drops of the *E. coli B* culture with a Pasteur pipette and 0.1 ml of the 10^{-4} tryptone broth phage dilution. Rapidly mix by rotating the tube between the palms of your hands and pour the contents over the hard tryptone agar plate labeled 10^{-5}, thereby forming a double-layered plate culture preparation. Swirl the plate gently and allow to harden.

5. Using separate Pasteur pipettes and 1-ml sterile pipettes, repeat Step 4 for the tryptone broth phage dilution tubes labeled 10^{-5} through 10^{-8} to effect the 10^{-6} through 10^{-9} tryptone soft agar overlays.

6. Following solidification of the soft agar overlay, incubate all plate cultures in an inverted position for 24 hours at 37°C.

Procedure Lab Two

1. Observe all plates for the presence of plaque-forming units that develop on the bacterial lawn.

2. Count the number of PFUs in the range of 30 to 300 on each plate.

3. Calculate the number of phage particles per ml of the stock phage culture based on your PFU count.

4. Record your results in the chart in the Lab Report.

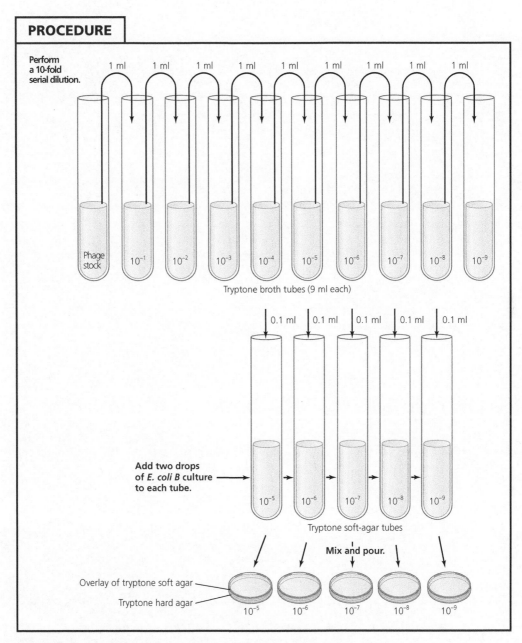

Figure 2 Dilution procedure for cultivation and enumeration of bacteriophages

Observations and Results

Phage Dilution	Number of PFUs	Calculation: PFUs × Dilution Factor	PFUs/ml of Stock Phage Culture
10^{-5}			
10^{-6}			
10^{-7}			
10^{-8}			
10^{-9}			

Review Questions

1. Discuss the effects of lytic and lysogenic infections on the life cycle of the host cell.

2. Discuss the factors responsible for the transformation of a lysogenic infection to one that is lytic.

3. Distinguish between the replicative and maturation stages of a lytic phage infection.

4. In this experimental procedure, why is it important to use a hard agar with a soft agar overlay technique to demonstrate plaque formation?

5. Explain what is meant by plaque-forming units.

6. Determine the number of PFUs per ml in a 10^{-9} dilution of a phage culture that shows 204 PFUs in the agar lawn.

7. The release of phage particles from the host bacterium always occurs by lysis of the cell and results in the death of the host. Animal viruses are released by either the lysis of the host cell or exocytosis, a reverse pinocytosis. Regardless of the mechanism of release, most infected cells die, while other viruses may escape the cell without damaging the host cell. Explain.

Photo Credit

Credits are listed in order of appearance.

Photo 1:   Experiment performed and photographed by L. Brent Selinger, Department of Biological Sciences, University of Lethbridge, Pearson Education

Isolation of Coliphages from Raw Sewage

Principle

Isolates of bacterial viruses (bacteriophages) can be obtained from a variety of natural sources, including soil, intestinal contents, raw sewage, and some insects such as cockroaches and flies. Their isolation from these environments is not an easy task because the phage particles are usually present in low concentrations. Therefore, isolation requires a series of steps:

1. Collection of the phage-containing sample at its source.
2. Addition of an enriched susceptible host cell culture to the sample to increase the number of phage particles for subsequent isolation.
3. Following incubation, centrifugation of the enriched sample for the removal of gross particles.
4. Filtration of the supernatant liquid through a bacteria-retaining membrane filter.
5. Inoculation of the bacteria-free filtrate onto a lawn of susceptible host cells grown on a soft agar plate medium.
6. Incubation and observation of the culture for the presence of phage particles, which is indicated by plaque formation in the bacterial lawn.

In the following experiment, you will use this procedure, as illustrated in **Figure 1**, for the isolation of *Escherichia coli* phage particles from raw sewage. Most bacteriophages that infect *E. coli* (coliphages) are designated by the letter T, indicating types. Seven types have been identified and are labeled T1 through T7. The T-even phages (T2, T4, and T6) differ from the T-odd phages in that the former vary in size, form, and chemical composition. All of the T phages are capable of infecting the susceptible *E. coli* B host cell.

CLINICAL APPLICATION

Phage Therapy

Phage therapy is the therapeutic use of bacteriophages to treat pathogenic bacterial infections. It is mainly used in Russia and the Republic of Georgia and is not universally approved elsewhere. In the West, no phage therapies are authorized for use on humans, although phages for killing food poisoning bacteria (*Listeria*) are now in use. They may also be used as a possible therapy against many strains of drug-resistant bacteria.

AT THE BENCH

Materials

Cultures

Lab One: 5-ml 24-hour broth cultures of *E. coli* B and 45-ml samples of fresh sewage collected in screw-capped bottles. Lab Two: 10-ml 24-hour broth cultures of *E. coli* B.

Media

Per designated student group: Lab One: One 5-ml tube of bacteriophage nutrient broth, 10 times normal concentration. Lab Two: Five tryptone agar plates and five 3-ml tubes of tryptone soft agar.

Equipment

Lab One: Sterile 250-ml Erlenmeyer flask and stopper. Lab Two: Sterile membrane filter apparatus, sterile 125-ml Erlenmeyer flask and stopper, 125-ml flask, 1000-ml beaker, centrifuge, Bunsen

Isolation of Coliphages from Raw Sewage

PROCEDURE

Pour in several centrifuge tubes and centrifuge sewage sample at 2500 rpm for 20 minutes.

E. coli B enriched sewage sample in 250-ml flask

Centrifuge

Remove tubes and decant supernatant into a 125-ml beaker.

Filter supernatant through membrane filter into vacuum flask.

Flask and membrane filter apparatus

Bacteria-free phage filtrate in vacuum flask

1 drop   2 drops   3 drops   4 drops   5 drops

Add 0.1 ml to tubes 1–5 of molten soft tryptone agar.

E. coli B culture

1   2   3   4   5

1   2   3   4   5

Plates of hard tryptone agar

Figure 1 Procedure for isolation of coliphages from raw sewage

burner, forceps, 1-ml sterile disposable pipettes, sterile Pasteur pipette, mechanical pipetting device, test tube rack, and glassware marking pencil.

Procedure Lab One

> ⚠ Use disposable gloves. It is essential to handle raw sewage with extreme caution because it may serve as a vehicle for the transmission of human pathogens.

Enrichment of Sewage Sample

1. Aseptically add 5 ml of bacteriophage nutrient broth, 5 ml of the *E. coli B* broth culture, and 45 ml of the raw sewage sample to an appropriately labeled sterile 250-ml Erlenmeyer flask.
2. Incubate the culture for 24 hours at 37°C.

Procedure Lab Two
Filtration and Seeding

1. Following incubation, pour the phage-infected culture into a 100-ml centrifuge bottle or several centrifuge tubes and centrifuge at 2500 rpm for 20 minutes.
2. Remove the centrifuge bottle or tubes, being careful not to stir up the sediment, and carefully decant the supernatant into a 125-ml beaker.

3. Pour the supernatant solution through a sterile membrane filter apparatus to collect the bacteria-free, phage-containing filtrate in the vacuum flask below.
4. Melt the soft tryptone agar by placing the five tubes in a boiling waterbath and cool to 45°C.
5. Label the five tryptone agar plates and the five tryptone agar tubes 1, 2, 3, 4, and 5, respectively.
6. Using a sterile 1-ml pipette, aseptically add 0.1 ml of the *E. coli B* culture to all the molten soft-agar tubes.
7. Using a sterile Pasteur pipette, aseptically add 1, 2, 3, 4, and 5 drops of the filtrate to the respectively labeled molten soft-agar tubes. Mix and pour each tube of soft agar into its appropriately labeled agar plate.
8. Allow agar to harden.
9. Incubate all the plates in an inverted position for 24 hours at 37°C.

Procedure Lab Three

1. Examine all the culture plates for plaque formation, which is indicative of the presence of coliphages in the culture.
2. Indicate the presence (+) or absence (−) of plaques in each of the cultures in the chart in the Lab Report.

Observations and Results

Drops of Phage Filtrate	1	2	3	4	5
Plaque Formation (+) or (−)					

Based on your observations, what is the relationship between the number of plaques observed and the number of drops of filtrate in each culture?

Review Questions

1. Why is enrichment of the sewage sample necessary for the isolation of phage?

2. How is enrichment of the sewage sample accomplished?

3. How are bacteria-free phage particles obtained?

4. Why must you exercise caution when handling raw sewage samples?

Photo Credits

Physical and Chemical Agents for the Control of Microbial Growth

LEARNING OBJECTIVES

Once you have completed the experiments in this section, you should

1. Know the basic methods for inhibiting microbial growth and the modes of antimicrobial action.

2. Be able to demonstrate the effects of physical agents, moist heat, osmotic pressure, and ultraviolet radiation on selected microbial populations.

3. Be able to demonstrate the effects on selected microbial populations of chemical agents used as disinfectants, antiseptics, and antibiotics.

Introduction

Control of microorganisms is essential in the home, industry, and medical fields to prevent and treat diseases and to inhibit the spoilage of foods and other industrial products. Common methods of control involve chemical and physical agents that adversely affect microbial structures and functions, thereby producing a microbicidal or microbistatic effect. A **microbicidal effect** is one that kills the microbes immediately; a **microbistatic effect** inhibits the reproductive capacities of the cells and maintains the microbial population at a constant size.

Chemical Methods for Control of Microbial Growth

1. **Antiseptics:** Chemical substances used on living tissue that kill or inhibit the growth of vegetative microbial forms.

2. **Disinfectants:** Chemical substances that kill or inhibit the growth of vegetative microbial forms on nonliving materials.

3. **Chemotherapeutic agents:** Chemical substances that destroy or inhibit the growth of microorganisms in living tissues.

Physical Methods for Control of Microbial Growth

The modes of action of the different chemical and physical agents of control vary, although they all produce damaging effects to one or more essential cellular structures or molecules in order to cause cell death or inhibition of growth. Sites of damage that can result in malfunction are the cell wall, cell membrane, cytoplasm, enzymes, or nucleic acids. The adverse effects manifest themselves in the following ways.

1. **Cell-wall injury:** This can occur in one of two ways. First, lysis of the cell wall will leave the wall-less cell, called a protoplast, susceptible to osmotic damage, and a hypotonic environment may cause lysis of the vulnerable protoplast. Second, certain agents inhibit cell wall synthesis, which is essential during microbial cell reproduction. Failure to synthesize a missing segment of the cell wall results in an unprotected protoplast.

2. **Cell-membrane damage:** This may be the result of lysis of the membrane, which will cause immediate cell death. Also, the selective nature of the membrane may be affected

Physical and Chemical Agents for the Control of Microbial Growth

Figure 1 **Physical methods used for the control of microbial growth**

without causing its complete disruption. As a result, there may be a loss of essential cellular molecules or interference with the uptake of nutrients. In both cases, metabolic processes will be adversely affected.

3. **Alteration of the colloidal state of cytoplasm:** Certain agents cause denaturing of cytoplasmic proteins. Denaturing processes are responsible for enzyme inactivation and cellular death by irreversibly rupturing the molecular bonds of these proteins and rendering them biologically inactive.

4. **Inactivation of cellular enzymes:** Enzymes may be inactivated competitively or noncompetitively. Noncompetitive inhibition is irreversible and occurs following the application of some physical agent, such as mercuric chloride ($HgCl_2$), that results in the uncoiling of the protein molecule, rendering it biologically inactive. Competitive inhibition occurs when a natural substrate is forced to compete for the active site on an enzyme surface with

a chemically similar molecular substrate, which can block the enzyme's ability to create end products. Competitive inhibitions are reversible.

5. **Interference with the structure and function of the DNA molecule:** The DNA molecule is the control center of the cell and may also represent a cellular target area for destruction or inhibition. Some agents have an affinity for DNA and cause breakage or distortion of the molecule, thereby interfering with its replication and role in protein synthesis.

Figure 1 illustrates the acceptable physical methods used for the control of microbial growth.

Awareness of the mode of action of the physical and chemical agents is absolutely essential for their proper selection and application in microbial control. The exercises in this section are designed to acquaint you more fully with several commonly employed agents and their uses.

Physical Agents of Control: Moist Heat

Principle

Temperature has an effect on cellular enzyme systems and therefore a marked influence on the rate of chemical reactions and thus the life and death of microorganisms. Despite the diversity among microorganisms' temperature requirements for growth, extremes in temperature can be used in microbial growth control. Sufficiently low temperatures will inactivate enzymes and produce a static effect. High temperatures destroy cellular enzymes, which become irreversibly denatured.

The application of heat is a common means of destroying microorganisms. Both dry and moist heat are effective. However, moist heat, which (because of the hydrolyzing effect of water and its greater penetrating ability) causes coagulation of proteins, kills cells more rapidly and at lower temperatures than does dry heat. **Sterilization,** the destruction of all forms of life, is accomplished in 15 minutes at 121°C with moist heat (steam) under pressure; dry heat requires a temperature of 160°C to 180°C for 1½ to 3 hours.

Microbes exhibit differences in their resistance to moist heat. As a general rule, bacterial spores require temperatures above 100°C for destruction, whereas most bacterial vegetative cells are killed at temperatures of 60°C to 70°C in 10 minutes. Fungi can be killed at 50°C to 60°C, and fungal spores require 70°C to 80°C for 10 minutes for destruction. Because of this variability, moist heat can either sterilize or disinfect. Common applications include free-flowing steam under pressure (autoclaving), free-flowing steam at 100°C (tyndallization), and the use of lower temperatures (pasteurization).

Free-flowing steam under pressure requires the use of an autoclave, a double-walled metal vessel that allows steam to be pressurized in the outer jacket (see **Figure 1**). At a designated pressure, the saturated steam is released into the inner chamber, from which all the air has been evacuated. The steam under pressure in the vacuumed inner chamber is now capable of achieving temperatures in excess of 100°C. The temperature is determined by the pounds of pressure applied per square inch:

Pressure (pounds/inch^2)	Temperature (°C)
0 (free-flowing steam)	100
10	115
15	121
20	126
25	130

A pressure of 15 pounds/inch^2 achieves a temperature of 121°C and sterilizes in 15 minutes. This is the usual procedure; however, depending on the heat sensitivity of the material to be sterilized, the operating pressure and time conditions can be adjusted.

Application of **free-flowing steam** requires exposure of the contaminated substance to a temperature of 100°C, which is achieved by boiling water. Exposures to boiling water for 30 minutes will result in disinfection only; all vegetative cells will be killed, but not necessarily the more heat-resistant spores.

Another procedure is **tyndallization,** also referred to as intermittent or fractional sterilization. This procedure requires exposure of the material to free-flowing steam at 100°C for 20 minutes on 3 consecutive days with intermittent incubation at 37°C. The steaming kills all vegetative cells. Any spores that may be present germinate during the period of incubation and are

From Experiment 41 of *Microbiology: A Laboratory Manual,* Tenth Edition. James G. Cappuccino, Natalie Sherman.

(a) An autoclave

(b) Schematic representation

Figure 1 The autoclave

destroyed during subsequent exposure to a temperature of 100°C. Repeating this procedure for 3 days ensures germination of all spores and their destruction in the vegetative form. Because tyndallization requires so much time, it is used only for sterilization of materials that are composed of thermolabile chemicals and that might be subject to decomposition at higher temperatures.

Pasteurization exposes fairly thermolabile products such as milk, wine, and beer for a given period of time to a temperature that is high enough to destroy pathogens and some spoilage-causing microorganisms that may be present, without necessarily destroying all vegetative cells. There are three types of pasteurization: The high-temperature, short-time (HTST) procedure requires a temperature of 71°C for 15 seconds. The low-temperature, long-time (LTLT) method

requires 63°C for 30 minutes, and the ultra high temperature (UHT) approach occurs at 138°C for 2 seconds.

CLINICAL APPLICATION

Autoclave Performance Testing

While the original "autoclave" was invented as a pressure cooker for food, modern autoclaves are precision instruments and require maintenance and periodic testing, especially if control of human pathogens is involved. Commonly, a sample of spores of the bacterium *Bacillus stearothermophilus* is sterilized in the chamber with a normal load, and then the sample is allowed to incubate—any growth indicates that the autoclave needs to be serviced.

AT THE BENCH

— Thermometer

— Beaker with water

— 10-ml test tube of nutrient broth

— Wire gauze

— Bunsen burner

Figure 2 Waterbath for moist heat experiment

Materials

Cultures

48- to 72-hour nutrient broth cultures (50 ml per 250-ml Erlenmeyer flask) of *Staphylococcus aureus* and *Bacillus cereus;* 72- to 96-hour Sabouraud broth cultures (50 ml per 250-ml Erlenmeyer flask) of *Aspergillus niger* and *Saccharomyces cerevisiae.*

Media

Per designated student group (pairs or groups of four): five nutrient agar plates, five Sabouraud agar plates, and one 10-ml tube of nutrient broth.

Equipment

Bunsen burner, 800-ml beaker (waterbath), tripod and wire gauze screen with heat-resistant pad, thermometer, sterile test tubes, glassware marking pencil, and inoculating loop.

Procedure Lab One

1. Label the covers of each of the nutrient agar and Sabouraud agar plates, indicating the experimental heat temperatures to be used: 25°C (control), 40°C, 60°C, 80°C, and 100°C.

2. Score the underside of all plates with a glassware marking pencil into two sections. On the nutrient agar plates, label one section *S. aureus* and the other *B. cereus.* On the Sabouraud agar plates, label one section *A. niger* and the second *S. cerevisiae.*

3. Using aseptic technique, inoculate the nutrient agar and Sabouraud agar plates labeled 25°C by making a single-line loop inoculation of each test organism in its respective section of the plate.

4. Using a sterile pipette and mechanical pipetter, transfer 10 ml of each culture to four sterile test tubes labeled with the name of the organism and the temperature (40°C, 60°C, 80°C, and 100°C).

5. Set up the waterbath as illustrated in **Figure 2**, inserting the thermometer in an uncapped tube of nutrient broth.

6. Slowly heat the water to 40°C; check the thermometer frequently to ensure that it does not exceed the desired temperature. Place the four cultures of the experimental organisms into the beaker and maintain the temperature at 40°C for 10 minutes. Remove the cultures and aseptically inoculate each organism in its appropriate section on the two plates labeled 40°C.

7. Raise the waterbath temperature to 60°C and repeat Step 6 for the inoculation of the two plates labeled 60°C.

8. Raise the waterbath temperature to 80°C and repeat Step 6 for the inoculation of the two plates labeled 80°C.

9. Raise the waterbath temperature to 100°C and repeat Step 6 for the inoculation of the two plates labeled 100°C.

10. Incubate the nutrient agar plate cultures in an inverted position for 24 to 48 hours at 37°C and the Sabouraud agar plate cultures for 4 to 5 days at 25°C in a moist chamber.

Procedure Lab Two

1. Observe all plates for the amount of growth of the test organisms at each of the temperatures.

2. Record your results in the chart provided in the Lab Report.

Observations and Results

1. Record your results in the chart as 0 = none; $1+$ = slight; $2+$ = moderate; $3+$ = abundant.

Microbial Species	AMOUNT OF GROWTH				
	25°C	40°C	60°C	80°C	100°C
B. cereus					
S. aureus					
A. niger					
S. cerevisiae					

2. List the microbial organisms in order of their increasing heat resistance.

   _____

   _____

   _____

   _____

Review Questions

1. Account for the microbistatic effect produced by low temperatures as compared to the microbicidal effect produced by high temperatures.

2. Cite the advantages of each of the modes of sterilization: tyndallization and autoclaving.

3. Discuss the detrimental effects of control agents on the following: the cytoplasm, the cell wall, nucleic acids, and the cell membrane.

4. Explain why milk is subjected to pasteurization rather than sterilization.

5. *A. niger* and *B. cereus* cultures used in this experiment contained spores. Why is *B. cereus* more heat resistant?

6. Account for the fact that aerobic and anaerobic bacterial spore-formers are more heat resistant than the tubercle bacillus, which is also known to tolerate elevated temperatures.

Photo Credit

Credits are listed in order of appearance.

Photo 1:   Courtesy of STERIS Corporation

Physical Agents of Control: Environmental Osmotic Pressure

LEARNING OBJECTIVE

Once you have completed this experiment, you should understand

1. The possible effect of osmotic pressure environments on microorganisms.

Principle

Osmosis is the net movement of water molecules (solvent) across a semipermeable membrane from a solution of their higher concentration to a solution of their lower concentration. The relative water concentrations of two solutions is determined by their solute concentrations. The **hypertonic solution** possesses a higher osmotic pressure and a higher solute concentration, and therefore it has a lower water concentration; it tends to draw in water. The **hypotonic solution** possesses a lower osmotic pressure and solute concentration, and therefore a higher water concentration; it tends to lose water. If two solutions have equal concentrations of solutes and therefore equal water concentrations, there is no osmosis and the solutions are **isotonic**.

The cell and its environment represent two solutions separated by the semipermeable cell membrane. The cell's cytoplasm contains colloidal and solute particles dispersed in water, as does the cell's environment. The **osmotic pressure of the environment** in relation to that of the cytoplasm of the cell plays a vital role in the life and death of a cell. The ideal environment of animal cells, which are bounded only by the fragile cell membrane, is completely or very nearly isotonic. In a hypertonic, high-pressure environment, all cells lose water by osmosis and become shriveled. This effect is called **plasmolysis.** As water is necessary for the occurrence of many chemical reactions, water loss adversely affects cell metabolism and reproduction. In a hypotonic, low-pressure environment, cells take in water and become swollen. This phenomenon is called **plasmoptysis.** In an environment with sufficiently low osmotic pressure, animal cells undergo **lysis,** which causes their deaths. Microorganisms and other organisms whose cells possess rigid cell walls are not usually susceptible to lysis in hypotonic environments and usually prefer a slightly hypotonic environment to maintain themselves in a turgid (distended) state. The effects of environmental osmotic pressure on cells unprotected by cell walls are illustrated in **Figure 1**.

Osmotic pressure can be used as an antimicrobial agent. Microorganisms are not usually adversely affected by low environmental osmotic pressure because of their small sizes and the presence of rigid cell walls. However, hypertonicity is a commonly used method of inhibiting microbial growth.

Because of their varied habitats, microorganisms are generally well adapted to exist in all types of osmotic pressure environments. Different groups of microorganisms require different degrees of salinity for growth, and as a rule, they can adjust to salt concentrations of 0.5% to 3%. Concentrations of 10% to 15% are inhibitory to the growth of most microbes, except for **halophiles,** which require high salinity concentrations for growth. This sensitivity is the basis of food preservation by the process of salting.

CLINICAL APPLICATION

Honey and Wound Healing

Honey has been applied as a wound dressing since at least the time of ancient Egypt, but interest in its antibacterial properties is on the rise today. The exact mechanism of honey's antibacterial actions is not totally understood, and may include anti-inflammatory effects and pH levels inhospitable to bacteria, but its osmotic pressure and tendency to dehydrate bacteria is at least part of its effectiveness.

AT THE BENCH

Materials

Cultures

24- to 48-hour nutrient broth cultures of *Staphylococcus aureus* and *Escherichia coli* and 48-hour *Halobacterium* salt broth culture of *Halobacterium salinarium.*

Physical Agents of Control: Environmental Osmotic Pressure

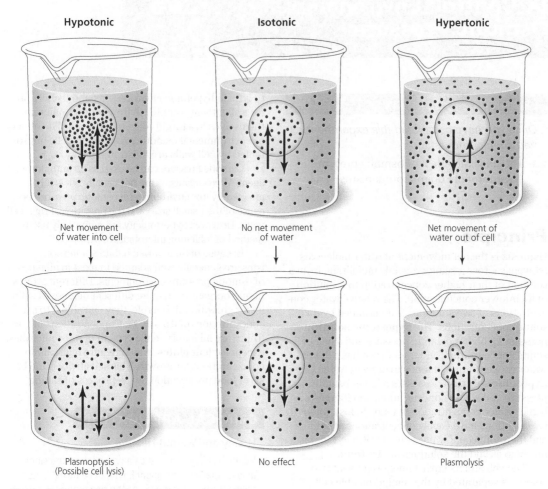

Figure 1 Osmotic environments

Media

Per student group: one nutrient agar plate of each of the following sodium chloride concentrations: 0.85%, 5%, 10%, 15%, and 25%.

Equipment

Bunsen burner, inoculating loop, and glassware marking pencil.

Procedure Lab One

1. Score the underside of each of the five nutrient agar plates into three sections with a glassware marking pencil.

2. Label each of the three sections on each plate with the name of the organism to be inoculated.

3. Using aseptic technique, inoculate each of the agar plates with the three experimental organisms by making a single-line loop inoculation of each organism in its labeled section.

4. Incubate all plates in an inverted position for 4 to 5 days at 25°C.

Procedure Lab Two

1. Observe each of the nutrient agar plate cultures for the amount of growth on each of the experimental species.

2. Record your observations in the Lab Report.

Observations and Results

1. Record your results in the chart as 0 = no growth; $1+$ = scant growth; $2+$ = moderate growth; $3+$ = abundant growth.

Microbial Species	SALT CONCENTRATION OF MEDIUM (%)				
	0.85	5	10	15	25
S. aureus					
E. coli					
H. salinarium					

2. For each of the experimental species, indicate (a) the salt concentration range in which growth will occur and (b) the optimal salt concentration.

Microbial Species	Range of Growth	Optimal NaCl Concentration
S. aureus		
E. coli		
H. salinarium		

Review Questions

1. Compare hypertonic, hypotonic, and isotonic solutions and their effects on cells.

2. Explain how hypertonicity can be used as a means of controlling microbial growth.

3. Early pioneers, traveling to the West, salted their meat products for preservation. Explain the microbiological mechanism by which the salt retarded the spoilage of their meat.

4. How do halophiles survive in their environment?

Physical Agents of Control: Electromagnetic Radiations

Principle

Certain forms of electromagnetic radiation are capable of producing a lethal effect on cells and therefore can be used for microbial control. Electromagnetic radiations that possess sufficient energy to be microbicidal are the short-wavelength radiations, that is, 300 nm and below. These include UV, gamma rays, and x-rays. The high-wavelength radiations, those above 300 nm, have insufficient energy to destroy cells. The electromagnetic spectrum and its effects on molecules are illustrated in **Figure 1**.

Gamma radiation, originating from unstable atomic nuclei, and **x-radiation,** originating from outside of the atomic nucleus, are representative of **ionizing forms of radiation.** Both transfer their energy through quanta (photons) to the matter through which they pass, causing excitation and the loss of electrons from molecules in their paths. This injurious effect is nonspecific in that any molecule in the path of the radiation will undergo ionization. Essential cell molecules can be directly affected through loss of their chemical structures and activity brought about by the ionization. Also, water, the most abundant chemical constituent of cells, commonly undergoes radiation breakdown, with the ultimate production of highly reactive H^+, OH^-, and, in the presence of oxygen, HO_2 free radicals. These may combine with each other, frequently forming hydrogen peroxide (H_2O_2), which is highly toxic to cells lacking catalase or other peroxidases, or the highly reactive free radicals may combine with any cellular constituents, again resulting in cell damage.

Because of their high energy content and therefore ability to penetrate matter, x-ray and gamma radiations can be used as means of sterilization, particularly of thermolabile materials. They are not commonly used, however, because of the expense of the equipment and the special facilities necessary for their safe use.

Ultraviolet light, which has a lower energy content than ionizing radiations, is capable of producing a lethal effect in cells exposed to the low penetrating wavelengths in the range of 210 nm to 300 nm. Cellular components capable of absorbing ultraviolet light are the nucleic acids; DNA is the primary site of damage. As the pyrimidines especially absorb ultraviolet wavelengths, the

Figure 1 The electromagnetic spectrum and its effects on molecules

major effect of this form of radiation is **thymine dimerization**, which is the covalent bonding of two adjacent thymine molecules on one nucleic acid strand in the DNA molecule. This dimer formation distorts the configuration of the DNA molecule, and the distortion interferes with DNA replication and transcription during protein synthesis.

Some cell types, including some microorganisms, possess enzyme systems for the repair of radiation-induced DNA damage. Two different systems may be operational: (1) The **excision repair system**, which functions in the absence of light; and (2) the **light repair system**, which is made operational by exposure of the irradiated cells to visible light in the wavelength range of 420 nm to 540 nm. The visible light serves to activate an enzyme that splits the dimers and reverses the damage.

Ultraviolet radiation, because of its low penetration ability, cannot be used as a means of sterilization, and its practical application is only for surface or air disinfection.

CLINICAL APPLICATION

Radiation Resistant Organisms

As lethal as radiation would seem to be, organisms vary tremendously in their ability to resist harm when exposed. Yeasts and bacterial spores are among the most resistant, while gram-positive bacteria are more resistant than gram-negative ones. Bacterial cocci also tend to be more resistant than bacilli, with viruses the most resistant of all. To effectively neutralize all contaminants, radiation dose and conditions must be carefully controlled.

AT THE BENCH

Materials

Cultures

24- to 48-hour nutrient broth cultures of *Serratia marcescens* and *Bacillus cereus*; sterile saline spore suspension of *Aspergillus niger*.

Media

Per student group: seven nutrient agar plates.

Equipment

Bunsen burner, inoculating loop, ultraviolet radiation source (254 nm), and glassware marking pencil.

Procedure Lab One

⚠️ **Wear disposable gloves and do not expose your eyes to the ultraviolet light source.**

1. Divide all nutrient agar plates into three sections by scoring the underside of each plate with a glassware marking pencil.

2. Label each of the sections on each plate with the name of the organism to be inoculated.

3. Using aseptic technique, inoculate all the plates by means of a streak inoculation *specifically* as shown in the following illustration:

4. Label the cover of each inoculated plate with the exposure time to ultraviolet radiation as 0 (control), 15 seconds, 30 seconds, 1 minute, and 3 minutes. Label two plates as 5 minutes; one of these plates will serve as the irradiated, covered control.

5. Irradiate all inoculated plates for the designated period of time by placing them 12 inches below the ultraviolet light source. Make sure first to remove all Petri dish covers except that of the 5-minute irradiated control plate.

6. Incubate all plates in an inverted position for 4 to 5 days at 25°C.

Procedure Lab Two

1. Observe each of the nutrient agar plate cultures for the amount of growth on each of the microbial species.

2. Record your observations in the chart provided in the Lab Report.

Name: _____

Date: _____ Section: _____

Observations and Results

Record your observations in the chart as 0 = no growth; 1+ = slight growth;
2+ = moderate growth; 3+ = abundant growth.

Microbial Species	TIME OF IRRADIATION						
	Seconds			Minutes			
	0	15	30	1	3	5	5*
B. cereus	3+	2+	2+	1+	0	1+	3+
S. marcescens	3+	2+	1+	1+	0	0	3+
A. niger	3+	2+	2+	2+	2+	1+	3+

*Irradiated, covered plate.

Review Questions

1. Discuss the effects of ionizing radiation on cellular constituents.

2. Explain why x-rays can be used for sterilization, whereas ultraviolet rays can be used only for surface disinfection of materials.

3. Explain the mechanism of action of ultraviolet radiation on cells.

4. Account for the greater susceptibility of *S. marcescens* than that of *B. cereus* to the effects of ultraviolet radiation.

5. Why is it not essential to shield your hands from ultraviolet light, whereas you must exercise great care to shield your eyes from this type of radiation?

Chemical Agents of Control: Chemotherapeutic Agents

Chemotherapeutic agents are chemical substances used in the treatment of infectious diseases. Their mode of action is to interfere with microbial metabolism, thereby producing a bacteriostatic or bactericidal effect on the microorganisms, without producing a like effect in host cells. Chemotherapeutic agents act on a number of cellular targets. Their mechanisms of action include inhibition of cell-wall synthesis, inhibition of protein synthesis, inhibition of nucleic acid synthesis, disruption of the cell membrane, and inhibition of folic acid synthesis. These drugs can be separated into two categories:

1. **Antibiotics** are synthesized and secreted by some true bacteria, actinomycetes, and fungi that destroy or inhibit the growth of other microorganisms. Today, some antibiotics are laboratory synthesized or modified; however, their origins are living cells.

2. **Synthetic drugs** are synthesized in the laboratory.

To determine a therapeutic drug of choice, one must know its mode of action, possible adverse side effects in the host, and the scope of its antimicrobial activity. The specific mechanism of action varies among different drugs, and the short-term or long-term use of many drugs can produce systemic side effects in the host. These vary in severity from mild and temporary upsets to permanent tissue damage (Table 1).

TABLE 1	Prototypic Antibiotics	
ANTIBIOTIC	**MODE OF ACTION**	**POSSIBLE SIDE EFFECTS**
Penicillin	Prevents transpeptidation of the N-acetylmuramic acids, producing a weakened peptidoglycan structure	Penicillin resistance; sensitivity (allergic reaction)
Streptomycin	Has an affinity for bacterial ribosomes, causing misreading of codons on mRNA, thereby interfering with protein synthesis	May produce damage to auditory nerve, causing deafness
Chloramphenicol	Has an affinity for bacterial ribosomes, preventing peptide bond formation between amino acids during protein synthesis	May cause aplastic anemia, which is fatal because of destruction of RBC-forming and WBC-forming tissues
Tetracyclines	Have an affinity for bacterial ribosomes; prevent hydrogen bonding between the anticodon on the tRNA–amino acid complex and the codon on mRNA during protein synthesis	Permanent discoloration of teeth in young children
Bacitracin	Inhibits cell-wall synthesis	Nephrotoxic if taken internally; used for topical application only
Polymyxin	Destruction of cell membrane	Toxic if taken internally; used for topical application only
Rifampin	Inhibits RNA synthesis	Appearance of orange-red urine, feces, saliva, sweat, and tears
Quinolone	Inhibits DNA synthesis	Affects the development of cartilage

From Experiment 44 of *Microbiology: A Laboratory Manual*, Tenth Edition. James G. Cappuccino, Natalie Sherman.
Copyright © 2014 by Pearson Education, Inc. All rights reserved.

Figure 1 Chemical similarity of sulfanilamide and PABA

Synthetic Agents

Sulfadiazine (a sulfonamide) produces a static effect on a wide range of microorganisms by a mechanism of action called **competitive inhibition**. The active component of the drug, sulfanilamide, acts as an **antimetabolite** that competes with the **essential metabolite**, p-aminobenzoic acid (PABA), during the synthesis of folic acid in the microbial cell. Folic acid is an essential cellular coenzyme involved in the synthesis of amino acids and purines. Many microorganisms possess enzymatic pathways for folic acid synthesis and can be adversely affected by sulfonamides. Human cells lack these enzymes, and the essential folic acid enters the cells in a preformed state. Therefore, these drugs have no competitive effect on human cells. The similarity between the chemical structure of the antimetabolite sulfanilamide and the structure of the essential metabolite PABA is illustrated in **Figure 1**.

PART A The Kirby-Bauer Antibiotic Sensitivity Test Procedure

LEARNING OBJECTIVE

Once you have completed this experiment, you should understand

1. The Kirby-Bauer procedure for the evaluation of the antimicrobial activity of chemotherapeutic agents.

Principle

The available chemotherapeutic agents vary in their scope of antimicrobial activity. Some have a limited spectrum of activity, being effective against only one group of microorganisms. Others exhibit broad-spectrum activity against a range of microorganisms. The drug susceptibilities of many pathogenic microorganisms are known, but it is sometimes necessary to test several agents to determine the drug of choice.

A standardized diffusion procedure with filter-paper discs on agar, known as the **Kirby-Bauer method**, is frequently used to determine the drug susceptibility of microorganisms isolated from infectious processes. This method allows the rapid determination of the efficacy of a drug by measuring the diameter of the zone of inhibition that results from diffusion of the agent into the medium surrounding the disc. In this procedure, filter-paper discs of uniform size are impregnated with specified concentrations of different antibiotics and then placed on the surface of an agar plate that has been seeded with the organism to be tested. The medium of choice is Mueller-Hinton agar, with a pH of 7.2 to 7.4, which is poured into plates to a uniform depth of 5 mm and refrigerated after solidification. Prior to use, the plates are transferred to an incubator at 37°C for 10 to 20 minutes to dry off the moisture that develops on the agar surface. The plates are then heavily inoculated with a standardized inoculum by means of a cotton swab to ensure the confluent growth of the organism. The discs are aseptically applied to the surface of the agar plate at well-spaced intervals. Once applied, each disc is gently touched with a sterile applicator stick to ensure its firm contact with the agar surface.

Following incubation, the plates are examined for the presence of growth inhibition, which is indicated by a clear zone surrounding each disc (**Figure 2**). The susceptibility of an organism to a drug is assessed by the size of this zone, which is affected by other variables such as

1. The ability and rate of diffusion of the antibiotic into the medium and its interaction with the test organism.

2. The number of organisms inoculated.

3. The growth rate of the organism.

A measurement of the diameter of the zone of inhibition in millimeters is made, and its size is compared to that contained in a standardized

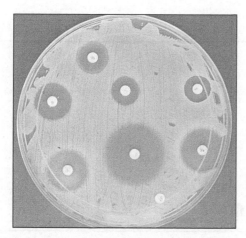

Figure 2 Kirby-Bauer antibiotic sensitivity test

chart, which is shown in Table 2. Based on this comparison, the test organism is determined to be resistant, intermediate, or susceptible to the antibiotic.

CLINICAL APPLICATION

Selection of Effective Antibiotics

Upon isolation of an infectious agent, a chemotherapeutic agent is selected and its effectiveness must be determined. This can be done using the Kirby-Bauer Antibiotic Sensitivity Test. This is the essential tool used in clinical laboratories to select the best agent to treat patients with bacterial infections.

AT THE BENCH

Materials
Cultures

0.85% saline suspensions of *Escherichia coli*, *Staphylococcus aureus*, *Pseudomonas aeruginosa*, *Proteus vulgaris*, *Mycobacterium smegmatis*, *Bacillus cereus*, and *Enterococcus faecalis* adjusted to an absorbance of 0.1 at 600 nm. *Note: For enhanced growth of* M. smegmatis, *add Tween™ 80 (1 ml/liter of broth medium) and incubate for 3 to 5 days in a shaking waterbath, if available.*

Media

Per designated student group: seven Mueller-Hinton agar plates.

Antimicrobial-Sensitivity Discs

Penicillin G, 10 µg; streptomycin, 10 µg; tetracycline, 30 µg; chloramphenicol, 30 µg; gentamicin, 10 µg; vancomycin, 30 µg; and sulfanilamide, 300 µg.

Sulfamethizde

Equipment

Sensi-Disc™ dispensers or forceps, Bunsen burner, sterile cotton swabs, glassware marking pencil, and millimeter ruler.

Procedure Lab One

1. Place agar plates right side up in an incubator heated to 37°C for 10 to 20 minutes with the covers adjusted so that the plates are slightly opened.

2. Label the covers of each of the agar plates with the name of the test organism to be inoculated.

3. Using aseptic technique, inoculate all agar plates with their respective test organisms as follows:

   a. Dip a sterile cotton swab into a well-mixed saline test culture and remove excess inoculum by pressing the saturated swab against the inner wall of the culture tube.

   b. Using the swab, streak the entire agar surface horizontally, vertically, and around the outer edge of the plate to ensure a heavy growth over the entire surface.

4. Allow all culture plates to dry for about 5 minutes.

5. Using the Sensi-Disc dispenser, apply the antibiotic discs by placing the dispenser over the agar surface and pressing the plunger, depositing the discs simultaneously onto the agar surface (**Figure 3**, Step 1a). Or, if dispensers are not available, distribute the individual discs at equal distances with forceps dipped in alcohol and flamed (Figure 3, Step 1b).

6. Gently press each disc down with the wooden end of a cotton swab or with sterile forceps to ensure that the discs adhere to the surface of the agar (Figure 3, Step 2). *Note: Do not press the discs into the agar.*

7. Incubate all plate cultures in an inverted position for 24 to 48 hours at 37°C.

Procedure Lab Two

1. Examine all plate cultures for the presence or absence of a zone of inhibition surrounding each disc.

PROCEDURE

Dispense antibiotic discs with the dispenser.

Space antibiotic discs equidistant from each other on the inoculated plate with a sterile forceps.

Gently touch each disc with a sterile applicator or forceps.

Following incubation, measure the diameter of each zone of inhibition with a millimeter ruler.

Figure 3 Kirby-Bauer antibiotic sensitivity procedure

2. Using a ruler graduated in millimeters, carefully measure each zone of inhibition to the nearest millimeter (Figure 3, Step 3). Record your results in the chart provided in the Lab Report.

3. Compare your results with Table 2 and determine the susceptibility of each test organism to the chemotherapeutic agent. Record your results in the Lab Report.

PART B Synergistic Effect of Drug Combinations

LEARNING OBJECTIVE

Once you have completed this experiment, you should be able to

1. Perform the disc–agar diffusion technique for determination of synergistic combinations of chemotherapeutic agents.

Principle

Combination chemotherapy, the use of two or more antimicrobial or antineoplastic agents, is being employed in medical practice with ever-increasing frequency. The rationale for using drug combinations is the expectation that effective combinations might lower the incidence of bacterial resistance, reduce host toxicity of the antimicrobial agents (because of decreased dosage requirements), or enhance the agents' bactericidal activity. Enhanced bactericidal activity is known as **synergism**. Synergistic activity is evident when the sum of the effects of the chemotherapeutic agents used in combination is significantly greater than the sum of their effects when used individually. This result is readily differentiated from an **additive (indifferent) effect**, which is evident when the interaction of two drugs produces a combined effect that is no greater than the sum of their separately measured individual effects.

A variety of *in vitro* methods are available to demonstrate synergistic activity. In this experiment, a disc–agar diffusion technique will be performed to demonstrate this phenomenon. This technique uses the Kirby-Bauer antibiotic susceptibility test procedure, as described in Part A of this experiment, and requires both Mueller-Hinton agar plates previously seeded with the test organisms and commercially prepared, antimicrobial-impregnated discs. The two discs, representing the drug combination, are placed on the inoculated agar plate and separated by a distance (measured in mm) that is equal to or slightly greater than one-half the sum of their individual zones of inhibition when obtained separately. Following the incubation period, an additive effect is exhibited by the presence of two distinctly separate circles of inhibition. If the drug combination is synergistic, the two inhibitory zones merge to form a "bridge" at their juncture, as illustrated in **Figure 4**.

The following drug combinations will be used in this experimental procedure:

1. **Sulfisoxazole, 150 μg, and trimethoprim, 5 μg.** Both antimicrobial agents are enzyme inhibitors that act sequentially in the metabolic pathway, leading to folic acid synthesis. The antimicrobial effect of each drug is enhanced when the two drugs are used in combination. The pathway thus exemplifies synergism.

2. **Trimethoprim, 5 μg, and tetracycline, 30 μg.** The modes of antimicrobial activity of these two chemotherapeutic agents differ; tetracycline acts to interfere with protein synthesis at the ribosomes. Thus, when used in combination, these drugs produce an additive effect.

CLINICAL APPLICATION

Multiple Drug Therapy

In antimicrobial therapy for drug-resistant bacteria such as the opportunistic pathogen *Pseudomonas aeruginosa,* multiple drugs may be used to take advantage of synergistic effects. Research has shown that use of ampicillin to degrade gram-negative cell walls allows easier entry of kanamycin, which then inhibits protein synthesis. Combination therapies taking advantage of synergism also allow use of lower doses of each drug, which reduces overall toxic effects on the patient.

AT THE BENCH

Materials
Cultures

0.85% saline suspensions of *Escherichia coli* and *Staphylococcus aureus* adjusted to an absorbance of 0.1 at 600 nm.

Media

Per designated student group: four Mueller-Hinton agar plates.

Antimicrobial-Sensitivity Discs

Tetracycline, 30 μg; trimethoprim, 5 μg; and sulfisoxazole, 150 μg.

Equipment

Bunsen burner, forceps, sterile cotton swabs, millimeter ruler, and glassware marking pencil.

Procedure Lab One

1. To inoculate the Mueller-Hinton agar plates, follow Steps 1 through 4 as described under the procedure in Part A of this experiment.

(a) Synergistic effect   (b) Additive effect

Figure 4 Synergistic and additive effects of drug combinations

2. Using the millimeter ruler, determine the center of the underside of each plate and mark with a glassware marking pencil.

3. Using the glassware marking pencil, mark the underside of each agar plate culture at both sides from the center mark at the distances specified below:

   a. *E. coli*–inoculated plate for trimethoprim and sulfisoxazole combination sensitivity: 12.5 mm on each side of center mark.

   b. *S. aureus*–inoculated plate for trimethoprim and sulfisoxazole combination sensitivity: 14.5 mm on each side of center mark.

   c. *E. coli*–inoculated plate for trimethoprim and tetracycline combination sensitivity: 14.0 mm on each side of center mark.

   d. *S. aureus*–inoculated plate for trimethoprim and tetracycline combination: 14.0 mm on each side of center mark.

4. Using sterile forceps, place the antimicrobial discs, in the combinations specified in Step 3, onto the surface of each agar plate culture at the previously marked positions. Gently press each disc down with the sterile forceps to ensure that it adheres to the agar surface.

5. Incubate all plate cultures in an inverted position for 24 to 48 hours at 37°C.

Procedure Lab Two

1. Examine all agar plate cultures to determine the zone of inhibition patterns exhibited. Distinctly separate zones of inhibition are indicative of an additive effect, whereas a merging of the inhibitory zones is indicative of synergism.

2. Record your observations and results in the chart provided in the Lab Report.

TABLE 2	Zone Diameter Interpretive Standards for Organisms Other Than *Haemophilus* and *Neisseria gonorrhoeae*			
		ZONE DIAMETER, NEAREST WHOLE mm		
ANTIMICROBIAL AGENT	**DISC CONTENT**	**RESISTANT**	**INTERMEDIATE**	**SUSCEPTIBLE**
Ampicillin				
when testing gram-negative bacteria	10 µg	≤ 13	14–16	≥ 17
when testing gram-positive bacteria	10 µg	≤ 28	—	≥ 29
Carbenicillin				
when testing *Pseudomonas*	100 µg	≤ 13	14–16	≥ 17
when testing other gram-negative organisms	100 µg	≤ 19	20–22	≥ 23
Cefoxitin	30 µg	≤ 14	15–17	≥ 18
Cephalothin	30 µg	≤ 14	16–17	≥ 18
Chloramphenicol	30 µg	≤ 12	13–17	≥ 18
Clindamycin	2 µg	≤ 14	15–20	≥ 21
Erythromycin	15 µg	≤ 13	14–22	≥ 23
Gentamicin	10 µg	≤ 12	13–14	≥ 15
Kanamycin	30 µg	≤ 13	14–17	≥ 18
Methicillin when testing staphylococci	5 µg	≤ 9	10–13	≥ 14
Novobiocin	30 µg	≤ 17	18–21	≥ 22
Penicillin G				
when testing staphylococci	10 units	≤ 28	—	≥ 29
when testing other bacteria	10 units	≤ 14	—	≥ 15
Rifampin	5 µg	≤ 16	17–19	≥ 20
Streptomycin	10 µg	≤ 11	12–14	≥ 15
Tetracycline	30 µg	≤ 14	15–18	≥ 19
Tobramycin	10 µg	≤ 12	13–14	≥ 15
Trimethoprim/sulfamethoxazole	1.25/23.75 µg	≤ 10	11–15	≥ 16
Vancomycin				
when testing enterococci	30 µg	≤ 14	15–16	≥ 17
when testing *Staphylococcus* spp.	30 µg	—	—	≥ 15
Sulfonamides	250 or 300 µg	≤ 12	—	≥ 17
Trimethoprim	5 µg	≤ 10	—	≥ 16

Source: Clinical and Laboratory Standards Institute. *Performance Standards for Antimicrobial Disk Susceptibility Tests*, Tenth Edition, 2008.

Observations and Results

PART A: Kirby-Bauer Antibiotic Sensitivity Test Procedure

1. Record the zone size and the susceptibility of each test organism to the chemotherapeutic agent as resistant (R), intermediate (I), or sensitive (S) in the charts below.

Chemotherapeutic Agent	GRAM-NEGATIVE								ACID-FAST	
	E. coli		P. aeruginosa		P. vulgaris				M. smegmatis	
	Zone Size	Susceptibility	Zone Size	Susceptibility	Zone Size	Susceptibility			Zone Size	Susceptibility
Penicillin	0	—	0	⊕						
Streptomycin	15	S	0							
Tetracycline	15	I	0							
Chloramphenicol	20	S	0							
Gentamicin	15	S	15ᴿ	S						
Vancomycin	0	—	0							
Sulfanilamide										

Chemotherapeutic Agent	GRAM-POSITIVE					
	S. aureus		E. faecalis		B. cereus	
	Zone Size	Susceptibility	Zone Size	Susceptibility	Zone Size	Susceptibility
Penicillin	0				0	
Streptomycin	10	R			20	
Tetracycline	0				15	
Chloramphenicol	20	S			30	
Gentamicin	15	S			20	
Vancomycin	20	R			0	
Sulfanilamide	20					

Inconclusive

2. For each of the chemotherapeutic agents, indicate the following:
   a. The spectrum of its activity as broad or limited.
   b. The type or types of organisms it is effective against as gram-positive, gram-negative, or acid-fast.

Chemotherapeutic Agent	Spectrum of Activity	Type(s) of Microorganisms
Penicillin		
Streptomycin		
Tetracycline		
Chloramphenicol		
Gentamicin		
Vancomycin		
Sulfanilamide		

PART B: Synergistic Effect of Drug Combinations

Cultures	Appearance of Zone Inhibition	Synergistic or Additive Effect
E. coli:		
trimethoprim and sulfisoxazole		
trimethoprim and tetracycline		
S. aureus:		
trimethoprim and sulfisoxazole		
trimethoprim and tetracycline		

Review Question

1. Your experimental results indicate that antibiotics such as tetracycline, streptomycin, and chloramphenicol have a broad spectrum of activity against prokaryotic cells. Why do these antibiotics lack inhibitory activity against eukaryotic cells such as fungi?

Photo Credits

Credits are listed in order of appearance.
Photo 1: James Cappuccino
Photo 2: James Cappuccino

Determination of Penicillin Activity in the Presence and Absence of Penicillinase

LEARNING OBJECTIVES

Once you have completed this experiment, you should be able to

1. Employ a broth culture system for the determination of the minimal inhibitory concentration (MIC) of penicillin.

2. Demonstrate the reversal of penicillin inhibition against the test organism in the presence of penicillinase (β-lactamase).

Figure 1 **Molecular structure of benzylpenicillin (penicillin G)**

Principle

In addition to the Kirby-Bauer paper disc–agar diffusion procedure, the broth tube dilution method may be used to determine the susceptibility of an organism to an antibiotic. The latter procedure, in which dilutions of the antibiotic are prepared in the broth medium, also permits the **minimal inhibitory concentration (MIC)** to be determined for the antibiotic under investigation. The **MIC** is the lowest concentration of an antimicrobial agent that inhibits the growth of the test microorganism. Quantitative data of this nature may be used by a clinician to establish effective antimicrobial regimens for the treatment of a bacterial infection in a host. This data is of particular significance when the toxicity of the antibiotic is known to produce major adverse effects in host tissues.

Penicillin is a potent antibiotic produced by the mold *Penicillium chrysogenum* (formerly called *P. notatum*). Sir Alexander Fleming's discovery of penicillin in 1928 provided the world with the first clinically useful antibiotic in the fight to control human infection. The activity of this antibiotic, as illustrated in **Figure 1**, is associated with the β-lactam ring within its molecular structure. Shortly after the clinical introduction of benzylpenicillin (penicillin G), pathogenic organisms such as *Staphylococcus aureus* were found to be resistant to this "wonder drug." Research

Figure 2 **Penicillinase activity.** Penicillin sensitivity is shown on the left; penicillin resistance is shown on the right.

revealed that some organisms were genetically capable of producing β-lactamase (penicillinase), an enzyme that breaks a bond in the β-lactam ring portion of the molecule. When the integrity of this ring is compromised, the inhibitory activity of the antibiotic is lost. Penicillinase activity is illustrated in **Figure 2**.

In this experiment, the MIC of penicillin will be determined against penicillin-sensitive and penicillinase-producing strains of *Staphylococcus*

Figure 3 Minimal inhibitory concentration tube set-up

AT THE BENCH

Materials
Cultures

1:1000 brain heart infusion (BHI) broth dilutions of 24-hour BHI broth cultures of *Staphylococcus aureus* ATCC® 27661™ (penicillin-sensitive strain) and *Staphylococcus aureus* ATCC 27659 (penicillinase-producing strain).

Media

Per designated student group: 40 ml of brain heart infusion broth in a 100-ml Erlenmeyer flask and 10 ml of sterile aqueous crystalline penicillin G solution (100 µg/ml).

aureus. The procedure to be followed involves specific concentrations of the penicillin prepared by means of a twofold serial dilution technique in an enriched broth medium. The tubes containing the antibiotic dilutions are then inoculated with a standardized concentration of the test organism (**Figure 3**). Table 1 illustrates the protocol for the antibiotic serial dilution–broth medium setup.

Following incubation, spectrophotometric absorbance readings will be used to determine the presence or absence of growth in the cultures. The culture that shows no growth in the presence of the lowest concentration of penicillin represents the minimal inhibitory concentration of this antibiotic against *S. aureus.*

TABLE 1	Antibiotic Serial Dilution–Broth Medium Setup									
	TUBE NUMBER									
Additions (ml) to:	**1**	**2**	**3**	**4**	**5**	**6**	**7**	**8**	**9**	**10**
Medium	0	2	2	2	2	2	2	2	2	2
Penicillin	2	2	Serial dilution (See protocol)							0
Test culture	2	2	2	2	2	2	2	2	2	2
Total volume	4	4	4	4	4	4	4	4	4*	4
Penicillin (µg/ml)	50	50	25	12.5	6.25	3.12	1.56	0.78	0.39	0
Control	(−)									(+)

*After 2 ml discarded

Equipment

Sterile 13 × 100-mm test tubes, test tube racks, sterile 2-ml and 10-ml pipettes, mechanical pipetting device, Bunsen burner, spectrophotometer, glassware marking pencil, and disinfectant solution in a 500-ml beaker.

Procedure Lab One

1. Into each of two test tube racks, place a set of 10 sterile 13 × 100-mm test tubes labeled 1 through 10. Label one rack Set I—penicillin-sensitive and the other rack Set II—penicillin-resistant. *Refer to Table 1 for Steps 2 through 7.*

2. Using a sterile 10-ml pipette and mechanical pipetting device, add 2 ml of BHI broth to the tubes labeled 2 through 10 in Sets I and II. *Note: Discard the pipette into the beaker of disinfectant.*

3. With a 2-ml sterile pipette, add 2 ml of the penicillin solution to Tubes 1 and 2 in Sets I and II. Discard the pipette. *Note: Mix the contents of the tubes well.*

4. **Set I Serial Dilution:** Using a sterile 2-ml pipette, transfer 2 ml from Tube 2 to Tube 3. Mix well and transfer 2 ml from Tube 3 to Tube 4. Continue this procedure through Tube 9 into beaker. Discard 2 ml from Tube 9. Tube 10 receives no antibiotic and serves as a positive control. Discard the pipette. *Note: Remember to mix the contents of each tube well between transfers.*

5. **Set II Serial Dilution:** Using a sterile 2-ml pipette, repeat Step 4.

6. Using a sterile 2-ml pipette, add 2 ml of the 1:1000 dilution of the *S. aureus* ATCC 27661 (penicillin-sensitive strain) to all tubes in Set I. Discard the pipette.

7. Repeat Step 6 to inoculate all the tubes in Set II with the 1:1000 dilution of *S. aureus* ATCC 27659 (penicillinase-producing strain). Discard the pipette.

8. Incubate both sets of tubes for 12 to 18 hours at 37°C.

Procedure Lab Two

1. Determine the absorbance readings for Tubes 2 through 10 in Sets I and II. Use the Number 1 tubes, the negative controls, as your blanks to adjust the spectrophotometer.

2. Record your absorbance readings in the chart in the Lab Report.

Name: _____

Date: _____ Section: _____

Lab Report

Observations and Results

Absorbance Readings at 600 nm

Tube Number	2	3	4	5	6	7	8	9	10
Penicillin concentration (μg/ml)	50	25	12.5	6.25	3.12	1.56	0.78	0.39	0
Set I									
Set II									

Set I: Minimal inhibitory concentration: _____

Set II: Minimal inhibitory concentration: _____

Review Questions

1. Was the ability of some microorganisms to produce β-lactamase present prior to their exposure to the antibiotic penicillin? Explain.

2. Can the results of an MIC test be used to determine whether an antibiotic is bactericidal or bacteriostatic? If not, set up an experimental procedure to determine whether the effect is bactericidal or bacteriostatic.

Photo Credits

Credits are listed in order of appearance.
Photo 1: James Cappuccino
Photo 2: Ashley Rex, Antimicrobial Test Laboratories

Chemical Agents of Control: Disinfectants and Antiseptics

Antiseptics and disinfectants are chemical substances used to prevent contamination and infection. Many are available commercially for disinfection and asepsis.

Table 1 shows the major groups of antimicrobial agents, their modes and ranges of action, and their practical uses.

(Text continues)

TABLE 1	Chemical Agents—Disinfectants and Antiseptics	
AGENT	**MECHANISM OF ACTION**	**USE**
Phenolic Compounds		
Phenol	1. Germicidal effect caused by alteration of protein structure resulting in protein denaturation. 2. Surface-active agent (surfactant) precipitates cellular proteins and disrupts cell membranes. (Phenol has been replaced by better disinfectants that are less irritating, less toxic to tissues, and better inhibitors of microorganisms.)	1. 5% solution: Disinfection. 2. 0.5% to 1% solutions: Antiseptic effect and relief of itching as it exerts a local anesthetic effect on sensory nerve endings.
Cresols	1. Similar to phenol. 2. Poisonous and must be used externally. 3. 50% solution of cresols in vegetable oil, known as Lysol®.	2% to 5% Lysol solutions used as disinfectants.
Hexachlorophene	Germicidal activity similar to phenol. (This agent is to be used with care, especially on infants, because after absorption it may cause neurotoxic effects.)	1. Reduction of pathogenic organisms on skin; added to detergents, soaps, lotions, and creams. 2. Effective against gram-positive organisms. 3. An antiseptic used topically.
Resorcinol	1. Germicidal activity similar to that of phenol. 2. Acts by precipitating cell protein.	1. Antiseptic. 2. Keratolytic agent for softening or dissolving keratin in epidermis.
Hexylresorcinol	Germicidal activity similar to that of phenol.	1. Treatment of worm infections. 2. Urinary antiseptic.

→

Chemical Agents of Control: Disinfectants and Antiseptics

TABLE 1	Chemical Agents—Disinfectants and Antiseptics (continued)	
AGENT	MECHANISM OF ACTION	USE
Thymol	1. Related to the cresols. 2. More effective than phenol.	1. Antifungal activity. 2. Treatment of hookworm infections. 3. Mouthwashes and gargle solutions.
Alcohols Ethyl: CH_3CH_2OH Isopropyl: $(CH_3)_2CHOH$	1. Lipid solvent. 2. Denaturation and coagulation of proteins. 3. Wetting agent used in tinctures to increase the wetting ability of other chemicals. 4. Germicidal activity increases with increasing molecular weight.	Skin antiseptics: Ethyl—50% to 70%. Isopropyl—60% to 70%.
Halogens Chlorine compounds: Sodium hypochlorite (Dakin's fluid): NaOCl Chloramine: $CH_3C_6H_4SO_2NNaCl$	1. Germicidal effect resulting from rapid combination with proteins. 2. Chlorine reacts with water to form hypochlorous acid, which is bactericidal. 3. Oxidizing agent. 4. Noncompetitively inhibits enzymes, especially those dealing with glucose metabolism, by reacting with SH and NH_2 groups on the enzyme molecule.	1. Water purification. 2. Sanitation of utensils in dairy and restaurant industries. 3. Chloramine, 0.1% to 2% solutions, for wound irrigation and dressings. 4. Microbicidal.
Iodine compounds: Tincture of iodine Povidone-iodine solution (Betadine®)	1. Mechanism of action is not entirely known, but it is believed that it precipitates proteins. 2. Surface-active agent.	1. Tinctures of iodine are used for skin antisepsis. 2. Treatment of goiter. 3. Effective against spores, fungi, and viruses.
Heavy Metals Mercury compounds: Inorganic: Mercury bichloride Mercurial ointments	1. Mercuric ion brings about precipitation of cellular proteins. 2. Noncompetitive inhibition of specific enzymes caused by reaction with sulfhydryl group (SH) on enzymes of bacterial cells.	1. Inorganic mercurials are irritating to tissues, toxic systemically, adversely affected by organic matter, and incapable of acting on spores. 2. Mercury compounds are mainly used as disinfectants of laboratory materials.
Organic mercurials: Mercurochrome (merbromin) Merthiolate (thimerosal) Metaphen (nitromersol) Merbak (acetomeroctol)	1. Similar to those of inorganic mercurials, but in proper concentrations are useful antiseptics. 2. Much less irritating than inorganic mercurials.	1. Less toxic, less irritating; used mainly for skin asepsis. 2. Do not kill spores.
Silver compounds: Silver nitrate	1. Precipitate cellular proteins. 2. Interfere with metabolic activities of microbial cells. 3. Inorganic salts are germicidal.	Asepsis of mucous membrane of throat and eyes.

TABLE 1 (continued)		
AGENT	**MECHANISM OF ACTION**	**USE**
Surface-Active Agents Wetting agents: Emulsifiers, soaps, and detergents	1. Lower surface tension and aid in mechanical removal of bacteria and soil. 2. If active portion of the agent carries a negative electric charge, it is called an anionic surface-active agent. If active portion of the agent carries a positive electric charge, it is called a cationic surface-active agent. 3. Exert bactericidal activity by interfering with or by depressing metabolic activities of microorganisms. 4. Disrupt cell membranes. 5. Alter cell permeability.	Weak action against fungi, acid-fast microorganisms, spores, and viruses.
Cationic agents: Quaternary ammonium compounds Benzalkonium chloride	1. Lower surface tension because of keratolytic, detergent, and emulsifying properties. 2. Their germicidal activities are reduced by soaps.	1. Bactericidal, fungicidal; inactive against spores and viruses. 2. Asepsis of intact skin. 3. Disinfectant for operating-room equipment. 4. Dairy and restaurant sanitization.
Anionic agents: Tincture of green soap Sodium tetradecyl sulfate	1. Neutral or alkaline salts of high-molecular-weight acids. Common soaps included in this group. 2. Exert their maximum activity in an acid medium and are most effective against gram-positive cells. 3. Same as all surface-active agents.	1. Cleansing agent. 2. Sclerosing agent in treatment of varicose veins and internal hemorrhoids.
Acids (H^+) Alkali (OH^-)	1. Destruction of cell wall and cell membrane. 2. Coagulation of proteins.	Disinfection; however, of little practical value.
Formaldehyde (liquid or gas)	Alkylating agent causes reduction of enzymes.	1. Room disinfection. 2. Alcoholic solution for instrument disinfection. 3. Specimen preservation.
Ethylene Oxide	Alkylating agent causes reduction of enzymes.	Sterilization of heat-labile material.
β-Propiolactone (liquid or gas)	Alkylating agent causes reduction of enzymes.	1. Sterilization of tissue for grafting. 2. Destruction of hepatitis virus. 3. Room disinfection.
Basic Dyes Crystal violet	Affinity for nucleic acids; interfere with reproduction in gram-positive organisms.	1. Skin antiseptic. 2. Laboratory isolation of gram-negative bacteria.

The efficiency of all disinfectants and antiseptics is influenced by a variety of factors, including the following:

1. **Concentration:** The concentration of a chemical substance markedly influences its effect on microorganisms, with higher concentrations producing a more rapid death. Concentration cannot be arbitrarily determined; the toxicity of the chemical to the tissues being treated and the damaging effect on nonliving materials must also be considered.

2. **Length of exposure:** All microbes are not destroyed within the same exposure time. Sensitive forms are destroyed more rapidly than resistant ones. The longer the exposure to the agent, the greater its antimicrobial activity. The toxicity of the chemical and environmental conditions must be considered in assessing the length of time necessary for disinfection or asepsis.

3. **Type of microbial population to be destroyed:** Microorganisms vary in their susceptibility to destruction by chemicals. Bacterial spores are the most resistant forms. Capsulated bacteria are more resistant than noncapsulated forms; acid-fast bacteria are more resistant than non–acid-fast; and older, metabolically less-active cells are more resistant than younger cells. Awareness of the types of microorganisms that may be present will influence the choice of agent.

4. **Environmental conditions:** Conditions under which a disinfectant or antiseptic affects the chemical agent are as follows:

   a. **Temperature:** Cells are killed as the result of a chemical reaction between the agent and cellular component. As increasing temperatures increase the rate of chemical reactions, application of heat during disinfection markedly increases the rate at which the microbial population is destroyed.

   b. **pH:** The pH conditions during disinfection may affect not only the microorganisms but also the compound. Extremes in pH are harmful to many microorganisms and may enhance the antimicrobial action of a chemical. Deviation from a neutral pH may cause ionization of the disinfectant; depending on the chemical agent, this may serve to increase or decrease the chemical's microbicidal action.

   c. **Type of material on which the microorganisms exist:** The destructive power of the compound on cells is due to its

combination with organic cellular molecules. If the material on which the microorganisms are found is primarily organic, such as blood, pus, or tissue fluids, the agent will combine with these extracellular organic molecules, and its antimicrobial activity will be reduced.

Numerous laboratory procedures are available for evaluating the antimicrobial efficiency of disinfectants or antiseptics. They provide a general rather than an absolute measure of the effectiveness of any agent because test conditions frequently differ considerably from those seen during practical use. The agar plate-sensitivity method, a commonly employed procedure, is presented.

LEARNING OBJECTIVE

Once you have completed this experiment, you should be able to

1. Evaluate the effectiveness of antiseptic agents against selected test organisms.

Principle

This procedure requires the heavy inoculation of an agar plate with the test organism. Sterile, color-coded filter-paper discs are impregnated with a different antiseptic and equally spaced on the inoculated agar plate. Following incubation, the agar plate is examined for zones of inhibition (areas of no microbial growth) surrounding the discs. A zone of inhibition is indicative of microbicidal activity against the organism. Absence of a zone of inhibition indicates that the chemical was ineffective against the test organism. *Note: The size of the zone of inhibition is not indicative of the degree of effectiveness of the chemical agent.* Antiseptic susceptibility is represented in **Figure 1**.

CLINICAL APPLICATION

MRSA and Disinfection

Methicillin-resistant *Staphylococcus aureus* (MRSA) has achieved notoriety for causing infections that are difficult to treat with conventional antimicrobials, but these strains have also demonstrated resistance to disinfection. One study has shown that resistance to methicillin is directly related to lack of susceptibility to benzalkonium chloride and other disinfectants. It may be that adjusted contact times are necessary to adequately kill these troublesome strains.

Figure 1 **Antiseptic susceptibility test**. Discs are saturated with chlorine bleach (CL), hydrogen peroxide (H$_2$O$_2$), isopropyl alcohol (A), and tincture of iodine (I).

AT THE BENCH

Materials

Cultures

24- to 48-hour Trypticase soy broth cultures of *Escherichia coli*, *Bacillus cereus*, *Staphylococcus aureus*, and *Mycobacterium smegmatis*, and a 7-day-old Trypticase soy broth culture of *Bacillus cereus*.

Media

Per designated student group: five Trypticase soy agar plates.

Antiseptics/Disinfectants

Per designated student group: 10 ml of each of the following dispensed in 25-ml beakers: tincture of iodine, 3% hydrogen peroxide, 70% isopropyl alcohol, and 5% chlorine bleach.

Equipment

Four different-colored, sterile Sensi-Discs; forceps; sterile cotton swabs; Bunsen burner; and glassware marking pencil.

Procedure Lab One

1. Aseptically inoculate the appropriately labeled agar plates with their respective test organisms by streaking each plate in horizontal and vertical directions and around the edge with a sterile swab.

2. Color-code the Sensi-Discs according to the chemical agents to be used (e.g., red = chlorine bleach).

3. Using forceps dipped in alcohol and flamed, expose five discs of the same color by placing them into the solution of one of the chemical agents. Drain the saturated discs on absorbent paper immediately prior to placing one on each of the inoculated agar plates. Place each disc approximately 2 cm in from the edge of the plate. Gently press the discs down with the forceps so that they adhere to the surface of the agar.

4. Impregnate the remaining discs as described in Step 3. Place one of each of the three remaining colored discs on the surface of each of the five inoculated agar plates equidistant from each other around the periphery of the plate.

5. Incubate all plate cultures in an inverted position for 24 to 48 hours at 37°C.

Procedure Lab Two

1. Observe all the plates for the presence of a zone of inhibition surrounding each of the impregnated discs.

2. Record your observations in the chart provided in the Lab Report.

Observations and Results

1. Indicate the absence of a zone of inhibition as (0), and the presence of a zone of inhibition as (+).

Bacterial Species	ANTIMICROBIAL AGENT			
	Tincture of Iodine	3% Hydrogen Peroxide	70% Isopropyl Alcohol	5% Chlorine Bleach
E. coli gram-negative				
S. aureus gram-positive				
M. smegmatis acid-fast				
B. cereus spore-former gram-positive				
B. cereus spore-former gram-positive 7-day-old				

2. Indicate which of the antiseptics exhibited microbicidal activity against each of the following groups of microorganisms.

Bacterial Group	Tincture of Iodine	3% Hydrogen Peroxide	70% Isopropyl Alcohol	5% Chlorine Bleach
Gram-negative				
Gram-positive				
Acid-fast				
Spore-former				

3. Which of the experimental chemical compounds appears to have the broadest range of microbicidal activity? The narrowest range of microbicidal activity?

Review Questions

1. Can the disinfection period (exposure time) be arbitrarily increased? Explain.

2. A household cleanser is labeled germicidal. Explain what this means to you.

Photo Credits

Credits are listed in order of appearance.

Photo 1:   Experiment performed and photographed by L. Brent Selinger, Department of Biological Sciences, University of Lethbridge, Pearson Education

Microbiology of Food

LEARNING OBJECTIVES

Once you have completed the experiments in this section, you should be familiar with

1. The endogenous and exogenous organisms that may be found in food products.
2. The analysis of food products as a means of determining their quality from the public health point of view.
3. The microbiological production of wine.

Introduction

Microbiologists have always been aware that foods, especially milk, have served as important inanimate vectors in the transmission of disease. Foods contain the organic nutrients that provide an excellent medium to support the growth and multiplication of microorganisms under suitable temperatures.

Food and dairy products may be contaminated in a variety of ways and from a variety of sources:

1. **Soil and water:** Food-borne organisms that may be found in soil and water and that may contaminate food are members of the genera *Alcaligenes, Bacillus, Citrobacter, Clostridium, Pseudomonas, Serratia, Proteus, Enterobacter,* and *Micrococcus.* The common soil and water molds include *Rhizopus, Penicillium, Botrytis, Fusarium,* and *Trichothecium.*

2. **Food utensils:** The type of microorganisms found on utensils depends on the type of food and the manner in which the utensils were handled.

3. **Enteric microorganisms of humans and animals:** The major members of this group are *Bacteroides, Lactobacillus, Clostridium,* *Escherichia, Salmonella, Proteus, Shigella, Staphylococcus,* and *Streptococcus.* These organisms find their way into the soil and water, from which they contaminate plants and are carried by wind currents onto utensils or prepared and exposed foods.

4. **Food handlers:** People who handle foods are especially likely to contaminate them because microorganisms on hands and clothing are easily transmitted. A major offending organism is *Staphylococcus,* which is generally found on hands and skin, and in the upper respiratory tract. Food handlers with poor personal hygiene and unsanitary habits are most likely to contaminate foods with enteric organisms.

5. **Animal hides and feeds:** Microorganisms found in water, soil, feed, dust, and fecal debris can be found on animal hides. Infected hides may serve as a source of infection for workers, or the microorganisms may migrate into the musculature of the animal and remain viable following its slaughter.

From Part 10 of *Microbiology: A Laboratory Manual*, Tenth Edition. James G. Cappuccino, Natalie Sherman.
Copyright © 2014 by Pearson Education, Inc. All rights reserved.

By enumerating microorganisms in milk and foods, the quality of a particular sample can be determined. Although the microorganisms cannot be identified, the presence of a high number suggests a good possibility that pathogens may be present. Even if a sample contains a low microbial count, it can still transmit infection.

In the laboratory procedures that follow, you will have an opportunity directly and indirectly to enumerate the number of microorganisms present in milk and other food products and to thereby determine the quality of the samples.

Microbiological Analysis of Food Products: Bacterial Count

LEARNING OBJECTIVES

Once you have completed this experiment, you should be able to determine

1. The total number of microorganisms present in food products.
2. The number of coliform bacteria in the selected food products.

Principle

Microorganisms in food may be harmful in some cases, while in others they are beneficial. Certain microorganisms are necessary in preparation of foods such as cheese, pickles, yogurt, and sausage. Other microorganisms, however, are responsible for serious and sometimes fatal food poisoning and spoilage.

CLINICAL APPLICATION

Microorganisms in Food

Some of the pathogens that are tested for in food include: *Escherichia coli*, *Listeria monocytogenes*, *Salmonella* species, and fungi of the genus *Aspergillus*.

AT THE BENCH

Materials

Cultures

Samples of fresh vegetables, ground beef, and dried fruit.

Media

Per designated student group: nine brain heart infusion agar deep tubes, three eosin–methylene blue (EMB) agar plates, three 99-ml sterile water blanks, and three 180-ml sterile water blanks.

Equipment

Bunsen burner, waterbath, Quebec or electronic colony counter, balance, sterile glassine weighing paper, blender with three sterile jars, sterile Petri dishes, 1-ml pipettes, mechanical pipetting device, inoculation loop, and glassware marking pencil.

Procedure Lab One

Figure 1 illustrates the procedure.

1. Label three sets of three Petri dishes for each of the food samples to be tested and their dilutions (10^{-2}, 10^{-3}, 10^{-4}). Label the three EMB agar plates with the names of the food.
2. Melt the brain heart infusion agar deep tubes in a waterbath, cool, and maintain at 45°C.
3. Place 20 g of each food sample, weighed on sterile glassine paper, into its labeled blender jar. Add 180 ml of sterile water to each of the blender jars and blend each mixture for 5 minutes. You will have made a 1:10 (10^{-1}) dilution of each food sample.
4. Transfer 1 ml of the 10^{-1} ground beef suspension into its labeled 99-ml sterile water blank, thereby effecting a 10^{-3} dilution, and 0.1 ml to the appropriately labeled 10^{-2} Petri dish. Shake the 10^{-3} sample dilution, and using a different pipette, transfer 1 ml to the plate labeled 10^{-3} and 0.1 ml to the plate labeled 10^{-4}. Add a 15-ml aliquot of the molten and cooled agar to each of the three plates. Swirl the plates gently to obtain a uniform distribution, and allow the plates to solidify.
5. Repeat Step 4 for the remaining two 10^{-1} test food sample dilutions.
6. Aseptically prepare a four-way streak plate and inoculate each 10^{-1} food sample dilution on its appropriately labeled EMB agar plate.
7. Incubate all plates in an inverted position for 24 to 48 hours at 37°C.

Procedure Lab Two

1. Following the instructions in the Lab Report, count and record the number of colonies on each plate.

Microbiological Analysis of Food Products: Bacterial Count

PROCEDURE

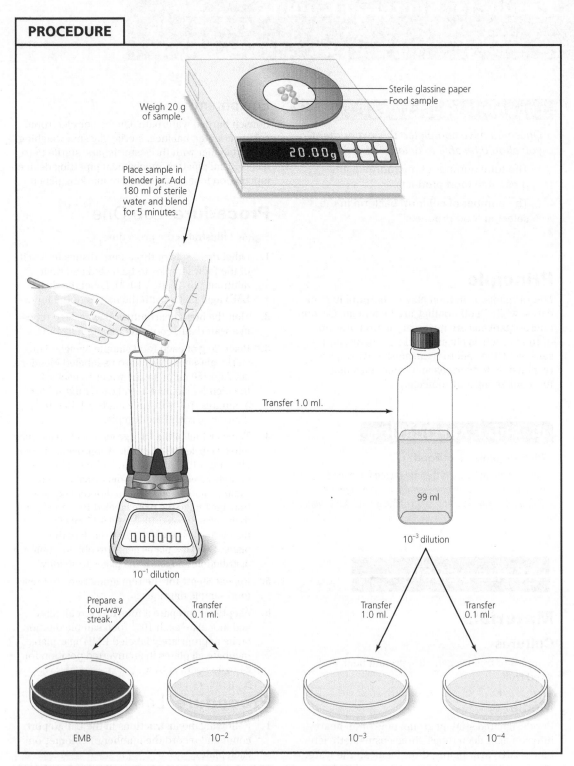

Weigh 20 g of sample.

Sterile glassine paper
Food sample

20.00 g

Place sample in blender jar. Add 180 ml of sterile water and blend for 5 minutes.

Transfer 1.0 ml.

99 ml

10^{-3} dilution

10^{-1} dilution

Prepare a four-way streak.

Transfer 0.1 ml.

Transfer 1.0 ml.

Transfer 0.1 ml.

EMB

10^{-2}

10^{-3}

10^{-4}

Figure 1 Preparation of a food sample for analysis

Observations and Results

1. Using either the Quebec or electronic colony counter, count the number of colonies on each plate. Count only statistically valid plates that contain between 30 and 300 colonies. Designate plates with fewer than 30 colonies as **too few to count (TFTC)** and plates with more than 300 colonies as **too numerous to count (TNTC).**

2. Determine the number of organisms per milliliter of each food sample on plates not designated as TFTC or TNTC by multiplying the number of colonies counted by the dilution factor.

3. Record in the chart below the number of colonies per plate and the number of organisms per milliliter of each food sample.

Type of Food	Dilution	Number of Colonies per Plate	Number of Organisms per ml
Ground beef	10^{-2}		
	10^{-3}		
	10^{-4}		
Fresh vegetables	10^{-2}		
	10^{-3}		
	10^{-4}		
Dried fruits	10^{-2}		
	10^{-3}		
	10^{-4}		

4. Examine the eosin–methylene blue agar plate cultures for colonies with a metallic green sheen on their surfaces, which is indicative of *E. coli*. Indicate in the chart below the presence or absence of *E. coli* growth and the possibility of fecal contamination of the food.

Sample	*E. coli* (+) or (−)	Fecal Contamination (+) or (−)
Ground beef		
Fresh vegetables		
Dried fruit		

Review Questions

1. Indicate some possible ways in which foods may become contaminated with enteric organisms.

2. Explain why it is not advisable to thaw and then refreeze food products without having cooked them.

3. Following a Fourth of July picnic lunch of ham, sour pickles, potato salad, and cream puffs, a group of students was admitted to the hospital with severe gastrointestinal distress. A diagnosis of staphylococcal food poisoning was made. Explain how the staphylococci can multiply in these foods and produce severe abdominal distress.

Wine Production

Principle

Wine is a product of the natural fermentation of the juices of grapes and other fruits, such as peaches, pears, plums, and apples, by the action of yeast cells. This biochemical conversion of juice to wine occurs when the yeast cells enzymatically degrade the fruit sugars fructose and glucose first to acetaldehyde and then to alcohol, as illustrated in **Figure 1**.

Grapes containing 20% to 30% sugar concentration will yield wines with an alcohol content of approximately 10% to 15%. Also present in grapes are acids and minerals whose concentrations

are increased in the finished product and that are responsible for the characteristic tastes and bouquets of different wines. For red wine, the crushed grapes must be fermented with their skins to allow extraction of their color into the juice. White wine is produced from the juice of white grapes.

The commercial production of wine is a long and exacting process. First, the grapes are crushed or pressed to express the juice, which is called **must.** Potassium metabisulfite is added to the must to retard the growth of acetic acid bacteria, molds, and wild yeast that are endogenous to grapes in the vineyard. A wine-producing strain of yeast, *Saccharomyces cerevisiae* var. *ellipsoideus*, is used to inoculate the must, which is then incubated for 3 to 5 days under aerobic conditions at 21°C to 32°C. This is followed by an anaerobic incubation period. The wine is then aged for a period of 1 to 5 years in aging tanks or wooden barrels. During this time, the wine is clarified of any turbidity, thereby producing volatile esters that are responsible for characteristic flavors. The clarified product is then filtered, pasteurized at 60°C for 30 minutes, and bottled.

Figure 1 **Biochemical pathway for alcohol production**

From Experiment 48 of *Microbiology: A Laboratory Manual*, Tenth Edition. James G. Cappuccino, Natalie Sherman.

This experiment is a modified method in which white wine is produced from white grape juice. You will examine the fermenting wine at 1-week intervals during the incubation period for:

1. Total acidity (expressed as % tartaric acid): To a 10-ml aliquot of the fermenting wine, add 10 ml of distilled water and 5 drops of 1% phenolphthalein solution. Mix and titrate to the first persistent pink color with 0.1N sodium hydroxide. Calculate total acidity using the following formula:

$$\% \text{ tartaric acid} = \frac{\text{ml alkali} \times \text{normality of alkali} \times 7.5}{\text{weight of sample in g}^*}$$

*1 ml = 1 g

2. Volatile acidity (expressed as % acetic acid): Following titration, calculate volatile acidity using the following formula:

$$\% \text{ acetic acid} = \frac{\text{ml alkali} \times \text{normality of alkali} \times 6.0}{\text{weight of sample in g}^*}$$

*1 ml = 1 g

3. Alcohol (expressed as volume %): Optional; can be determined by means of an ebulliometer.

4. Aroma: Fruity, yeastlike, sweet, none.

5. Clarity: Clear, turbid.

AT THE BENCH

Materials

Cultures

50 ml of white grape juice broth culture of *Saccharomyces cerevisiae* var. *ellipsoideus* incubated for 48 hours at 25°C.

Media

Per designated student group: 500 ml of pasteurized Welch's® commercial white grape juice.

Reagents

1% phenolphthalein solution, 0.1N sodium hydroxide, and sucrose.

Equipment

1-liter Erlenmeyer flask, one-holed rubber stopper containing a 2-inch glass tube plugged with cotton, pan balance, spatula, glassine paper, 10-ml graduated cylinder, ebulliometer (optional), and burette or pipette for titration.

Procedure

1. Pour 500 ml of the white grape juice into the 1-liter Erlenmeyer flask. Add 20 g of sucrose and the 50 ml of *S. cerevisiae* grape juice broth culture (10% starter culture). Close the flask with the stopper containing a cotton plugged air vent.

2. After 2 days and 4 days of incubation, add 20 g of sucrose to the fermenting wine.

3. Incubate the fermenting wine for 21 days at 25°C.

4. Using uninoculated white grape juice:

   a. Perform a titration to determine total acidity and volatile acidity.

   b. Note aroma and clarity.

   c. Determine volume % alcohol (optional).

5. Record your results in the chart in the Lab Report.

6. At 7-day intervals, using samples of the fermenting wine, repeat Steps 4a though 4c and record your results in the Lab Report.

Name: _____

Date: _____ Section: _____

Observations and Results

	Grape Juice	FERMENTING WINE		
		7 days	14 days	21 days
% Tartaric acid				
% Acetic acid				
Volume % alcohol				
Aroma				
Clarity				

Review Questions

1. What is the purpose of adding sulfite to the must?

2. Explain what occurs during the aging process in the commercial preparation of wine.

3. What are the chemical end products of fermentation?

4. How are white and red wines produced?

5. Why is wine pasteurized? Would it be preferable to sterilize the wine? Explain.

Microbiology of Water

LEARNING OBJECTIVES

Once you have completed the experiments in this section, you should be familiar with

1. The types of microorganisms present in water.
2. The methods to determine the potability of water using standard qualitative and quantitative procedures.

Introduction

The importance of potable (drinking) water supplies cannot be overemphasized. With increasing industrialization, water sources available for consumption and recreation have been adulterated with industrial as well as animal and human wastes. As a result, water has become a formidable factor in disease transmission. Polluted waters contain vast amounts of organic matter that serve as excellent nutritional sources for the growth and multiplication of microorganisms. The presence of nonpathogenic organisms is not of major concern, but intestinal contaminants of fecal origin are important. These pathogens are responsible for intestinal infections such as **bacillary dysentery, typhoid fever, cholera,** and **paratyphoid fever.**

The World Health Organization (WHO) estimates that 1.7 million deaths per year result from unsafe water supplies. Most of these are from diarrheal diseases, and 90% of these deaths occur in children living in developing countries where sanitary facilities and potable water are at a minimum. The WHO indicates that about 3.4 million deaths annually are caused by dangerous waterborne enteric bacterial pathogens such as *Shigella dysenteriae*, *Campylobacter jejuni*, *Salmonella typhi*, and *Vibrio cholerae*.

In addition to bacterial infections, unsafe water supplies are responsible for numerous parasitological infections, including helminth diseases such as schistosomiasis and especially guinea worm *(Dracunculus medinensis)*, which infects about 200 million people worldwide each year. Intestinal, hepatic, and pulmonary flukes such as *Fasciolopsis buski*, *Clonorchis sinensis*, and *Paragonimus westermani* are responsible for human infection and are all associated with unsafe water and sanitation. The parasitic protozoa *Entamoeba histolytica*, *Giardia intestinalis* (formerly called *G. lamblia*), and *Balantidium coli* are just a few of the protozoa responsible for major diarrheal disease in humans.

Although waterborne infections occur in the United States, their incidence in comparison to the rest of the world is much lower, and they occur sporadically. This can be attributed to the diligent attention given to our water supplies and sewage disposal systems.

Analysis of water samples on a routine basis would not be possible if each pathogen required detection. Therefore, water is examined to detect *Escherichia coli*, the bacterium that indicates fecal pollution. Since *E. coli* is always present in the human intestine, its presence in water alerts public health officials to the possible presence of other human or animal intestinal pathogens. However, in the tropics and subtropics it is not considered a reliable indicator of fecal pollution because the soil in these regions naturally contains high levels of *E. coli*. Therefore, *E. coli* is present in the water anytime there is surface runoff. Both qualitative and quantitative methods are used to determine the sanitary condition of water.

From Part 11 of *Microbiology: A Laboratory Manual*, Tenth Edition. James G. Cappuccino, Natalie Sherman.

Standard Qualitative Analysis of Water

Principle

The three basic tests to detect coliform bacteria in water are presumptive, confirmed, and completed (Figure 1). The tests are performed sequentially on each sample under analysis. They detect the presence of coliform bacteria (indicators of fecal contamination), the gram-negative, non–spore-forming bacilli that ferment lactose with the production of acid and gas that is detectable following a 24-hour incubation period at 37°C.

The Presumptive Test

The **presumptive test** is specific for detection of coliform bacteria. Measured aliquots of the water to be tested are added to a lactose fermentation broth containing an inverted gas vial. Because these bacteria are capable of using lactose as a carbon source (the other enteric organisms are not), their detection is facilitated by the use of this medium. In this experiment, you will use lactose fermentation broth containing an inverted Durham tube for gas collection.

Tubes of this lactose medium are inoculated with 10-ml, 1-ml, and 0.1-ml aliquots of the water sample. The series consists of at least three groups, each composed of five tubes of the specified medium. The tubes in each group are then inoculated with the designated volume of the water sample, as described under "Procedure: Lab One." The greater the number of tubes per group, the greater the sensitivity of the test. Development of gas in any of the tubes is *presumptive* evidence of the presence of coliform bacteria in the sample. The presumptive test also enables the microbiologist to obtain some idea of the number of coliform organisms present by means of the **most probable number (MPN) test.** The MPN is estimated by determining the number of tubes in each group that show gas following the incubation period (Table 1).

The Confirmed Test

The presence of a positive or doubtful presumptive test immediately suggests that the water sample is nonpotable. Confirmation of these results is necessary because positive presumptive tests may be the result of organisms of noncoliform origin that are not recognized as indicators of fecal pollution.

The **confirmed test** requires that selective and differential media such as eosin–methylene blue (EMB) or Endo agar be streaked from a positive lactose broth tube obtained from the presumptive test. Eosin–methylene blue contains the dye methylene blue, which inhibits the growth of gram-positive organisms. In the presence of an acid environment, EMB forms a complex that precipitates out onto the coliform colonies, producing dark centers and a green metallic sheen. The reaction is characteristic for *Escherichia coli*, the major indicator of fecal pollution. Endo agar is a nutrient medium containing the dye fuchsin, which is present in the decolorized state. In the presence of acid produced by the coliform bacteria, fuchsin forms a dark pink complex that turns the *E. coli* colonies and the surrounding medium pink.

From Experiment 49 of *Microbiology: A Laboratory Manual*, Tenth Edition. James G. Cappuccino, Natalie Sherman.

Standard Qualitative Analysis of Water

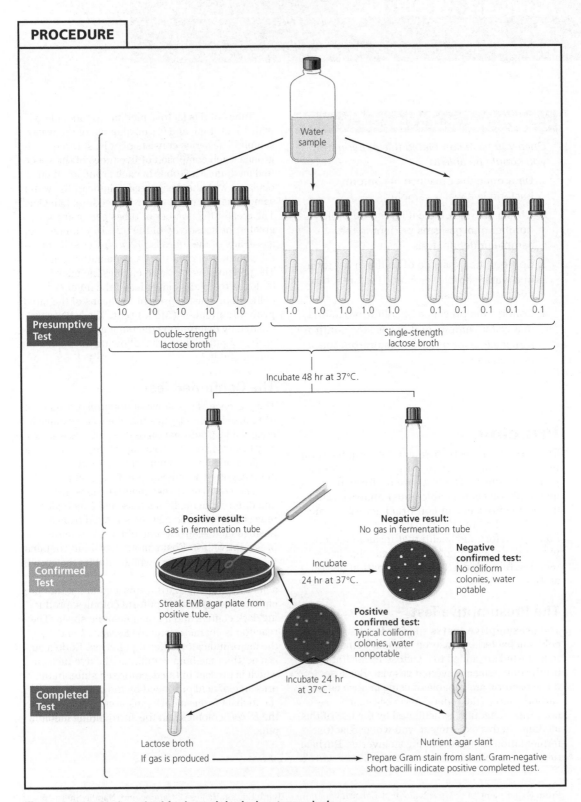

Figure 1 Standard method for bacteriological water analysis

The Completed Test

The **completed test** is the final analysis of the water sample. It is used to examine the coliform colonies that appeared on the EMB or Endo agar plates used in the confirmed test. An isolated colony is picked up from the confirmatory test plate and inoculated into a tube of lactose broth and streaked on a nutrient agar slant to perform a Gram stain. Following inoculation and incubation, tubes showing acid and gas in the lactose broth and presence of gram-negative bacilli on microscopic examination are further confirmation of the presence of *E. coli*, and they are indicative of a positive completed test.

CLINICAL APPLICATION

Testing for Safe Water

The analysis of water used for human consumption and recreational use is routinely performed for safety. Water sources are regularly tested for the presence of *Escherichia coli* to determine the quality and safety of municipal water supplies. Several testing methods are available for this purpose including: most probable numbers (MPN), ATP testing, membrane filtration, and the use of pour plates.

AT THE BENCH

Materials

Cultures

Lab One: Water samples from sewage plant, pond, and tap. Lab Two: One 24-hour-old positive lactose broth culture from each of the three series from the presumptive test. Lab Three: One 24-hour coliform-positive EMB or Endo agar culture from each of the three series of the confirmed test.

Media

Lab One (per designated student group): 15 double-strength lactose fermentation broths (LB2X) and 30 single-strength lactose fermentation broths (LB1X). Lab Two (three each per designated student group): eosin–methylene blue agar plates or Endo agar plates. Lab Three (three each per designated student group): nutrient agar slants and lactose fermentation broths.

Reagents

Lab Three: Crystal violet, Gram's iodine, 95% ethyl alcohol, and safranin.

Equipment

Lab One: Bunsen burner, 45 test tubes, test tube rack, sterile 10-ml pipettes, sterile 1-ml pipettes, sterile 0.1-ml pipettes, mechanical pipetting device, and glassware marking pencil. Lab Two: Bunsen burner, glassware marking pencil, and inoculating loop. Lab Three: Bunsen burner, staining tray, inoculating loop, lens paper, bibulous paper, microscope, and glassware marking pencil.

Procedure Lab One
Presumptive Test

⚠ **Exercise care in handling sewage waste water sample because enteric pathogens may be present.**

1. Set up three separate series consisting of three groups, a total of 15 tubes per series, in a test tube rack; for each tube, label the water source and volume of sample inoculated as illustrated.

Series 1: Sewage water	5 tubes of LB2X-10 ml 5 tubes of LB1X-1 ml 5 tubes of LB1X-0.1 ml
Series 2: Pond water	5 tubes of LB2X-10 ml 5 tubes of LB1X-1 ml 5 tubes of LB1X-0.1 ml
Series 3: Tap water	5 tubes of LB2X-10 ml 5 tubes of LB1X-1 ml 5 tubes of LB1X-0.1 ml

2. Mix sewage plant water sample by shaking thoroughly.
3. Flame bottle and then, using a 10-ml pipette, transfer 10-ml aliquots of water sample to the five tubes labeled LB2X-10 ml.
4. Flame bottle and then, using a 1-ml pipette, transfer 1-ml aliquots of water sample to the five tubes labeled LB1X-1 ml.
5. Flame bottle and then, using a 0.1-ml pipette, transfer 0.1-ml aliquots of water sample to the five tubes labeled LB1X-0.1 ml.

(a)   (b)   (c)   (d)   (e)

Figure 2 Possible MPN presumptive test results. **(a)** Uninoculated control tube, **(b, c)** inoculated tubes with no change, **(d)** inoculated tube with acid production only, and **(e)** inoculated tube with acid and gas production—the only positive result of the five tubes.

6. Repeat Steps 2 through 5 for the tap and pond water samples.

7. Incubate all tubes for 48 hours at 37°C.

Procedure Lab Two

Presumptive Test

1. Examine the tubes from your presumptive test after 24 and 48 hours of incubation. Your results are positive if the Durham tube fills 10% or more with gas in 24 hours, doubtful if gas develops in the tube after 48 hours, and negative if there is no gas in the tube after 48 hours. Refer to **Figure 2** for a summary of possible MPN presumptive test results. **Figure 3** shows actual results from an MPN presumptive test for a water sample. Record your results in the Lab Report.

2. Determine the MPN using Table 1, and record your results in the Lab Report.

Confirmed Test

1. Label the covers of the three EMB plates or the three Endo agar plates with the source of the water sample (sewage, pond, and tap).

2. Using a positive 24-hour lactose broth culture from the sewage water series from the presumptive test, streak the surface of one EMB or one Endo agar plate to obtain discrete colonies.

3. Repeat Step 2 using the positive lactose broth cultures from the pond and tap water series from the presumptive test to inoculate the remaining plates.

(a) Positive results (acid and gas) in five 10-ml tubes

(b) Positive results (acid and gas) in five 1-ml tubes

(c) Negative results (acid only) in five 0.1-ml tubes

Figure 3 MPN presumptive test results for a water sample. The results of this test (5 positive, 5 positive, and 5 negative) indicate 240 coliforms per 100 ml of water (see Table 1). This represents a positive presumptive test for the presence of coliforms in the tested water sample.

4. Incubate all plate cultures in an inverted position for 24 hours at 37°C.

Procedure Lab Three

Confirmed Test

1. Examine all the plates from your confirmed test for the presence or absence of *E. coli* colonies (refer to the description of the confirmed test in the experiment introduction). Record your results in the Lab Report.

2. Based on your results, determine whether each of the samples is potable or nonpotable. The presence of *E. coli* is a positive confirmed test, indicating that the water is nonpotable. The absence of *E. coli* is a negative test, indicating that the water is not contaminated with fecal wastes and is therefore potable. Record your results in the Lab Report.

Completed Test

1. Label each tube of nutrient agar slants and lactose fermentation broths with the source of its water sample.

2. Inoculate one lactose broth and one nutrient agar slant with a positive isolated *E. coli* colony obtained from each of the experimental water samples during the confirmed test.

3. Incubate all tubes for 24 hours at 37°C.

Procedure Lab Four

Completed Test

1. Examine all lactose fermentation broth cultures for the presence or absence of acid and gas. Record your results in the Lab Report.

2. Prepare a Gram stain, using the nutrient agar slant cultures of the organisms that showed a positive result in the lactose fermentation broth.

3. Examine the slides microscopically for the presence of gram-negative short bacilli, which are indicative of *E. coli* and thus nonpotable water. In the Lab Report, record your results for Gram stain reaction and morphology of the cells.

Standard Qualitative Analysis of Water

TABLE 1	The MPN Index per 100 ml for Combinations of Positive and Negative Presumptive Test Results When Five 10-ml, Five 1-ml, and Five 0.1-ml Portions of Sample Are Used

NUMBER OF TUBES WITH POSITIVE RESULTS						NUMBER OF TUBES WITH POSITIVE RESULTS					
FIVE OF 10 ML EACH	FIVE OF 1 ML EACH	FIVE OF 0.1 ML EACH	MPN INDEX PER 100 ML	95% CONFIDENCE LIMITS		FIVE OF 10 ML EACH	FIVE OF 1 ML EACH	FIVE OF 0.1 ML EACH	MPN INDEX PER 100 ML	95% CONFIDENCE LIMITS	
				LOWER	UPPER					LOWER	UPPER
0	0	0	<2	0	6	4	2	1	26	7	67
0	0	1	2	<0.5	7	4	3	0	27	9	78
0	1	0	2	<0.5	7	4	3	1	33	9	78
0	2	0	4	<0.5	11	4	4	0	34	11	93
1	0	0	2	0.1	10	5	0	0	23	7	70
1	0	1	4	0.7	10	5	0	1	31	11	89
1	1	0	4	0.7	12	5	0	2	43	14	100
1	1	1	6	1.8	15	5	1	0	33	10	100
1	2	0	6	1.8	15	5	1	1	46	14	120
2	0	0	5	<0.5	13	5	1	2	63	22	150
2	0	1	7	1	17	5	2	0	49	15	150
2	1	0	7	1	17	5	2	1	70	22	170
2	1	1	9	2	21	5	2	2	94	34	230
2	2	0	9	2	21	5	3	0	79	22	220
2	3	0	12	3	28	5	3	1	110	34	250
3	0	0	8	2	22	5	3	2	140	52	400
3	0	1	11	4	23	5	3	3	180	70	400
3	1	0	11	5	35	5	4	0	130	36	400
3	1	1	14	6	36	5	4	1	170	58	400
3	2	0	14	6	36	5	4	2	220	70	440
3	2	1	17	7	40	5	4	3	280	100	710
3	3	0	17	7	40	5	4	4	350	100	710
4	0	0	13	4	35	5	5	0	240	70	710
4	0	1	17	6	36	5	5	1	350	100	1100
4	1	0	17	6	40	5	5	2	540	150	1700
4	1	1	21	7	42	5	5	3	920	220	2600
4	1	2	26	10	70	5	5	4	1600	400	4600
4	2	0	22	7	50	5	5	5	≥2400	700	---

Sources: pp 9–51, *Standard Methods for the Examination of Water and Wastewater,* 20th Edition (1998). M. J. Taras, A. E. Greenberg, R. D. Hoak, and M. C. Rand, eds. American Public Health Association, Washington, D.C. Copyright 1998, American Public Health Association, and *Bacteriological Analytical Manual (BAM),* 8th Edition, Food and Drug Administration, 1998.

Name: _____

Date: _____ Section: _____

Observations and Results

Presumptive Test

Using Table 1, determine and record the MPN.

Example: If gas appeared in all five tubes labeled LB2X-10, in two of the tubes labeled LB1X-1, and in one labeled LB1X-0.1, the series would be read as 5-2-1. From the MPN table, such a reading would indicate approximately 70 microorganisms per 100 ml of water, with a 95% probability that between 22 and 170 microorganisms are present.

Water Sample	GAS LB2X-10 Tube 1	2	3	4	5	LB1X-1 Tube 1	2	3	4	5	LB1X-0.1 Tube 1	2	3	4	5	Reading	MPN	95% Probability Range
Sewage																		
Pond																		
Tap																		

Confirmed Test

Water Sample	COLIFORMS EMB Plate	Endo Agar Plate	Potable	Nonpotable
Sewage				
Pond				
Tap				

Completed Test

Water Source	Lactose Broth A/G (+) or (−)	GRAM STAIN	POTABILITY	
		Reaction/Morphology	Potable	Nonpotable
Sewage				
Pond				
Tap				

Review Questions

1. What is the rationale for selecting *E. coli* as the indicator of water potability?

2. Why is this procedure qualitative rather than quantitative?

3. Explain why it is of prime importance to analyze water supplies that serve industrialized communities.

4. Account for the presence of microorganisms in natural bodies of water and sewage systems. What is their function? Explain.

Photo Credits

Credits are listed in order of appearance.

Photo 1:   Experiment performed and photographed by L. Brent Selinger, Department of Biological Sciences, University of Lethbridge, Pearson Education

Photo 2: Experiment performed and photographed by L. Brent Selinger, Department of Biological Sciences, University of Lethbridge, Pearson Education

Quantitative Analysis of Water: Membrane Filter Method

LEARNING OBJECTIVES

Once you have completed this experiment, you should be able to

1. Determine the quality of water samples using the membrane filter method.

Principle

Bacteria-tight **membrane filters** capable of retaining microorganisms larger than 0.45 micrometer (μm) are frequently used for analysis of water. These filters offer several advantages over the conventional, multiple-tube method of water analysis: (1) results are available in a shorter period of time, (2) larger volumes of sample can be processed, and (3) because of the high accuracy of this method, the results are readily reproducible. A disadvantage involves the processing of turbid specimens that contain large quantities of suspended materials; particulate matter clogs the pores and inhibits passage of the specific volume of water.

A water sample is passed through a sterile membrane filter that is housed in a special filter apparatus contained in a suction flask. Following filtration, the filter disc that contains the trapped microorganisms is aseptically transferred to a sterile Petri dish containing an absorbent pad saturated with a selective, differential liquid medium. Following incubation, the colonies present on the filter are counted with the aid of a microscope.

This experiment is used to analyze a series of dilutions of water samples collected upstream and downstream from an outlet of a sewage treatment plant. A total count of coliform bacteria determines the potability of the water sources. Also, the types of fecal pollution, if any, are established by means of a fecal coliform count, indicative of human pollution, and a fecal streptococcal count, indicative of pollution from other animal origins. The ratio of the fecal coliforms to fecal streptococci per milliliter of sample is interpreted as follows: Between 2 and 4 indicates human and animal pollution; >4 indicates human pollution; and <0.7 indicates poultry and livestock pollution.

CLINICAL APPLICATION

Rapid Water Analysis

In the late 1950s the membrane filter method was introduced as an alternative to the most probable number method (MPN). Microbiological analysis of water by the membrane filter procedure is a rapid method that isolates discrete bacteria that are able to be accurately counted, whereas the MPN method only allows for the approximate determination of the number of organisms and does not separate species without further testing.

AT THE BENCH

Materials

Cultures

Water samples collected upstream (labeled U) and downstream (labeled D) from an outlet of a sewage treatment plant.

Media

Per designated student group for analysis of one water sample: one 20-ml tube of m-Endo broth, one 20-ml tube of m-FC broth, one 20-ml tube of KF broth, four 90-ml sterile water blanks, and one 300-ml flask of sterile water.

Equipment

Sterile membrane filtration apparatus (i.e., Millipore®; Pall® Gelman; sterile, plastic, disposable membrane filters), 1-liter suction flask, 15 sterile membrane filters and absorbent pads, 15 sterile 50-mm Petri dishes, 12 10-ml pipettes,

From Experiment 50 of *Microbiology: A Laboratory Manual*, Tenth Edition. James G. Cappuccino, Natalie Sherman.

mechanical pipetting device, small beaker of 95% alcohol, membrane forceps, waterproof tape, watertight plastic bags, 44.5°C waterbath, dissecting microscope, and glassware marking pencil.

Procedure Lab One

The following instructions are for analysis of one of the provided water samples using the Millipore system. Different samples may be assigned to individual groups.

> ⚠️ **Use disposable gloves when handling the water samples in this experiment.**

1. Label the four 90-ml water blanks with the source of the water sample and dilution (10^{-1}, 10^{-2}, 10^{-3}, and 10^{-4}).

2. Using 10-ml pipettes, aseptically perform a 10-fold serial dilution of the assigned undiluted water sample, using the four 90-ml water blanks to effect the 10^{-1}, 10^{-2}, 10^{-3}, and 10^{-4} dilutions.

3. Arrange the 15 Petri dishes into three sets of five plates. Label each set as follows:

   a. For total coliform count (TCC) and dilutions (undiluted, 10^{-1}, 10^{-2}, 10^{-3}, and 10^{-4}).

   b. For fecal coliform count (FCC) and dilutions as in Step 3a.

   c. For fecal streptococcal count (FSC) and dilutions as in Step 3a.

Membrane Filter Technique

Refer to **Figure 1** as you read the instructions below.

1. Using sterile forceps dipped in 95% alcohol and flamed, add a sterile absorbent pad to all Petri dishes.

2. With sterile 10-ml pipettes, aseptically add the following:

   a. To each pad in the plates labeled TCC, 2 ml of m-Endo broth.

   b. To each pad in the plates labeled FCC, 2 ml of m-FC broth.

   c. To each pad in the plates labeled FSC, 2 ml of KF broth.

3. Aseptically assemble the sterile paper-wrapped membrane filter unit as follows:

   a. Unwrap and insert the sintered glass filter base into the neck of a 1-liter side-arm suction flask.

   b. With sterile forceps, place a sterile membrane filter disc, grid side up, on the sintered glass platform.

   c. Unwrap and carefully place the funnel section of the apparatus on top of the filter disc. Using the filter clamp, secure the funnel to the filter base.

   d. Attach a rubber hose from the side-arm on the vacuum flask to a vacuum source.

4. Using the highest sample dilution (10^{-4}) and a pipette, place 20 ml of the dilution into the funnel and start the vacuum.

   a. When the entire sample has been filtered, wash the inner surface of the funnel with 20 ml of sterile water.

5. Disconnect the vacuum, unclamp the filter assembly, and with sterile forceps, remove the membrane filter.

6. Place the filter on the medium-saturated pad in the Petri dish labeled TCC, 10^{-4}.

7. Aseptically place a new membrane on the platform, reassemble the filtration apparatus, and repeat Steps 4 through 6 twice, adding the filter discs to the 10^{-4} dilution plates labeled FCC and FSC.

8. Repeat Steps 4a through 7, using 20 ml of the 10^{-3}, 10^{-2}, and 10^{-1} dilutions and the undiluted samples.

9. Incubate the plates in an inverted position as follows:

   a. TCC and FSC plates for 24 hours at 37°C.

   b. FCC plates sealed with waterproof tape and placed in a weighted watertight plastic bag, which is then submerged in a 44.5°C waterbath for 24 hours.

Quantitative Analysis of Water: Membrane Filter Method

PROCEDURE

1 Aseptically place an absorbent pad in a 50-mm petri dish.

2 Saturate the absorbent pad with the specified selective broth medium.

3 Assemble the filter apparatus and insert membrane filter.

Funnel

Membrane filter

Base

Rubber

Fused, porous glass platform

4 Pour test sample into funnel, filter under vacuum, and rinse with sterile water.

Cotton plug

To vacuum

Holding clamp

Sterile flask

5 Aseptically remove filter.

6 Place filter in Petri dish on top of medium-saturated pad and incubate.

Figure 1 Membrane filter technique

Figure 2 Development of colonies on a membrane filter following incubation

Procedure Lab Two

1. Using sterile membrane forceps, remove the filter discs from the Petri dishes and allow to dry on absorbent paper for 1 hour.

2. Using membrane forceps, place each dry filter disc into its Petri dish cover. *Keep the discs within the covers at all times for further observation.*

3. Examine all filter discs under a dissecting microscope. Refer to **Figure 2**, which shows colonies developing on the membrane filter. Perform colony counts on each set of discs as follows:

   a. TCC: Count colonies on m-Endo agar that present a golden metallic sheen (performed on a disc showing 20 to 80 of these colonies).

   b. FCC: Count colonies on m-FC agar that are blue (performed on a disc showing 20 to 60 of these colonies).

   c. FSC: Count colonies on KF agar that are pink to red (performed on a disc showing 20 to 100 of these colonies).

   Dilution samples that show fewer colonies than indicated are designated as TFTC, and those showing a greater number of colonies are designated as TNTC.

4. For each of the three counts, determine the number of fecal organisms present in 100 ml of the water sample, using the following formula:

$$\frac{\text{colony count} \times \text{dilution factor}}{\text{ml of sample used}} \times 100$$

5. Record your results in the Lab Report.

Name: _____

Date: _____   Section: _____

Observations and Results

| | UPSTREAM WATER | | | | | |
| | TCC | | FCC | | FSC | |
Dilution	Count	Cells/100 ml	Count	Cells/100 ml	Count	Cells/100 ml
Undiluted						
10^{-1}						
10^{-2}						
10^{-3}						
10^{-4}						

| | DOWNSTREAM WATER | | | | | |
| | TCC | | FCC | | FSC | |
Dilution	Count	Cells/100 ml	Count	Cells/100 ml	Count	Cells/100 ml
Undiluted						
10^{-1}						
10^{-2}						
10^{-3}						
10^{-4}						

Determine the fecal coliform to fecal streptococcal (FC:FS) ratio. Record your results in the chart below.

| | UPSTREAM WATER | | | DOWNSTREAM WATER | | |
| | Cells/ml* | | | Cells/ml* | | |
Dilution	FCC	FSC	FC:FS Ratio	FCC	FSC	FC:FS Ratio
Undiluted						
1021						
1022						
1023						
1024						

*Cells/ml $= \dfrac{\text{Cells/100 ml}}{100}$

Based on your FC:FS ratio, indicate the type of fecal pollution, if any, in the two samples:

   a. Upstream water sample:

   b. Downstream water sample:

Review Questions

1. What are the advantages of the membrane filter method in the analysis of water samples?

2. What are the disadvantages of the membrane filter method?

3. What is the purpose of determining the FC:FS ratio?

4. Cite some other microbiological applications of the membrane filter technique in environmental studies.

Photo Credit

Credits are listed in order of appearance.

Photo 1:   L. Brent Selinger, Department of Biological Sciences, University of Lethbridge, Pearson Education

Microbiology of Soil

Once you have completed the experiments in this section, you should be able to

1. Understand the characteristics and activities of soil microorganisms.
2. Enumerate soil microorganisms.
3. Demonstrate the ability of some soil microorganisms to produce antibiotics.
4. Demonstrate the use of enrichment cultures for the isolation of specific soil microorganisms.

Introduction

Soil is often thought of as an inert substance by the average layperson. However, contrary to this belief, it serves as a repository for many life forms, including a huge and diverse microbial population. The beneficial activities of these soil inhabitants far outweigh their detrimental effects.

Life on this planet could not be sustained in the absence of microorganisms that inhabit the soil. This flora is essential for degradation of organic matter deposited in the soil, such as dead plant and animal tissues and animal wastes. Hydrolysis of these macromolecules by microbial enzymes supplies and replenishes the soil with basic elemental nutrients. By means of enzymatic transformations, plants assimilate these nutrients into organic compounds essential for their growth and reproduction. In turn, these plants serve as a source of nutrition for animals and man. Thus, many soil microorganisms play a vital role in a number of elemental cycles, such as the nitrogen cycle, the carbon cycle, and the sulfur cycle.

Nitrogen Cycle

The nitrogen cycle is concerned with the enzymatic conversion of complex nitrogenous compounds in the soil and atmosphere into nitrogen compounds that plants are able to use for the synthesis of essential macromolecules such as nucleic acids, amino acids, and proteins. The four distinct phases in this cycle are as follows:

1. **Ammonification:** Soil microorganisms sequentially degrade nitrogenous organic compounds derived from dead plants and animals deposited in the soil. The degraded nitrogenous organic compounds are converted to inorganic nitrogen compounds and then to ammonia.

2. **Nitrification:** In this two-step process, (1) ammonia is oxidized to nitrite ions (NO_2^-) by an aerobic species of *Nitrosomonas*, and then (2) nitrites are converted to nitrate ions (NO_3^-) by another aerobic species, *Nitrobacter*. Nitrates are released into the soil and are assimilated as a nutritional source by plants.

3. **Denitrification:** Nitrates (NO_3^-) that are not used by plants are reduced to gaseous nitrogen ($N_2\uparrow$) and are liberated back into the atmosphere by certain groups of microorganisms.

4. **Nitrogen fixation:** This vital process involves the chemical combination of gaseous nitrogen ($N_2\uparrow$) with other elements to form fixed nitrogen (nitrogen-containing compounds), which are useful for plant growth. The two types of microorganisms involved in this process are free-living and symbiotic. Free-living microorganisms include *Azotobacter*,

From Part 12 of *Microbiology: A Laboratory Manual*, Tenth Edition. James G. Cappuccino, Natalie Sherman.

Figure 1 The nitrogen cycle

Pseudomonas, *Clostridium*, and *Bacillus* as well as some species of yeast. Symbiotic microorganisms, such as *Rhizobium*, grow in tumorlike nodules in the roots of leguminous plants, and use nutrients in the plant sap to fix gaseous nitrogen as ammonia for its subsequent assimilation into plant proteins. Animals then consume the leguminous plants and convert plant protein to animal protein, completing the process. The nitrogen cycle is shown in **Figure 1**.

Carbon Cycle

Carbon dioxide is the major carbon source for the synthesis of organic compounds. The carbon cycle is basically represented by the following two steps:

1. Oxidation of organic compounds to carbon dioxide with the production of energy and heat by heterotrophs.

2. Fixation of carbon dioxide into organic compounds by green plants and some bacteria, the autotrophic soil flora.

Sulfur Cycle

Elemental sulfur and proteins cannot be utilized by plants for growth. They must first undergo enzymatic conversions into inorganic

sulfur-containing compounds. The basic steps in the sulfur cycle are

1. Degradation of proteins into hydrogen sulfide (H_2S) by many heterotrophic microorganisms.

2. Oxidation of H_2S to sulfur (S) by a number of bacterial genera, such as *Beggiatoa*.

3. Oxidation of sulfur to utilizable sulfate (SO_4^{2-}) by several chemoautotrophic genera, such as *Thiobacillus*.

Some soil microorganisms also play a role in the enzymatic transformation of other elements, such as phosphorus, iron, potassium, zinc, manganese, and selenium. These biochemical changes make the minerals available to plants in a soluble form.

Many members of the soil flora, because of their fermentative and synthetic capabilities, play an important role in the synthesis of a variety of industrial products:

1. **Food.** *Penicillium* spp. are used in the production of such cheeses as Camembert, Roquefort, and Brie.

2. **Beverages.** *Saccharomyces* spp. are utilized in the wine, beer, and ale industries.

3. **Vitamins.** *Eremothecium ashbyii* and *Pseudomonas denitrificans*, respectively, synthesize riboflavin (vitamin B_2) and cobalamin (vitamin B_{12}).

4. **Enzymes.** Amylases, pectinases, and proteases are produced by *Aspergillus* spp.

5. **Antibiotics.** *Penicillium* spp. (penicillin), *Streptomyces* spp. (kanamycins and tetracyclines), and *Bacillus* spp. (bacitracin).

6. **Steroids.** *Rhizopus*, *Streptomyces*, and *Curvularia* are microorganisms that are used to carry out specific reactions, bioconversions, to aid in the manufacture of these lipid compounds.

7. **Industrial chemicals.** *Clostridium acetobutylicum* is used in the production of acetone and butanol, and *Aspergillus niger* is used in the synthesis of citric acid.

The major adverse effect of soil organisms is the ability of some species to produce disease in plants and animals. Soil-borne human pathogens include members of the spore-forming bacterial genera *Clostridium* and *Bacillus*, and some fungal genera, such as *Cryptococcus* and *Coccidioides*.

Microbial Populations in Soil: Enumeration

LEARNING OBJECTIVES

Once you have completed this experiment, you should be

1. Familiar with the microbial soil flora.
2. Able to determine the number of bacteria and fungi present in a soil sample.

Principle

Soil contains myriads of microorganisms, including bacteria, fungi, protozoa, algae, and viruses. The most prevalent are bacteria, including the moldlike actinomycetes, and fungi:

Simple bacteria	Predominantly members of the orders Pseudomonadales and Eubacteriales
Actinomycetes (moldlike bacteria)	Predominantly members of the genus *Streptomyces*; characterized by pleomorphism and filamentous structure
Fungi	Predominantly members of the zygomycetes (*Rhizopus*, *Mucor*, and *Absidia*) and deuteromycetes (*Penicillium*, *Aspergillus*, *Alternaria*, *Stemphylium*, and *Cladosporium*)

It is essential to bear in mind that the soil environment differs from one location to another and from one period of time to another. Therefore, factors such as moisture, pH, temperature, gaseous oxygen content, and organic and inorganic composition of soil are crucial in determining the specific microbial flora of a particular sample.

Just as the soil differs, microbiological methods used to analyze soil also vary. A single technique cannot be used to count all the different types of microorganisms present in a given soil sample because no one laboratory cultivation procedure can provide all the physical and nutritional requirements necessary for the growth of a greatly diverse microbial population. In this experiment, only the relative numbers of bacteria, actinomycetes, and fungi are determined. The method used is the serial dilution–agar plate procedure. Different media are employed to support the growth of these three types of microorganisms: glycerol yeast agar for the isolation of actinomycetes, Sabouraud agar for the isolation of fungi, and nutrient agar for the isolation of bacteria. The glycerol yeast agar and Sabouraud agar are supplemented with 10 μg of chlortetracycline (Aureomycin) per milliliter of medium to inhibit the growth of bacteria.

CLINICAL APPLICATION

Soil Testing

The enumeration of organisms in soil helps to establish the level of soil fertility as well as the types and kinds of pathogens it contains. From a clinical view, many bacterial pathogens originate from a soil environment. Current thought is that the ability of *Bacillus* species (for example, *B. subtilis* and *B. anthracis*) and *Mycobacterium* species (for example, *M. tuberculosis*) to survive in a soil environment—one that contains low nutrients, low moisture, and that necessitates sporulation or slow growth—aids the bacteria in infecting human tissues and surviving the immune response.

AT THE BENCH

Materials

Soil

1-g sample of finely pulverized, rich garden soil in a flask containing 99 ml of sterile water; flask labeled 1:100 dilution (10^{-2}).

From Experiment 51 of *Microbiology: A Laboratory Manual*, Tenth Edition. James G. Cappuccino, Natalie Sherman.
Copyright © 2014 by Pearson Education, Inc. All rights reserved.

Media

Per designated student group: four glycerol yeast agar deep tubes, four Sabouraud agar deep tubes, four nutrient agar deep tubes, and two 99-ml flasks of sterile water.

Equipment

Bunsen burner, 12 Petri dishes, Quebec colony counter, mechanical hand counter, sterile 1-ml pipettes, mechanical pipetting device, L-shaped bent glass rod, turntable (optional), 95% alcohol in a 500-ml beaker, and glassware marking pencil.

Procedure Lab One

Refer to **Figure 1** as you read the following instructions.

1. Liquefy the glycerol yeast, Sabouraud, and nutrient agar deep tubes in an autoclave or by boiling. Cool the molten agar tubes and maintain in a waterbath at 45°C.

2. Divide the Petri dishes into three groups of four; using a glassware marking pencil, label the groups as nutrient agar, glycerol yeast extract agar, and Sabouraud agar. Then, label each set of Petri dishes as follows:

   Nutrient agar: 10^{-4}, 10^{-5}, 10^{-6}, and 10^{-7} (to be used for enumeration of bacteria).

   Glycerol yeast extract agar: 10^{-3}, 10^{-4}, 10^{-5}, and 10^{-6} (to be used for enumeration of actinomycetes).

   Sabouraud agar: 10^{-2}, 10^{-3}, 10^{-4}, and 10^{-5} (to be used for enumeration of fungi).

3. With a glassware marking pencil, label the soil sample flask as Flask 1, and label the 99-ml sterile water Flasks 2 and 3.

4. Vigorously shake the provided soil sample dilution of 1:100 (10^{-2}) approximately 30 times, with your elbow resting on the table.

5. With a sterile 1-ml pipette, transfer 1 ml of the provided soil sample dilution to Flask 2 and shake vigorously as before. The final dilution is 1:10,000 (10^{-4}).

6. Using another sterile 1-ml pipette, transfer 1 ml of Dilution 2 to Flask 3 and shake vigorously as before. The final dilution is 1:1,000,000 (10^{-6}).

7. Using sterile 1-ml pipettes and aseptic technique, add the proper amount of each dilution into each Petri dish as indicated in a–c and shown in Figure 1.

   a. **For actinomycetes**—in plates labeled glycerol yeast extract agar:

      Transfer 0.1 ml of Dilution 1 into plate to effect a 10^{-3} dilution.

      Transfer 1 ml of Dilution 2 into plate to effect a 10^{-4} dilution.

      Transfer 0.1 ml of Dilution 2 into plate to effect a 10^{-5} dilution.

      Transfer 1 ml of Dilution 3 into plate to effect a 10^{-6} dilution.

   b. **For molds**—in plates labeled Sabouraud agar:

      Transfer 1 ml of Dilution 1 into plate to effect a 10^{-2} dilution.

      Transfer 0.1 ml of Dilution 1 into plate to effect a 10^{-3} dilution.

      Transfer 1 ml of Dilution 2 into plate to effect a 10^{-4} dilution.

      Transfer 0.1 ml of Dilution 2 into plate to effect a 10^{-5} dilution.

   c. **For bacteria**—in plates labeled nutrient agar:

      Transfer 1 ml of Dilution 2 into plate to effect a 10^{-4} dilution.

      Transfer 0.1 ml of Dilution 2 into plate to effect a 10^{-5} dilution.

      Transfer 1 ml of Dilution 3 into plate to effect a 10^{-6} dilution.

   Transfer 0.1 ml of Dilution 3 into plate to effect a 10^{-7} dilution.

8. Check the temperature of the molten agar medium to be sure that the temperature is 45°C. Remove the tubes from the waterbath and wipe the outside surface dry with a paper towel. Using the pour-plate technique, pour the liquefied agar into the plates and rotate gently to ensure uniform distribution of the cells in the medium.

9. Incubate the plates in an inverted position at 25°C. Perform colony counts on nutrient agar plate cultures in 2 to 3 days and on the remaining agar plate cultures in 4 to 7 days.

Microbial Populations in Soil: Enumeration

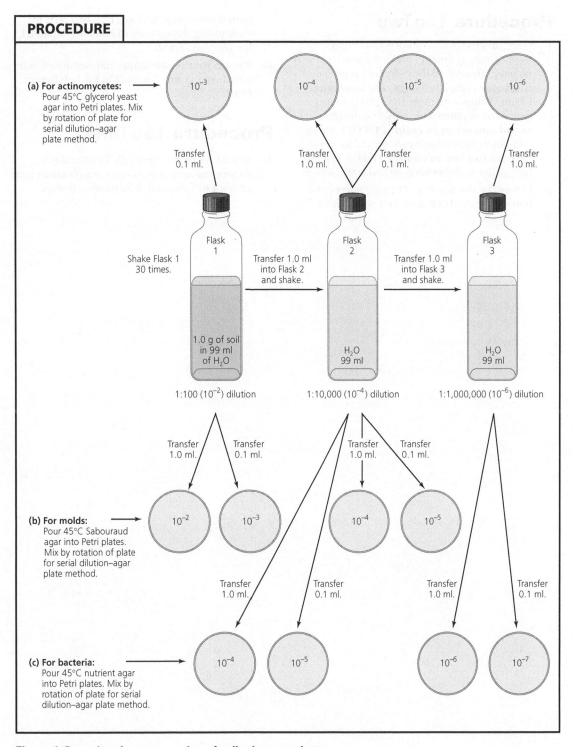

Figure 1 Procedure for enumeration of soil microorganisms

Procedure Lab Two

1. Using an electronic colony counter or a Quebec colony counter and a mechanical hand counter, observe all the colonies on each nutrient agar plate 2 to 3 days after incubation begins. Plates with more than 300 colonies cannot be counted and should be designated as **too numerous to count (TNTC)**; plates with fewer than 30 colonies should be designated as **too few to count (TFTC).** Count only plates with between 30 and 300 colonies.

2. Determine the number of organisms per milliliter of original culture on all plates other than those designated as TFTC or TNTC by multiplying the number of colonies counted by the dilution factor.

3. Record your observations and calculated cell counts per gram of sample in the Lab Report chart.

Procedure Lab Three

1. Repeat Steps 1–3 from Lab Two for the Sabouraud agar and glycerol yeast extract agar plates 4 to 7 days after incubation begins.

Observations and Results

Organism	Dilution	Number of Colonies	Organisms per Gram of Soil
Bacteria	10^{-4}		
	10^{-5}		
	10^{-6}		
	10^{-7}		
Actinomycetes	10^{-3}		
	10^{-4}		
	10^{-5}		
	10^{-6}		
Molds	10^{-2}		
	10^{-3}		
	10^{-4}		
	10^{-5}		

Based on your results, which of the three types of soil organisms was most abundant in your sample? Least abundant?

Review Questions

1. Would you expect to be able to duplicate your results if a soil sample were taken from the same location at a different time of the year? Explain.

2. In the experiment performed, why wasn't the same medium used for enumeration of all three types of soil organisms?

3. Would you expect to be able to isolate an anaerobic organism from any of your cultures? Explain.

4. Explain why most microorganisms are present in the upper layers of the soil.

5. Following the nuclear disaster at Chernobyl, the regional microbial flora was destroyed. What impact did this have on higher forms of plant and animal life in this area?

Isolation of Antibiotic-Producing Microorganisms and Determination of Antimicrobial Spectrum of Isolates

Principle

Soil is the major repository of microorganisms that produce **antibiotics** capable of inhibiting the growth of other microorganisms. Clinically useful antibiotics have been isolated from five groups of soil microorganisms—*Streptomyces*, *Amycolatopsis* (including some species formerly classified as *Streptomyces*), *Bacillus*, *Penicillium*, and *Acremonium*—that represent three microbial types, namely, actinomycetes, true bacteria, and molds.

Although soils from all parts of the world are continually screened in industrial laboratories for the isolation of new antibiotic-producing microorganisms, industrial microbiology is directing its energies toward chemical modification of existing antibiotic substances. This is accomplished by adding or replacing chemical side chains, reorganizing intramolecular bonding, or producing mutant microbial strains capable of excreting a more potent form of the antibiotic. The establishment of chemical congeners has been responsible for the circumvention of antibiotic resistance, minimizing adverse side effects in the host and increasing the effective spectrum of a given antibiotic.

In Part A of this experiment, you will use the **crowded-plate** technique for isolation of antibiotic-producing microorganisms from two soil samples, one of which is seeded with *Streptomyces griseus* to serve as a positive control. Figure 1 illustrates the procedure to be followed. In Part B, isolates exhibiting antibiotic activity will be screened against several different microorganisms to establish their effectiveness.

CLINICAL APPLICATION

Testing New Antibiotics

Soil is the major reservoir housing microorganisms that produce antibiotics, which are used offensively to reduce competition for available nutrients. The most prolific antibiotic producers are within the phylum *Actinobacteria*. The genus *Streptomyces* are the major producers of currently used antibiotics (for example, neomycin, streptomycin, and tetracyclin) along with the genus *Actinomycetes* (for example, erythromycin). Interestingly, hundreds of new antibiotics are isolated annually using procedures such as the crowded plate technique, but most have a limited spectrum and only a few are found to be clinically acceptable.

AT THE BENCH

Materials

Cultures

For Part B: 24-hour Trypticase soy broth cultures of *Escherichia coli*, *Staphylococcus aureus*, *Mycobacterium smegmatis*, and *Pseudomonas aeruginosa*.

Soil Suspensions

For Part A: 1:500 dilution of soil sample suspension (0.1 g of soil per 50 ml of tap water) to serve as an unknown; 1:500 dilution of soil sample

From Experiment 52 of *Microbiology: A Laboratory Manual*, Tenth Edition. James G. Cappuccino, Natalie Sherman. Copyright © 2014 by Pearson Education, Inc. All rights reserved.

Isolation of Antibiotic-Producing Microorganisms and Determination of Antimicrobial Spectrum of Isolates

PROCEDURE

Figure 1 Crowded-plate technique for isololation of antibiotic-producing microorganisms

seeded with *S. griseus* (0.1 g of soil per 50 ml of tap water) to serve as a positive control.

Media

Per designated student group: Part A: Six 15-ml Trypticase soy agar deep tubes, and two Trypticase soy agar slants. Part B: Two Trypticase soy agar plates.

Equipment

Part A: 500-ml beaker, test tubes, test tube rack, sterile Petri dishes, inoculating needle, hot plate, thermometer, 1-ml and 5-ml pipettes, mechanical pipetting device, and magnifying hand lens.
Part B: Bunsen burner, inoculating loop, and glassware marking pencil.

PART A Isolation of Antibiotic-Producing Microorganisms

Procedure Lab One

1. Label two sets of three sterile Petri dishes with the types of soil samples being used and dilutions (1:1000, 1:2000, and 1:4000).

2. Place six Trypticase soy agar deep tubes into a beaker of water and bring to 100°C on a hot plate. Once agar is liquefied, add cool water to the waterbath. Cool to 45°C, checking the temperature with a thermometer.

3. Prepare a serial dilution of the unknown and positive control 1:500 soil samples as follows (refer to **Figure 1**):

a. Label three test tubes 1, 2, and 3. With a pipette, add 5 ml of tap water to each tube.

b. Shake the provided 1:500 soil sample thoroughly for 5 minutes to effect a uniform soil-water suspension.

c. Using a 5-ml pipette, transfer 5 ml from the 1:500 dilution to Tube 1 and mix. The final dilution is 1:1000.

d. Using another pipette, transfer 5 ml from Tube 1 to Tube 2 and mix. The final dilution is 1:2000.

e. Using another pipette, transfer 5 ml from Tube 2 to Tube 3 and mix. The final dilution is 1:4000.

f. Using separate 1-ml pipettes, transfer 1 ml of the 1:1000, 1:2000, and 1:4000 dilutions to their appropriately labeled Petri dishes.

g. Pour one tube of molten Trypticase soy agar, cooled to 45°C, into each plate and mix by gentle rotation.

h. Allow all plates to solidify.

4. Incubate all plates in an inverted position for 2 to 4 days at 25°C.

Procedure Lab Two

1. Examine all crowded-plate dilutions for colonies exhibiting zones of growth inhibition. Use a hand magnifying lens if necessary. Record in the Lab Report the number of colonies showing zones of inhibition.

2. Aseptically isolate one colony showing a zone of growth inhibition from each soil culture with an inoculating needle and streak onto Trypticase soy agar slants labeled with the soil sample from which the isolate was obtained.

3. Incubate the slants for 2 to 4 days at 25°C. These will serve as stock cultures of antibiotic-producing isolates to be used in Part B.

PART B Determination of Antimicrobial Spectrum of Isolates

Procedure Lab One

1. Label the Trypticase soy agar plates with the soil sample source of the isolate.

2. Using aseptic technique, make a single-line streak inoculation of each isolate on the surface of an agar plate so as to divide the plate in half as shown:

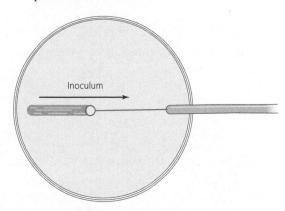

3. Incubate the plates in an inverted position for 3 to 5 days at 25°C.

Procedure Lab Two

1. Following incubation, on the bottom of each plate draw four lines perpendicular to the growth of the antibiotic-producing isolate as shown:

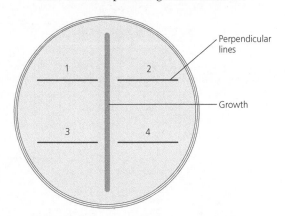

2. Aseptically make a single-line streak inoculation of each of the four test cultures following the inoculation template on each plate. Start close to, but not touching, the growth of the antibiotic-producing isolate and streak toward the edge of the plate.

3. Incubate the plates in an inverted position for 24 hours at 37°C.

Procedure Lab Three

1. Examine all plates for inhibition of test organisms, and record your observations in the Lab Report.

Observations and Results

PART A: Isolation of Antibiotic-Producing Microorganisms

| Soil Sample | NUMBER OF COLONIES SHOWING INHIBITION ZONE | | |
| | Dilutions | | |
	1:1000	1:2000	1:4000
Unknown			
Positive control			

PART B: Determination of Antimicrobial Spectrum of Isolates

1. Draw a representation of the observed antibiotic activity against the test organisms.

Antibiotic-Producing Isolate 1

Antibiotic-Producing Isolate 2

2. Based on your observations, record in the chart the presence (+) or absence (−) of antibiotic activity against each of the test organisms and the spectrum of antimicrobial activity (broad or narrow).

| Soil Sample | TEST ORGANISMS | | | | |
	E. coli Gram-Negative	*S. aureus* Gram-Positive	*P. aeruginosa* Gram-Negative	*M. smegmatis* Acid-Fast	Spectrum
Unknown					
Positive control					

Review Questions

1. Why is it frequently advantageous to modify antibiotics in industrial laboratories?

2. Is the ability to produce antibiotics limited only to bacterial species? Explain.

3. Do you feel that sufficient test organisms were used in Part B to determine fully the spectrum of activity of each isolated antibiotic? Explain.

Isolation of *Pseudomonas* Species by Means of the Enrichment Culture Technique

LEARNING OBJECTIVES

Once you have completed this experiment, you should

1. Understand the enrichment culture technique for the isolation of a specific microbial cell type.

Principle

The enrichment culture technique is used for the isolation of a specific type of microorganism from an environment that is replete with different types of microbes. In such an environment, the desired organism may be present only in very small numbers because of the competitive activities of this diverse microbial population. Under these circumstances, the use of conventional enriched media is not suitable for the selection of a specific cell type. These special-purpose media are supplemented with a variety of enriching nutrients capable of supporting the growth of many organisms rather than a single cell type in the test sample. Enrichment broths, on the other hand, are designed to contain a limited number of specific substrates that will preferentially promote the growth of the desired microorganisms.

The enrichment culture technique employs such a specifically designed enrichment broth for the initial inoculation of the test sample. Once growth occurs in the primary culture, it is sequentially transferred into a fresh medium of the same composition until the desired microorganisms are predominant in the culture. These organisms are capable of exponential growth because of their ability to adapt to the medium and to enzymatically use the incorporated substrate(s) as an energy source. Most of the competitors, however, are incapable of utilizing the substrate(s) and therefore remain in the lag phase of the growth curve. In some instances the organisms to be isolated do not grow more rapidly than their competitors. Instead, they produce a growth inhibitor that greatly suppresses the growth of the competing population. After the serial transfer through the broth medium, the culture is streaked on an agar plate of the same composition as the enrichment broth for the isolation and subsequent identification of the discrete colonies.

The use of the enrichment culture technique has a wide range of applications in clinical, industrial, and environmental microbiology. Enrichment methods may be used to isolate and cultivate specific soil microorganisms for the production of industrial products such as steroids, enzymes, and vitamins. Likewise, a beneficial environmental application may involve the isolation by enrichment of petroleum-utilizing microorganisms such as *Pseudomonas* that would be capable of degrading environmentally destructive oil spills in waterways.

In this experimental procedure, a compost or a rich garden soil sample will be used to isolate *Pseudomonas* species by means of the enrichment culture procedure. Members of the genus *Pseudomonas* can utilize mandelic acid aerobically as their sole carbon and energy source. Therefore, this compound is the most important factor in the enrichment broth, which also contains a number of inorganic salts. The pseudomonads are gram-negative, motile organisms that generally produce a diffusible yellow-green pigment. In addition, they commonly reduce nitrates (NO_3^-) and produce an alkaline or proteolytic reaction in litmus milk. The schema for the experimental procedure to be followed is illustrated in **Figure 1**.

From Experiment 53 of *Microbiology: A Laboratory Manual*, Tenth Edition. James G. Cappuccino, Natalie Sherman.

Isolation of *Pseudomonas* Species by Means of the Enrichment Culture Technique

Figure 1 Enrichment culture procedure schema

AT THE BENCH

Materials

Cultures

Rich garden soil or compost sample.

Media

Per designated student group: Two Erlenmeyer flasks containing 20 ml of basal salts broth supplemented with 2 ml of 2.5% mandelic acid, two agar plates of the same composition as the broth, one Trypticase nitrate broth, one litmus milk, and one Trypticase soy agar slant.

Reagents

Crystal violet, Gram's iodine, 95% ethanol, safranin, Solution A (sulfanilic acid), Solution B (alpha-naphthylamine), and zinc powder. *Note: Solutions A and B are not Barritt's reagent.*

Equipment

Sterile 10-ml, 5-ml, and 1-ml pipettes, mechanical pipetting device, microspatula, Bunsen burner, staining tray, glass slides, lens paper, bibulous paper, inoculating loop, and glassware marking pencil.

Procedure Lab One

Primary Broth Culture Preparation

1. Inoculate an appropriately labeled Erlenmeyer flask containing the enrichment broth by adding an amount of the soil sample equivalent to the size of a pea with a microspatula. Gently swirl the flask to mix the culture.

2. Incubate the primary broth culture for 24 hours at 30°C.

Procedure Lab Two

Secondary Broth Culture Preparation

1. Examine the primary culture for presence of growth. If growth is not present, return the flask to the incubator for an additional 24 hours.

2. If growth is present, aseptically transfer 1 ml of the primary culture to an appropriately labeled Erlenmeyer flask containing fresh enrichment medium. Swirl the flask.

3. Incubate the secondary broth culture for 24 hours at 30°C.

4. Prepare and examine a Gram-stained smear from the primary culture. Record your observations of cellular morphology and Gram reaction in the Lab Report.

5. Refrigerate the primary broth culture.

Procedure Lab Three

Primary Agar Plate Preparation

1. If growth is present in the secondary broth culture, aseptically perform a four-way streak inoculation on the appropriately labeled agar plate of the enrichment medium.

2. Incubate the agar plate culture in an inverted position for 24 hours at 30°C.

3. Prepare and examine a Gram-stained smear of the secondary broth culture. Record your observations of cellular morphology and Gram reaction in the Lab Report.

4. Refrigerate the secondary broth culture.

Procedure Lab Four

Secondary Agar Plate Preparation

1. Examine the primary plate culture for the presence of discrete colonies. Record your observations of the cultural characteristics of these colonies in the Lab Report. Using a discrete colony:

   a. Aseptically prepare and examine a Gram-stained smear. Record your observations of cellular morphology and Gram reaction in the Lab Report.

   b. Aseptically perform a four-way streak inoculation on an appropriately labeled agar plate of the enrichment medium.

2. Incubate the secondary agar plate culture in an inverted position for 24 hours at 30°C.

3. Refrigerate the primary agar plate culture.

Procedure Lab Five

Pure Culture Isolation

1. Examine the secondary agar plate culture. Record your observations of the cultural characteristics of these colonies in the Lab Report. If the cultural characteristics of discrete colonies appear to be similar:

   a. Prepare and examine a Gram-stained smear from a discrete colony. Record your observations of cellular morphology and Gram reaction in the Lab Report.

   b. Pick a discrete colony and aseptically inoculate a Trypticase soy agar slant by means of a streak inoculation.

2. Incubate the agar slant culture for 24 to 48 hours at 30°C.

3. Refrigerate the secondary agar plate culture.

Procedure Lab Six

Genus Identification of Isolate

1. Prepare and examine a Gram-stained smear from the Trypticase agar slant culture. Record your observations of cellular morphology and Gram reaction in the Lab Report.

2. Using the Trypticase agar slant culture, aseptically inoculate the appropriately labeled tubes of Trypticase nitrate broth and litmus milk by means of a loop inoculation.

3. Incubate the litmus milk and Trypticase nitrate broth cultures for 24 to 48 hours at 30°C.

Procedure Lab Seven

1. Observe the litmus milk culture. Determine the type of reaction that has taken place and record in the Lab Report.

2. Perform the nitrate reduction test on the Trypticase nitrate broth culture. Record your results in the Lab Report.

Observations and Results

Gram Reactions and Colony Characteristics

Culture	Gram Stain; Cellular Morphology	Cultural Characteristics
Primary broth culture		
Secondary broth culture		
Primary agar plate culture		
Secondary agar plate culture		
Trypticase soy agar slant culture		

Litmus Milk Reaction

Record the type of reaction below.

Nitrate Reduction Test

Record whether or not the organism was capable of nitrate reduction ($+$ or $-$) below.

Review Questions

1. A child is hospitalized with a severe gastroenteritis that is suspected to be food poisoning caused by a *Salmonella* species. Explain why the hospital laboratory supervisor uses an enrichment broth technique rather than selective media to confirm her suspicions.

2. A patient is afflicted with a disease that generates a large volume of gelatinous abdominal ascites. Drainage by surgical means is not successful. The use of a microbial enzyme capable of degrading this viscous ascites is suggested. Explain how you would go about isolating an organism that is enzymatically competent to act on this unusual substrate.

Bacterial Genetics

LEARNING OBJECTIVES

Once you have completed the experiments in this section, you should be able to demonstrate the applicability of bacterial test systems in genetic-related studies. The procedures include

1. Enzyme induction.
2. Transfer of genetic material by means of conjugation.
3. Isolation of a streptomycin-resistant mutant.
4. Detection of potential chemical carcinogens.

Introduction

In recent years, bacteria have proved to be essential organisms in research into the structure and function of DNA, the universal genetic material. Their use is predicated on the following:

1. Their haploid genetic state, which allows the phenotypic, observable expression of a genetic trait in the presence of a single mutant gene.

2. Their rapid rate of growth, which permits observation of transmission of a trait through many generations.

3. The availability of large test populations, which allows isolation of spontaneous mutants and their induction by chemical and physical mutagenic agents.

4. Their low cost of maintenance and propagation, which make it possible to perform a large number of experimental procedures.

In the following experiments, bacterial test systems are used to demonstrate enzyme induction, screening for chemical carcinogens, and the genetic phenomena of mutation and genetic transfer. The last two mechanisms introduce genetic variability, which is essential for evolutionary survival in asexually reproducing bacterial populations.

Point mutations are permanent, sudden qualitative alterations in genetic material that arise as a result of the addition, deletion, or substitution of one or more bases in the region of a single gene. As a result, one or more amino acid substitutions occur during translation, and a protein that may be inactive, reduced in activity, or entirely different is synthesized. **Spontaneous mutations** are the result of the chemical and physical components in the organism's natural environment. The rate at which they occur is extremely low in all organisms. For example, in *Escherichia coli*, the spontaneous mutation rate at a single locus (specific site on the DNA) is estimated to be about 1×10^{-7}, and the possibility of a mutation at any locus in the genome is approximately 1×10^{-4}. **Induced mutations** are genetic changes resulting from the organism's exposure to an artificial physical or chemical mutagen, that is, an agent capable of inducing a mutation. The resultant mutations are of the same type that occur spontaneously;

however, their rate is increased, and in some cases dramatically so.

Transfer of genetic material and its subsequent incorporation into the bacterial genome is also a source of genetic variation in some bacteria. This transfer may occur by means of the following:

1. **Conjugation:** A mating process between "sexually" differentiated bacterial strains that allows unidirectional transfer of genetic material.

2. **Transduction:** A bacteriophage-mediated transfer of genetic material from one cell to another.

3. **Transformation:** A genetic alteration in a cell, resulting from the introduction of free DNA from the environment across the cell membrane.

Enzyme Induction

Principle

Although bacteria possess a single chromosome, each cell is capable of synthesizing hundreds of different enzymes. Studies have shown that these enzymes are not present within the cells in equal concentrations. Some enzymes, called **constitutive enzymes,** are synthesized at a constant rate regardless of conditions in the cell's environment. Synthesis of other enzymes, called **adaptive enzymes,** occurs only when necessary, and it is subject to regulatory mechanisms that are dependent on the environment. One such mechanism, **induction,** requires the presence of a substrate, the inducer, in the environment to initiate synthesis of its specific enzyme, called an **inducible enzyme.** An extensively studied inducible enzyme in *E. coli* is **β-galactosidase,** which acts on the disaccharide lactose to yield the monosaccharides glucose and galactose. The gene for β-galactosidase is a member of a cluster of genes, called an **operon,** that is involved in the metabolism of lactose. The member genes of the lactose *(lac)* operon function as a unit, all being transcribed only when the inducer, lactose, is present in the surrounding medium. See **Figure 1**.

To illustrate β-galactosidase induction, two test strains of *E. coli* will be used: a prototrophic (wild type) strain (lactose-positive) and an auxotrophic (mutant) strain (lactose-negative), which carries a mutation in the gene for β-galactosidase as well as a mutation in the lactose operon regulatory gene. Both test strains will be grown in the following media:

1. Inorganic synthetic medium lacking an organic carbon and energy source that is required by the heterotrophic *E. coli.*
2. Inorganic synthetic medium plus glucose, which can be utilized by both strains as a carbon and energy source.
3. Inorganic synthetic medium plus lactose, which can be utilized only by the prototrophic strain.

Orthonitrophenyl-β-D-galactoside (ONPG), a colorless analog of lactose, can serve as the substrate for the induction of β-galactosidase synthesis. As the inducer, it is hydrolyzed to galactose and a yellow nitrophenolate ion. Following a short incubation period, growth in all the cultures will be determined by spectrophotometry. Induction of β-galactosidase synthesis and activity will be indicated by the appearance of a yellow color in the medium following addition of ONPG, which occurs only in the presence of the nitrophenolate ion. Absence of this macroscopically visible color change indicates that enzyme induction in the lactose-negative strain did not occur.

CLINICAL APPLICATION

Enzyme Inducers and Cancer

Inducer molecules can include hormones produced by the body as well as toxins and drugs. Both enzyme induction and inhibition are used by the body to control a number of interactions that play a role in many cellular reactions from digestion to cell death. One important type of current research is the deliberate induction of human enzymes that protect against environmental carcinogens. Such intervention may provide advance protection against cell damage.

(a) Lactose operon.

Genes of lactose operon

☐ Regulator gene (*Lac I*):
produces repressor protein.

☐ Promoter gene:
binding site for RNA polymerase

☐ Operator gene:
binding site for repressor protein

☐ Structural genes:
Lac Z: codes for β-galactosidase
Lac Y: codes for galactoside permease
Lac A: codes for galactoside transacetylase

(b) **No lactose present.** The regulator gene (*Lac I*) expresses the repressor protein. Because no lactose is present, the repressor protein binds to the operator gene, blocking the RNA polymerase and stopping mRNA trascription of structural genes.

(c) **Lactose present.** Lactose acts as an inducer, binding to the repressor protein and inactivating it. The repressor protein cannot bind to the operator gene; therefore mRNA transcription of the structural genes can proceed.

Figure 1 Enzyme induction: The mechanism of operation of the lactose operon

AT THE BENCH

Materials

Cultures

25-ml inorganic synthetic broth suspensions of 12-hour nutrient agar cultures of a lactose-positive *E. coli* strain (ATCC e 23725) and a lactose-negative *E. coli* strain (ATCC e 23735) adjusted to an absorbance of 0.1 at 600 nm.

Media

Per designated student group: dropper bottles of sterile 10% glucose, 10% lactose, and water.

Reagents

Dropper bottles of toluene and orthonitrophenyl-β-D-galactoside (ONPG).

Equipment

1-ml and 5-ml sterile pipettes, mechanical pipetting device, six sterile 13- × 100-mm test tubes, test tube racks, six sterile 25-ml Erlenmeyer flasks, Bausch & Lomb Spectronic 20 spectro-photometer, shaking waterbath incubator, and glassware marking pencil.

Procedure

1. Label three sterile test tubes and three sterile 25-ml Erlenmeyer flasks as "Lac⁺" (lactose-positive) and the name of the substrate to be

added (glucose, lactose, or water). Similarly label three sterile tubes and flasks "Lac⁻" (lactose-negative) for each test organism.

2. Using sterile 5-ml pipettes, aseptically transfer 5 ml of the Lac⁺ and Lac⁻ inorganic synthetic broth cultures to their respectively labeled test tubes.

3. Using a sterile 1-ml pipette, aseptically add 0.5 ml of the glucose and lactose solutions and 0.5 ml of sterile distilled water to the appropriately labeled tubes.

4. Determine the absorbance of all cultures at a wavelength of 600 nm. Record your results in the Lab Report.

5. Aseptically transfer each culture to its appropriately labeled flask. *(Note: If side-arm flasks are available, additions and absorbance readings may be made directly.)*

6. Incubate all flasks for 2 hours in a shaking waterbath at 37°C and 100 strokes per minute.

7. Following incubation, transfer all cultures back to their appropriately labeled test tubes.

8. Determine and record in the Lab Report the absorbance for each culture at a wavelength of 600 nm. Based on your observations, indicate whether growth has occured in each of the cultures.

9. To each culture, add 5 drops of toluene and shake vigorously (toluene ruptures the cells, releasing intact enzymes).

10. To each culture, add 5 drops of ONPG solution.

11. Incubate all cultures for 40 minutes at 37°C.

12. Following the addition of ONPG, observe the cultures for the presence of yellow coloration indicative of β-galactosidase synthesis and activity. In the Lab Report, record the colors of your cultures and the presence (+) or absence (−) of the β-galactosidase activity.

Observations and Results

Cultures	ABSORBANCE AT 600 nm		Growth (+) or (−)	Color of Culture with ONPG	β-Galactosidase (+) or (−)
	Prior to Incubation	Following Incubation			
Lac⁺ E. coli Glucose					
Lactose					
Water					
Lac⁻ E. coli Glucose					
Lactose					
Water					

Explain the absence of growth in some of the cultures.

Review Questions

1. Distinguish between constitutive enzymes and inducible enzymes.

2. Explain what is meant by an operon.

3. Explain the purpose of the ONPG in the procedure.

4. Compare and contrast the methods for DNA transfer in microbial cells.

5. How can you explain why *Staphylococcus aureus*, which was initially sensitive to penicillin, is now resistant to this antibiotic?

Principle

Genetic variability is essential for the evolutionary success of all organisms. In diploid eukaryotes, the processes of **crossing over** (exchange of genetic material between homologous chromosomes) and **meiosis** contribute to this variability. In haploid, asexually reproducing prokaryotic organisms, genetic recombination may occur by **conjugation, transduction,** and **transformation.** In this experiment, only the process of conjugation is considered.

Conjugation is a mating process during which a unidirectional transfer of genetic material occurs at physical contact between two "sexually" differentiated cell types. This differentiation, or existence of different mating strains in some bacteria, is determined by the presence of a **fertility factor,** or **F factor,** within the cell. Cells that lack the F factor are recipients (females) of the genetic material during conjugation and are designated as **F⁻**. Cells possessing the F factor have the ability to act as genetic donors (males) during mating. If this F factor is extrachromosomal (a **plasmid** or **episome**), the cells are designated as **F⁺**; most commonly only the F factor is transferred during conjugation. If this factor becomes incorporated into the bacterial chromosome, there is a transfer of chromosomal genes, although generally not involving the entire chromosome or the F factor. The resulting cells are designated **Hfr,** for **high-frequency recombinants.**

In this experiment, you will prepare a mixed culture representing a cross between an Hfr prototrophic (wild type) strain of *E. coli* that is streptomycin-sensitive and an F⁻ auxotrophic (mutant) *E. coli* strain that requires threonine (thr), leucine (leu), and thiamine (thi) and is streptomycin-resistant (Str-r). Following a short incubation period, isolation of only the threonine and leucine recombinants will be performed by plating the mixed culture on a minimal medium containing streptomycin and thiamine. The streptomycin is incorporated into the medium to inhibit the growth of the wild-type, streptomycin-sensitive (Str-s) parental Hfr cells. The thiamine is required as an essential growth factor for the thiamine-negative (thi⁻) recombinant cells. Because of its distant location on the chromosome, this marker will not be transferred during the short mating period. A genetic map denotes the time in minutes required for the transfer of a marker (operon) from the donor cell to the recipient cell. **Figure 1** is the genetic map showing the site of origin of transfer and location of relevant markers in this experiment.

Figure 1 Genetic map of *Escherichia coli*

From Experiment 55 of *Microbiology: A Laboratory Manual*, Tenth Edition. James G. Cappuccino, Natalie Sherman.
Copyright © 2014 by Pearson Education, Inc. All rights reserved.

CLINICAL APPLICATION

Antibiotic Resistance

Conjugation is a major cause of the spread of antibiotic resistance and represents a serious problem in antibiotic therapy of immunosuppressed patients. Bacteria that carry several resistant genes are called multi-drug-resistant superbugs. The indiscriminate use of antibiotics both within the health care profession and the illegal sale of drugs without prescriptions are mainly responsible for the increased spread of antibiotic resistance.

AT THE BENCH

Materials

Cultures

12-hour nutrient broth cultures of F^- *E. coli* strain thr$^-$, leu$^-$, thi$^-$, and Str-r (ATCC e 23724); and Hfr *E. coli* strain Str-s (ATCC e 23740).

Media

Per designated student group: three plates of minimal medium plus streptomycin and thiamine.

Equipment

Bunsen burner, beaker with 95% ethyl alcohol, L-shaped bent glass rod, 1-ml sterile pipettes, mechanical pipetting device, sterile 13- × 100-mm test tube, waterbath shaker, and glassware marking pencil.

Procedure Lab One

1. With separate sterile 1-ml pipettes, aseptically transfer 1 ml of the F^- *E. coli* culture and 0.3 ml of the Hfr *E. coli* culture into the sterile 13 × 100-mm test tube.

2. Mix by gently rotating the culture between the palms of your hands.

3. Incubate the culture for 30 minutes at 37°C in a waterbath shaker at the lowest speed setting.

4. Appropriately label two minimal plus streptomycin and thiamine agar plates, to be used for the control plates in Step 5.

5. To prepare control plates of the parental Hfr and F^- *E. coli* strains, aseptically add 0.1 ml of each *E. coli* strain to its appropriately labeled agar plate.

6. Use the spread-plate technique as shown in **Figure 2** and as instructed below.

    a. Dip the bent glass rod into the beaker of 95% ethyl alcohol.

    b. Sterilize the glass rod by flaming with a Bunsen burner.

    c. Remove the glass rod from the Bunsen burner, allow flame to extinguish, and cool the glass rod.

    d. Spread the inoculum over the agar surface by rotating the plate.

7. Following incubation of the mixed culture, vigorously agitate it to terminate the genetic transfer.

8. Appropriately label a minimal plus streptomycin and thiamine plate. Aseptically add 0.1 ml of the mixed culture. Spread the inoculum over the entire surface with a sterile glass rod.

9. Incubate all plates in an inverted position for 48 hours at 37°C.

Procedure Lab Two

1. Observe all plates for growth of colonies.

2. Record your observations in the Lab Report.

Bacterial Conjugation

PROCEDURE

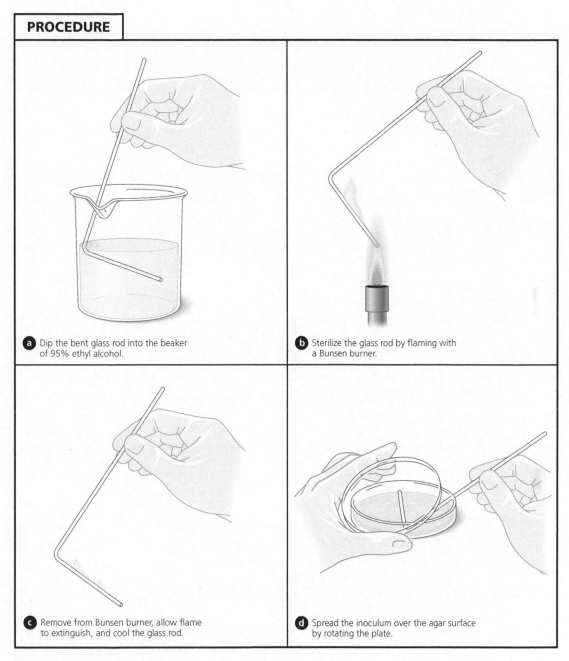

a Dip the bent glass rod into the beaker of 95% ethyl alcohol.

b Sterilize the glass rod by flaming with a Bunsen burner.

c Remove from Bunsen burner, allow flame to extinguish, and cool the glass rod.

d Spread the inoculum over the agar surface by rotating the plate.

Figure 2 **Spread-plate technique**

Observations and Results

1. Observe all plates for the presence (+) or absence (−) of colonies. Record your results in the chart.

	Hfr *E. coli* Plate	F⁻ *E. coli* Plate	Mixed-Culture Plate
Growth (+) or (−)			

2. Do you expect any growth to be present on the two parental *E. coli* minimal agar plates? Explain.

3. Did genetic recombination occur? Explain how your observations support your answer.

Review Questions

1. Explain how genetic variations may be introduced in eukaryotic and prokaryotic cells.

2. Explain the significance of the F factor.

3. Distinguish between F^+ and Hfr bacterial strains.

4. Explain the importance of the streptomycin marker in the parental *E. coli* strains.

Isolation of a Streptomycin-Resistant Mutant

Principle

Mutation, a change in the base sequence of a single gene, although infrequent, is one of the sources of genetic variability in cells. In some instances, these changes enable the cell to survive in an otherwise deleterious environment. An example of such a genetic adaptation is the development of **antibiotic resistance** in a small population of microorganisms prior to the advent and large-scale use of these agents. This microbial characteristic of antibiotic resistance is of major clinical importance because the number of drug-resistant microbial strains continues to increase. This occurs due to their extensive use and frequent misuse, which over the years have selected for the drug-resistant strains by their microbicidal effects on the sensitive cell forms. These agents select for the resistant mutant and do not act as inducers of the mutation.

In a drug-resistant organism, the mutated gene enables the cell to circumvent the antimicrobial effect of the drug by a variety of mechanisms, including the following:

1. The production of an enzyme that alters the chemical structure of the antibiotic, as in penicillin resistance.

2. A change in the selective permeability of the cell membrane, as in streptomycin resistance.

3. A decrease in the sensitivity of the organism's enzymes to inhibiting mechanisms, as in the resistance to streptomycin, which interferes with the translation process at the ribosomes.

4. An overproduction of a natural substrate (metabolite) to compete effectively with the drug (antimetabolite), as in the resistance to sulfonamides, which produce their antimicrobial effect by competitive inhibition.

The following procedure is designed to allow you to isolate a streptomycin-resistant mutant from a prototrophic (wild type, streptomycin-sensitive) *Escherichia coli* culture by means of the **gradient-plate technique.** This requires preparation of a double-layered agar plate as illustrated in **Figure 1**. The lower, slanted agar-medium layer lacks streptomycin. When poured over the lower slanted layer, the molten agar medium containing the antibiotic will produce a streptomycin concentration gradient in the surface layer. Following a spread-plate inoculation of the prototrophic test

LSC = Low streptomycin concentration
HSC = High streptomycin concentration

Figure 1 Preparation of a streptomycin gradient plate

From Experiment 56 of *Microbiology: A Laboratory Manual*, Tenth Edition. James G. Cappuccino, Natalie Sherman.

culture and incubation, the appearance of colonies in a region of high streptomycin concentration is indicative of streptomycin-resistant mutants.

CLINICAL APPLICATION

Searching for Resistance Mutations

Once strains of bacteria that are known to be resistant are isolated, microbiologists attempt to find the gene or genes responsible. A gene called *sasX*, found in methicillin-resistant *Staphylococcus aureus* (MRSA), has almost doubled in frequency over the past decade. It is located in a mobile genetic element that allows its easy transfer to other bacteria. This gene helps the bacterium to more effectively colonize nasal tissues and evade the host's immune system. Targeting this gene may provide a route for highly effective therapies.

AT THE BENCH

Materials

Cultures

24-hour nutrient broth culture of *E. coli.*

Media

Per designated student group: two 10-ml Trypticase soy agar deep tubes.

Reagent

Stock streptomycin solution (10 mg per 100 ml of sterile distilled water).

Equipment

Sterile Petri dish (100 × 15 mm), sterile 1-ml pipettes, mechanical pipetting device, inoculating loop, bent glass rod, beaker with 70% ethanol, waterbath, and glassware marking pencil.

Procedure Lab One

1. In a hot waterbath, melt two Trypticase soy agar tubes. Cool and maintain at 45°C.

2. Place a pencil under one end of a sterile Petri dish, pour in a sufficient amount of the molten agar medium to cover the entire bottom surface, and allow to solidify in the slanted position.

3. Using a sterile 1-ml pipette, add 0.1 ml of the streptomycin solution to a second tube of molten Trypticase soy agar. Mix by rotating the tube between the palms of your hands.

4. Place the dish in a horizontal position, pour in a sufficient amount of the molten agar medium containing streptomycin to cover the gradient agar layer, and allow to solidify.

5. With a sterile 1-ml pipette, add 0.2 ml of the *E. coli* test culture. With an alcohol-dipped and flamed bent glass rod, spread the culture over the entire agar surface.

6. Incubate the appropriately labeled culture in an inverted position for 48 hours at 37°C.

Procedure Lab Two

1. Observe the plate for the appearance of discrete colonies and indicate their positions in the "Initial Incubation" diagram in the Lab Report.

2. Select one or two isolated colonies present in the middle of the streptomycin concentration gradient. With a sterile inoculating loop, streak the selected colonies toward the high-concentration end of the plate.

3. Incubate the plate in an inverted position for 48 hours at 37°C.

Procedure Lab Three

1. Observe the plate for a line of growth from the streaked colonies into the area of high streptomycin concentration. Growth in this area is indicative of streptomycin-resistant mutants.

2. Indicate the observed line(s) of growth in the "Second Incubation" diagram in the Lab Report.

Observations and Results

1. Indicate the positions of discrete colonies in the diagram below (LSC = low streptomycin concentration; HSC = high streptomycin concentration).

LSC ——   —— HSC

Initial incubation

2. Indicate the observed line(s) of growth in the diagram below.

LSC ——   —— HSC

Second incubation

Review Questions

1. What mechanisms are responsible for antibiotic resistance?

2. Why is it necessary to use an antibiotic gradient-plate preparation for isolation of mutants?

3. Why has there been an increase in drug-resistant bacterial strains in recent years?

4. Does the streptomycin in the medium cause the mutations? Explain.

The Ames Test: A Bacterial Test System for Chemical Carcinogenicity

Principle

Our exposure to a wide variety of chemical compounds has increased markedly over the past decades. Oncological epidemiologists strongly suspect that the intrusion of these chemicals in the form of industrial pollutants, pesticides, food additives, hair dyes, cigarette smoke, and the like may play a significant role in the induction of malignant transformations in humans. From a genetic aspect there is strong evidence linking **carcinogenicity** to **mutagenicity.** Research indicates that approximately 90% of the chemicals proved to be carcinogens are mutagens; they cause cancer by inducing mutations in somatic cells. These mutations are most frequently a result of base substitutions, the substitution of one base for another in the DNA molecule, and frameshift mutations, a shift in the reading frame of a gene because of the addition or deletion of a base.

In view of the rapid advent of new products and new industrial processes with their resultant pollutants, it is essential to determine their potential genetic hazards. Despite the fact that mammalian cell structure and human enzymatic pathways differ from those in bacteria, the chemical nature of DNA is common to all organisms; this permits the use of bacterial test systems for the rapid detection of possible mutagens and therefore possible carcinogens.

The **Ames test** is a simple and inexpensive procedure that uses a bacterial test organism to screen for mutagens. The test organism is a histidine-negative (his^-) and biotin-negative (bio^-) auxotrophic strain of *Salmonella typhimurium* that will not grow on a medium deficient in histidine unless a back mutation to his^+ (histidine-positive) has occurred. It is recognized that the mutagenic effect of a chemical is frequently influenced by the enzymatic pathways of an organism, whereby nonmutagens are transformed into mutagens and vice versa when introduced into human systems. In mammals, this toxification or detoxification frequently occurs in the liver. The Ames test generally requires the addition of a liver homogenate, S-9, which serves as a source of activating enzymes, to make this bacterial system more comparable to a mammalian test system.

In the Ames test, by means of the spot method, molten agar containing the test organism, S-9 mix, and a trace of histidine to allow the bacteria to undergo the several cell divisions necessary for mutation to occur is poured on a minimal agar plate. A disc impregnated with the test chemical is then placed in the center of the test plate. Following diffusion of the test compound from the disc, a concentration gradient of the chemical is established. Following incubation, a qualitative indication of the mutagenicity of the test chemical can be determined by noting the number of colonies present on the plate. Each colony represents a $his^- \rightarrow his^+$ revertant. A positive result, indicating mutagenicity, is obtained when an obvious increase in the number of colonies is evident compared to the number of spontaneous revertants on the negative control plate.

In the following procedure, you will perform a modified Ames test; you will not use the S-9 mix to test for the mutagenicity of nitro compounds, which, as in humans, are activated by the bacterial nitroreductases. Four minimal agar plates are inoculated with the *S. typhimurium* test organism. One plate, the negative control, is not exposed to a test chemical. Any colonies developing on this plate are representative of spontaneous $his^- \rightarrow his^+$ mutations. The second plate, the positive control, is exposed to a known nitrocarcinogen, 2-nitrofluorene. The remaining two plates are used to determine the mutagenicity of two commercial hair dyes.

From Experiment 57 of *Microbiology: A Laboratory Manual*, Tenth Edition. James G. Cappuccino, Natalie Sherman.

The Ames Test: A Bacterial Test System for Chemical Carcinogenicity

AT THE BENCH

Materials

Cultures

24-hour nutrient broth cultures of *S. typhimurium*, Strain TA 1538 (ATCC. e 29631).

Media

Per designated student group: four minimal agar plates and four 2-ml top agar tubes.

Reagents

Sterile biotin-histidine solution, 2-nitrofluorene dissolved in alcohol, and two commercial hair dyes.

Equipment

1-ml sterile pipettes, mechanical pipetting device, sterile discs, forceps, waterbath, Bunsen burner, and glassware marking pencil.

Procedure Lab One

⚠️ **Wear disposable gloves and a laboratory coat when handling 2-nitrofluorene. For disposal of this chemical, place excess into a sealable container and put it inside a fume hood for subsequent removal according to your institution's policy for disposal of hazardous materials.**

Refer to **Figure 1** as you read the following instructions.

1. Label three minimal agar plates with the name of the test chemical to be used. Label the fourth plate as a negative control.

2. Melt four tubes of top agar in a hot waterbath and maintain the molten agar at 45°C.

3. To each molten top agar tube, aseptically add 0.2 ml of the sterile biotin-histidine solution and 0.1 ml of the *S. typhimurium* test culture. Mix by rotating the test tube between the palms of your hands.

4. Aseptically pour the top agar cultures onto the minimal agar plates and allow to solidify.

5. Using sterile forceps, dip each disc into its respective test chemical solution and drain by touching the side of the container.

6. Place the chemical-impregnated discs in the center of the respectively labeled minimal agar plates. Place a sterile disc on the plate labeled negative control. With the sterile forceps, *gently* press down on the discs so that they adhere to the surface of the agar.

7. Incubate all plates in an inverted position for 24 hours at 37°C.

Procedure Lab Two

1. Count the number of large colonies present on each plate and record on the chart in the Lab Report.

2. Determine and record the number of chemically induced mutations by subtracting the number of colonies on the negative control plate, representative of spontaneous mutations, from the number of colonies on each test plate.

3. Determine and record in the Lab Report the relative mutagenicity of the test compounds on the basis of the number of induced mutations: If below 10, (−); if greater than 10, (1+); if greater than 100, (2+); and if greater than 500, (3+).

The Ames Test: A Bacterial Test System for Chemical Carcinogenicity

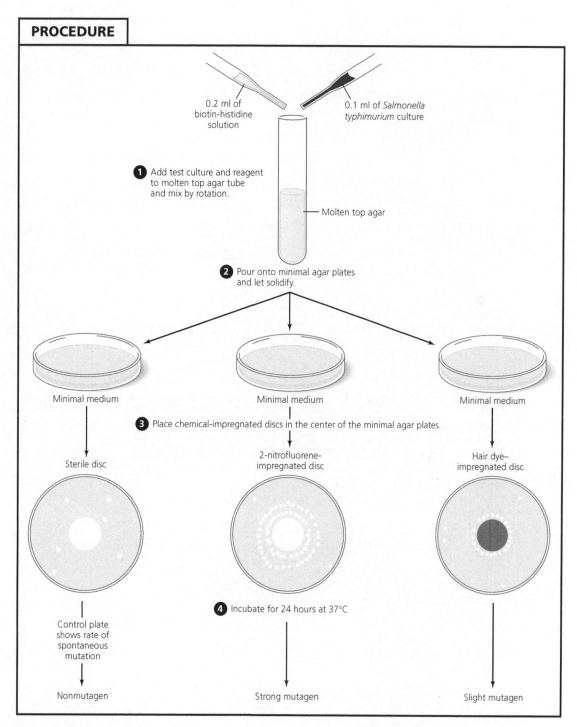

Figure 1 The Ames test

Observations and Results

Test Chemical	Number of Colonies	Number of Induced Mutations	Degree of Mutagenicity ($-$), (1+), (2+), or (3+)*
Negative control			
2-Nitrofluorene			
Hair dye 1			
Hair dye 2			

* If below 10, ($-$); if greater than 10, (1+); if greater than 100, (2+); and if greater than 500, (3+).

Review Questions

1. What is the purpose of the S-9 in the Ames test?

2. What is the purpose of the biotin-histidine solution in the Ames test?

3. What is the relationship between chemical carcinogenicity and mutagenicity?

4. What are the advantages of using bacterial systems instead of mammalian systems to test for chemical carcinogenicity?

5. What are the disadvantages of using bacterial systems instead of mammalian systems to test for chemical carcinogenicity?

Biotechnology

LEARNING OBJECTIVES

Once you have completed the experiments in this section, you should be familiar with the

1. Process of bacterial transformation.
2. Isolation of bacterial plasmids.
3. Use of restriction endonucleases to cut (digest) DNA molecules into small fragments.
4. Use of agarose gel electrophoresis to separate DNA fragments and determine their size.

Introduction

In the past, microbiologists focused on macro-molecular cellular components. In recent years, however, this focus has rapidly shifted, and biological studies can now be easily carried out at the molecular level. **Molecular biology** is the study of life at the molecular level. This rapidly expanding field is based on the ability to manipulate the genes of an organism. As technology has expanded, so too have researchers' abilities to modify an organism's genetic structure by removing the genetic material from one organism and combining it with that of another organism. Commonly, this is referred to as **genetic engineering,** or **recombinant DNA technology.**

Most often, genomic manipulation begins with isolating plasmid DNA and foreign DNA and cutting them with the same restriction enzyme. The foreign DNA inserts itself into the plasmid and the recombinant plasmid is introduced into a bacterium. The bacteria are then grown and screened to select the desired gene. An example of the use of this technology is the exploration of human genetic structure to identify and ameliorate genetic diseases, particularly through prenatal diagnosis.

Scientists are also interested in the genetic engineering of hormones (e.g., pancreatic insulin), which are normally obtained only in their natural state. Genetically engineered organisms also help produce vaccines and antibiotic substances and remediate environmental toxins that threaten human and environmental health. The role of genetic engineering technology in clinical and forensic science is commonplace today. For example, DNA profiling is used to resolve paternity disputes, and it was used to identify the bones of Czar Nicholas, the last Russian czar, and his family. This technology is also used extensively in criminology as a tool to help establish guilt or innocence of individuals involved in criminal cases.

The many applications of recombinant DNA technology have brought about significant advances in medicine, pharmacology, basic research, industry, and agriculture. In medicine, advances in biotechnology now allow insulin-deficient diabetics to use different types of genetically engineered insulin (e.g., rapid acting, moderate acting, or slow acting) to meet diverse medical needs, rather than relying on the slower-acting insulin obtained from

From Part 14 of *Microbiology: A Laboratory Manual*, Tenth Edition. James G. Cappuccino, Natalie Sherman.

the pancreas of slaughtered animals. Other proteins such as somatostatin, human growth hormone, interferon, interleukin-2—a regulator of the immune system—and blood clotting factor VIII have all been cloned using genetic engineering and are in clinical use. Biotechnology plays a prominent role in agriculture as well. Plants have been made resistant to herbicides such as glyphosate and pathogens such as the European corn borer. These few examples illustrate the amazing achievements made by the use of recombinant

DNA technology. More fascinating biotechnological advances are anticipated in the years ahead.

In the experiments that follow, you will explore some of the basic techniques in biotechnology. You will transform an antibiotic-susceptible cell into an antibiotic-resistant one by means of a plasmid. You will isolate plasmid DNA from bacterial cells and cut it into small fragments using restriction endonucleases. Finally, using agarose gel electrophoresis, you will separate these DNA fragments and determine their size.

Bacterial Transformation

Principle

Transformation is a process whereby small pieces of host cell genomic DNA are able to enter a recipient cell and become incorporated into a homologous area on the recipient cell's genome. Historically, transformation had its origin in the pioneering experiments of Fred Griffith in London in the late 1920s. Working with *Streptococcus pneumoniae*, he noted that when an encapsulated smooth (S) strain that was lethal for mice was heat-killed and mixed with a living culture of an avirulent nonencapsulated rough (R) strain and then injected into mice, the result was fatal **(Figure 1)**. Subsequent isolation of the organisms from the tissues of the dead mice revealed that the rough avirulent strain had been converted to a smooth, encapsulated, and lethal strain of *S. pneumoniae*.

This unusual experiment by Griffith, done long before DNA was determined to be the genetic basis for life, was simply termed by him as a "transformation." Today, in retrospect, we realize that this experiment proved to be the first indication of gene activity and the first demonstration of genetic recombination in bacteria. Later, Avery, McLeod, and McCarty, research scientists at the then Rockefeller Institute, were able to show that the transforming factor in Griffith's experiment was not a protein, as had been previously suspected, but a little-studied organic chemical called deoxyribonucleic acid (DNA).

During the **transformation** process, the donor cells forcibly lyse, releasing small segments of DNA containing 10 to 20 genes. These small segments have the ability to pass through the cell wall and cell membrane of a **competent cell** (a cell that is able to take up DNA from its environment). During naturally occurring transformations, a double-stranded DNA segment passes through the cell wall and into the cell's cytoplasm, and if there is sufficient sequence similarity, the foreign DNA undergoes homologous recombination with the recipient chromosome. The genome of the recipient cell has now been modified to contain DNA with genetic characteristics of the donor cell. Naturally occurring transformations are of great interest medically because they may serve as a vehicle for genetic exchange among pathogenic organisms. Interestingly, it appears that a larger percentage of pathogenic bacteria, such as *Streptococcus pneumoniae*, *Neisseria gonorrhoeae*, and *Haemophilus influenzae*, is capable of natural transformation than the nonpathogenic bacteria. This raises the intriguing possibility that the exchange of genetic material allows pathogenic cells to acquire the ability to evade a host's bodily defenses.

Bacterial Transformation

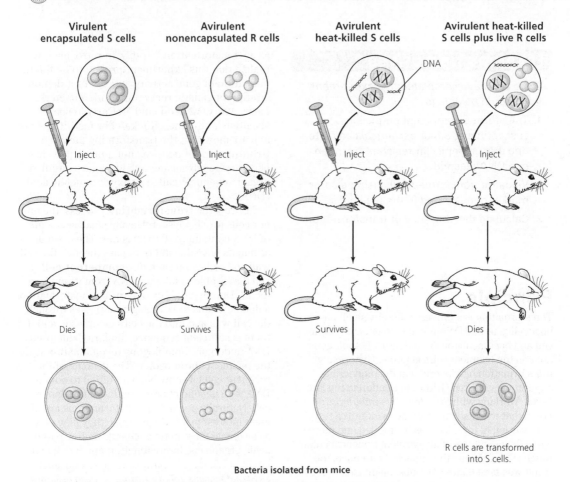

Figure 1 Griffith's experiment on transformation. An avirulent rough strain of *Streptococcus pneumoniae* becomes lethal when transformed after mixing with the DNA of a heat-killed virulent smooth strain of *S. pneumoniae*.

Not all bacteria are naturally transformable, however, and methods have been developed to produce competency in various types of cells and transform those cells artificially. This process was initiated in the 1970s, when it was shown that treating a recipient cell with a cold calcium chloride ($CaCl_2$) solution allows the passage of donor DNA into the cell. The porosity of the cell wall is already almost sufficient to allow the passage of intact DNA; it is the cell membrane that is the true barrier, and its permeability is altered by this drastic treatment with $CaCl_2$, allowing DNA to pass through the membrane and into the cell. With our rapidly advancing knowledge in the field of molecular genetics, it is now possible to artificially induce transformations by the use of **plasmids.**

Plasmids are small, circular pieces of extrachromosomal DNA with a length of 5,000 to 100,000 base pairs (bp), capable of autonomous replication in the bacterial cytoplasm. Another membrane-altering method is **electroporation.** In this method, cells are suspended in a DNA solution and subjected to high-voltage electric impulses that destabilize the cell membrane, resulting in increased permeability and enabling DNA to pass into the cells. **Transduction** is a method of horizontal passage of genetic material from one bacterial cell to another by means of a bacteriophage. **Conjugation** occurs when bacterial DNA is transferred from one cell to another via the formation of a protoplasmic bridge, called a conjugative, or sex, pilus.

In the following experiment, the transformation of *E. coli* is artificial because the cells must be treated with a salt concentration and temperature shocks, an environment that is not natural for these cells. You will use a competent strain of *E. coli* in which the *lac* operon has been deleted, leaving it devoid of a β-galactosidase gene. The procedure directs you to suspend the *E. coli* in cold $CaCl_2$ and then introduce an ampicillin-resistant plasmid (pBLU®). The plasmid confers ampicillin resistance because it carries the β-lactamase gene amp^r, as shown in **Figure 2**. This suspension is incubated in ice and then heated. The cold shock and heat shock in the presence of $CaCl_2$ alters the permeability of the outer surfaces of the cell and facilitates the passage of the DNA into the cellular cytoplasm.

Figure 2 **Plasmid map of pBLU**

AT THE BENCH

Materials
Cultures
18- to 24-hour Luria-Bertani (LB) agar base streak plate cultures of *Escherichia coli.*

Media
Per designated student group: two LB agar base plates, three LB agar base plates plus ampicillin (Amp), three LB agar base plates plus ampicillin/X-Gal, and one tube of LB broth. *Note: X-Gal is a colorimetric analog of lactose that is cleaved by β-galactosidase to yield blue-colored colonies.*

Reagent
50 mM $CaCl_2$ solution.

Plasmid pBLU is 5437 bp long and has the gene for β-lactamase (penicillinase) and the gene for β-galactosidase.

Equipment
Sterile plastic 13- × 100-mm test tubes or plastic 1.5-ml centrifuge tubes, adjustable micropipette (0.5 to 100 μl) with sterile plastic micropipette

CLINICAL APPLICATION

Transferring Genes Between Bacteria
Bacterial transformation is the exchange of genetic material (DNA) between strains of bacteria by the transfer of a fragment of naked DNA from a donor cell to a recipient cell, followed by recombination in the recipient chromosome. Called "horizontal gene transfer," this allows for the transfer of genes between bacteria of the same or different species. Human and other genes are routinely transferred into bacteria in order to synthesize products for medical and commercial use, such as human insulin, human growth hormone, and vaccines.

Bacterial Transformation

Figure 3 Transformation procedure

tips (10 to 100 μl) (or 1.0-ml graduated, individually wrapped, disposable plastic transfer pipettes), glass beads (6-mm diameter), glassware marking pencil, disposable plastic inoculating loops (standard wire loops may be used), Bunsen burner, waterbath, 500-ml beaker of crushed ice, 500-ml beaker labeled "waste," 500-ml beaker containing disinfectant solution, and a Quebec colony counter (or permanent marker); if the spread-plate method is used, bent glass rod, beaker of alcohol, and turntable.

Procedure Lab One

Refer to **Figure 3** as you read the numbered instructions.

Note: If using a plastic transfer pipette (Figure 4), it is essential that you calibrate it to deliver a volume of 100 μl (0.1 ml), required for plasmid transfer. Once calibrated, it should be marked with a permanent glassware marker and retained to be used as a guide in the transformation experiment. Ask your instructor for help if needed.

1. With a glassware marking pencil, label two 13- × 100-mm test tubes, one as "DNA+" and the other as "DNA−." The DNA+ tube will receive the plasmid.

2. Using a sterile pipette, transfer 250 μl (0.25 ml) of ice-cold CaCl₂ solution into each tube.

3. Place both tubes in a 500-ml beaker of crushed ice.

4. Using a sterile inoculation loop, obtain a large mass of cells approximately 5 mm in size (about the size of a pencil eraser) from the *E. coli* starter plate, and inoculate the tube labeled "DNA+." *Note: Be sure to immerse the loop directly into the CaCl₂ and shake the loop vigorously to dislodge the inoculum. Discard the plastic loops in the beaker labeled "waste" or sterilize the wire loop by flaming it.*

5. Disperse the cells by gently tapping the tube with your finger until a uniform milky-white translucent cell suspension is obtained.

6. Repeat Steps 4 and 5 to inoculate the tube marked "DNA−," using an equal amount of inoculum and a sterile inoculating loop.

7. Using a sterile pipette, deliver 10 μl (0.01 ml) of pBLU plasmid into the DNA+ tube. Tap the tube several times with your finger to ensure complete mixing of the plasmid and cell suspension. *Note: Discard the plastic tip or*

Figure 4 Plastic transfer pipette

disposable pipette into a beaker containing disinfectant solution.

8. Return the DNA+ tube to the crushed-ice beaker and incubate for 15 minutes. During this time, label your agar plates as described in Step 9.

9. Label the 8 LB agar plates as follows:

   Plate 1: LB+

   Plates 2, 3: LB/Amp+

   Plates 4, 5: LB/Amp/X-Gal+

   Plate 6: LB−

   Plate 7: LB/Amp−

   Plate 8: LB/Amp/X-Gal−

10. Remove both tubes from ice after 15 minutes; place them in a test tube rack and immediately into a 42°C waterbath with *gentle agitation* for 90 seconds (heat shocking).

11. Return both tubes to the crushed-ice beaker for 1 minute.

12. With a sterile pipette, add 250 μl (0.25 ml) of LB broth to both the DNA+ and DNA− tubes. Tap the tubes with your finger to achieve uniform cell suspension. (These are the transformation tubes.)

13. Incubate both tubes in a test tube rack for 10 minutes. *Note: This is the **recovery period,** when the cells convert their newly modified genotype into a functionally ampicillin-resistant phenotype.*

403

14. Using a new plastic micropipette tip or disposable plastic transfer pipette for each inoculation, inoculate 100 μl (0.1 ml) of cells from the DNA+ transformation tube onto the surface of LB plates 1–5, and inoculate 100 μl (0.1 ml) of cells from the DNA− transformation tube onto plates 6–8.

15. Place six sterile 6-mm glass beads on the surface of each inoculated plate. Replace the cover and spread the cell suspension by gently moving the plate up and down and then side to side a few times. *Note: Do not swirl or rotate the plate.*

16. Repeat Steps 14 and 15 for the remaining plates.

17. Allow the plates to set for a few minutes so that the inoculum may be absorbed by the agar.

18. Remove the glass beads from the plate by lifting the cover slightly while holding the plate vertically over the beaker of disinfectant, allowing the beads to leave the plate. *Note: This step may be eliminated if the spread-plate procedure is used.*

19. Incubate all plates at 37°C for 24 to 36 hours or at room temperature for 48 to 72 hours.

Procedure Lab Two

1. In the Lab Report, predict whether each plate will experience growth or no growth. Use a plus (+) sign for growth and a minus (−) for no growth.

2. Without removing the cover of the Petri plates, observe the colonies through the bottom of each plate.

3. Perform a colony count on each plate using an electronic colony counter if available, or use a permanent marker to mark each colony on the bottom of the plate as it is counted. Plates with more than 300 colonies should be designated as **TNTC (too numerous to count)**; plates with fewer than 30 colonies are designated as **TFTC (too few to count).** Record your results in the Lab Report.

4. For each plate, did transformation occur? Record your results in the Lab Report.

Observations and Results

Plate Number	Designation	Growth + or −	Transformation Yes or No	Number of Colonies
1	LB+			
2	LB/Amp+			
3	LB/Amp+			
4	LB/Amp/X-Gal+			
5	LB/Amp/X-Gal+			
6	LB−			
7	LB/Amp−			
8	LB/Amp/X-Gal−			

Determine the sum of the colonies on the two experimental plates for LB/AMP+ and the two LB/AMP/X-Gal+ plates. Determine the averages and use these figures to calculate the transformation efficiency, using the following protocol.

Avg. LB/Amp+ colonies _____   Avg. LB/Amp/X-Gal+ colonies _____

  a. The concentration of the plasmid used in this experiment was 0.005 µg/µl. Keep in mind that you used 10 µl.

  Total mass of plasmid = volume × concentration
  Total mass of plasmid = _____

  b. Calculate the total volume of the cell suspension.

  Total volume = volume of $CaCl_2$ solution + volume of plasmid + volume of LB broth
  Total volume = _____

  c. Calculate the fraction of cell suspension spread on each plate.

  Fraction spread = volume of suspension spread on plate / total volume
  Fraction spread = _____

d. Calculate the mass of DNA plasmid in the cell suspension spread on each plate.

Mass of DNA plasmid spread = total mass of plasmid × fraction spread

Mass of DNA plasmid spread = _____

e. Calculate the transformation efficiency (the number of colonies per μg of plasmid DNA).

Transformation efficiency = average of colonies counted/mass of plasmid spread

Express your results using scientific notation.

TRANSFORMATION EFFICIENCY	
LB/Amp+	**LB/Amp/X-Gal+**

Review Questions

1. Why do you think that it is necessary to autoclave transformed cells immediately after the termination of the experiment?

2. How would you explain to an untrained neighbor the process scientists use to change the genes (genotype) of an organism to give it useful new traits?

3. At a neighboring lab bench, students find that there are a few white colonies scattered among a few hundred blue colonies on their LB/Amp/X-Gal+ plates.

a. How would you explain this result?

b. To confirm your hypothesis, you ask to see their LB/Amp/X-Gal− plate. What do you see that supports your hypothesis?

Isolation of Bacterial Plasmids

LEARNING OBJECTIVES

Once you have completed this experiment, you should be able to

1. Isolate plasmids from plasmid-bearing bacteria.
2. Separate plasmids using agarose gel electrophoresis.
3. Compare electrophoretic mobilities of plasmids.

Figure 1 Illustration of a plasmid, showing a selectable marker and a multiple cloning site

Principle

Isolating pure DNA is a necessary step in studies that incorporate cloning, gene sequencing, gene mapping, or any other recombinant DNA technique. Many microorganisms contain small pieces of circular DNA called **plasmids** that exist separately from the host-cell genome. In studies that use recombinant DNA techniques, plasmid DNA is often preferred over chromosomal DNA because it is smaller and easier to manipulate. Plasmids that are commonly used as cloning vectors possess three important elements: an origin of replication, which allows the plasmid to be replicated independently of the cell's chromosome; a selectable marker, so the presence of the plasmid in the cell can be detected; and a cloning site into which a gene can be inserted. Although a selectable marker is not a required element of a plasmid, it can be useful in order to signal that the plasmid has been incorporated into the host cell. Plasmid genes that code for resistance to antibiotics are able to confer this resistance to the host cell, and a test of the host cell reveals that the transfer has occurred. In fact, antibiotic-resistance genes are among the most commonly used selectable markers.

Because plasmids are circular and capable of self-replication, they are able to serve as vectors for transportation of cloned fragments of DNA into other cells for genetic engineering purposes. To do this, plasmids must have a multiple cloning site, or **polylinker,** which is a DNA segment with several unique insertion sites for restriction endonucleases located next to each other as shown in **Figure 1.**

Gel electrophoresis is a technique used to separate different sizes of DNA fragments from a sample of DNA. Because DNA is negatively charged, when a sample is loaded into a porous agarose gel and subjected to an electric current with a positive charge at one end of the gel and a negative charge at the other, DNA fragments will migrate through the pores in the gel, toward the positively charged end. Different-sized fragments of linear and circular DNA move through the gel at different speeds, thus traveling different distances in the gel over a set time period. Larger, longer pieces snake their way through the pores more slowly, while shorter, smaller pieces move more quickly and travel further toward the positively charged end of the gel.

There are two types of circular DNA: closed and nicked. Closed circular DNA has all of its nucleotides linked with phosphodiester bonds and is supercoiled. Nicked circular DNA has at least one broken phosphodiester linkage. Nicked DNA is sometimes referred to as "relaxed" because

From Experiment 59 of *Microbiology: A Laboratory Manual*, Tenth Edition. James G. Cappuccino, Natalie Sherman.

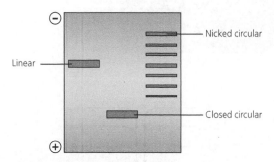

Figure 2 Gel migration pattern for linear, nicked circular, and closed circular DNA

some of the tension present in covalently coiled and twisted DNA has been released. **Figure 2** illustrates the relative distance that each type of DNA described previously (linear, closed circular, and nicked circular) travels in an electrophoresed agarose gel.

Isolating plasmids is a multistep process, which involves rupturing a plasmid-bearing bacterium, using a variety of reagents to remove cellular components, and suspending plasmid DNA in an aqueous solution. After a plasmid-bearing organism is cultured, cells are lysed using alkali to release the plasmid DNA. The cellular debris is then precipitated by using a detergent and potassium acetate. Following centrifugation, the pellet that forms is removed, and alcohol is added to the supernatant to precipitate the DNA. The DNA precipitate is resuspended in Tris-EDTA buffer.

In the following experiment, two different strains of plasmid-bearing *Escherichia coli* will be used—*E. coli*-1 and *E. coli*-2. Half of the class will isolate *E. coli*-1 plasmid DNA, and the other half will isolate *E. coli*-2 plasmid DNA.

CLINICAL APPLICATION

Plasmids and Genetic Engineering

Plasmids are mostly found in bacteria and are used in recombinant DNA research to transfer genes between cells. Plasmids that confer antibiotic resistance (R Plasmids) have been of special interest because of their medical importance, and also because of their significant role in genetic engineering.

AT THE BENCH

Materials

Cultures

24-hour Luria-Bertani broth, 50 μg/ml of ampicillin, cultures of plasmid-bearing *Escherichia coli* ATCC 39991 (plasmid designation pIVEV) and *Escherichia coli* ATCC 53100 (plasmid designation pDGR-2).

Reagents

Glucose-Tris-ethylenediaminetetraacetic acid (EDTA) buffer, Tris-EDTA buffer, Tris-acetate-EDTA buffer, 5M potassium acetate (KOAc), sodium hydroxide containing 1% sodium dodecyl-sulfate (NaOH/SDS), 95% ethanol at 0°C, 70% ethanol, molten agarose at 55°C, gel electrophoresis running dye, Carolina Blu stain or 0.025% methylene blue stain, and *Hin*dIII-cut bacteriophage lambda (λ) DNA (used as the standard for comparing fragment sizes).

Note: Although it is cheaper to prepare your own solutions, your instructor may have ordered a kit containing premade solutions.

Equipment

Microcentrifuge, 2-ml microcentrifuge tubes, digital micropipette—10, 100, and 200 μl, small and large micropipette tips, waterbath, rubber micro test tube racks capable of floating, glassware marking pencil, ice bucket, crushed ice, a light box or overhead projector, millimeter ruler, agarose gel casting tray, staining tray, plastic sandwich size bags, and an electrophoretic apparatus.

Procedure

Using a Micropipette

Before the start of the experiment, familiarize yourself with the use of a micropipette, the function of which is to accurately deliver microliter volumes of solution. Not all micropipettes work the same way. Some are designed to deliver a fixed volume, while others can deliver variable volumes. Your instructor will demonstrate the proper handling and use of these expensive instruments.

Using samples of colored water, practice using a micropipette, attaching different-sized micropipette tips and delivering various sample volumes to digestion tubes.

1. Set the scale on the pipette to the volume you wish to deliver.

2. Place a tip on the micropipette by pushing it firmly onto the pipette.

3. Depress the plunger to the first stop. This is necessary to remove all of the air from the tip.

4. To load the pipette, dip the pipette tip into the solution and release the plunger slowly to draw up the solution.

5. Touch the end of the tip to the side of the tube to remove any excess solution.

6. To deliver the solution, touch the side of the micropipette tip to the inside of the tube receiving the solution to produce a capillary.

7. Depress the plunger to the *first stop* and then continue depressing the plunger to the *second stop* to deliver the full volume of sample, blowing out the last bit in the tip.

8. Continue depressing the plunger while you remove the pipette tip from the tube. *Note: Releasing the plunger before removing the tip of the pipette from the tube will cause fluid to suck back into the tip.*

Before the laboratory session, *E. coli*-1 and *E. coli*-2 were inoculated in their medium and grown overnight. Before the start of the lab, your instructor dispensed 1 ml of culture into a microcentrifuge tube and spun it for 1 minute in a centrifuge. The supernatant was discarded, and the pellet retained. Another 1 ml of culture was added to the tube, and the process was repeated.

Isolating the Plasmid

Obtain a microcentrifuge tube from your instructor with a retained pellet labeled "EC-1" or "EC-2." With a glassware marking pencil, label the tube with your group name or number to identify it later. Refer to **Figure 3** as you complete the following steps.

1. Add 100 μl of GTE (glucose, Tris, and EDTA) buffer to your tube and resuspend the pelleted cells by tapping with your finger or mixing by vortex. *Note: The EDTA in the buffer chelates the divalent metal ions, Ca^{2+} and Mg^{2+}, which destabilizes the cell membrane and*

PROCEDURE

Prior to the lab, your instructor centrifuged 1 ml of *E. coli* culture for 1 minute. The supernatant was discarded and the pellet retained. Another 1 ml of *E. coli* culture was added to the pellet. It was centrifuged for 1 minute. The supernatant was discarded and the pellet retained for this experiment.

① Add 100 μl of GTE buffer. Resuspend pellet. Incubate at room temperature for 5 min.

② Add 200 μl of NaOH/SDS. Mix gently by inversion. Incubate in ice bucket for 5 min.

③ – ④ Remove from ice bucket. Add 500 μl of KOAc. Mix gently by inversion. Incubate in ice bucket for 5 min.

⑤ – ⑥ Supernatant / Pellet. Remove from ice bucket. Centrifuge for 5 min. Decant supernatant to a new tube.

⑦ – ⑩ Add 1 ml 95% ethanol at 0°C to the new tube containing supernatant. Incubate in ice bucket for 15 min. Centrifuge for 15 min. Decant and discard supernatant.

⑪ – ⑭ Add 500 μl of cold 70% ethanol. Mix gently. Centrifuge for 5 min. Decant and discard supernatant. Allow pellet to air dry for 15 min.

⑮ – ⑯ Plasmid. Add 100 μl of TAE buffer. Resuspend pellet. Store in freezer, if necessary.

Figure 3 Procedure for isolating bacterial plasmid DNA

inhibits the activity of DNases. The glucose maintains the osmolarity, preventing the buffer from bursting the cell.

2. Add 200 μl of NaOH/SDS solution and mix gently by inversion about four to five times. Incubate the tube in an ice bucket for 5 minutes. *Note: This is a highly alkaline solution that lyses the cell, releasing the cytoplasm into the buffer, and separates the chromosomal DNA into single strands (ssDNA) and complexes with cellular proteins.*

3. Remove the tube from the ice bucket. Then add 500 μl of potassium acetate (KOAc) and mix thoroughly by gentle inversion. *Note: The KOAc promotes the precipitation of chromosomal ssDNA and large RNA molecules, which are insoluble in this salt.*

4. Reincubate the tube in the ice bucket for another 5 minutes.

5. Remove the tube from the ice bucket and centrifuge for 5 minutes. Be sure the tubes are balanced in the centrifuge. *Note: In this step, pellets form from all of the cellular debris and organic molecules precipitated in the previous steps.*

6. Carefully decant the supernatant solution into a new microcentrifuge tube. *Note: The plasmid remains in the supernatant solution. The pellet and the tube are discarded.*

7. Add 1 ml of 95% ethanol at 0°C to the supernatant fluid in the new tube. *Note: The ethanol precipitates the plasmid.*

8. Incubate the plasmid in the ice bucket for 15 minutes.

9. Centrifuge the tube for 15 minutes to make the precipitated plasmid form a pellet.

10. Decant and discard the supernatant. *Note: Care must be taken not to shake the tube before or after decanting the supernatant. Do not be concerned if you do not see a pellet. It is there, provided that you were careful during the decanting step.*

11. Add 500 μl of cold 70% ethanol to the pellet and gently tap the tube with your finger or rock the tube back and forth. *Note: This step washes the plasmid by removing the excess salt. The plasmid is insoluble in ethanol.*

12. Centrifuge the tube for 5 minutes.

13. Decant and discard the supernatant fluid.

14. Allow the pellet to dry for about 15 minutes until you no longer smell alcohol.

15. Add 100 μl of TAE (Tris-acetate-EDTA) buffer to resuspend the pellet.

16. The plasmid may be placed in the freezer until the next lab class, or you may proceed to the electrophoresis step. *Note: If the electrophoresis is to be done during this class period, practice loading and casting the gel, which is described next.*

Casting the Agarose Gel

Note: Not all casting trays are the same. Your instructor will indicate which type will be used and whether there are special considerations during the setup.

Your instructor prepared the 0.8% agarose gel in a 1X TAE buffer solution before class and maintained it at 55°C in a waterbath. It is ready to pour. One or two drops of Carolina Blu stain was added to the agarose buffer solution to give a small tinge of blue to the gel. At this concentration, the pores that form the gel lattice are such that they allow the free migration of the cut DNA fragments between 0.5 and 10 kilobases (kb).

1. Place the casting tray inside the casting tray box on a level surface.

2. Close off the ends of the tray with the rubber dams by tightening the knob on the top of the casting tray box.

3. Place a well-forming comb in the first notch at the end of the casting tray.

4. Pour 60–70 ml of agarose solution that has been cooled to 55°C into the tray. Use a toothpick or applicator stick to move the bubbles to the edge of the gel before it solidifies.

5. Allow the gel to solidify completely. It should be firm to the touch after 20 minutes.

6. Slowly remove the rubber dams and *very gently* remove the well-forming comb by pulling it straight up. *Note: Use extreme care not to damage or tear the wells.*

7. Place the gel on the platform in the electrophoresis box so that the formed wells are properly oriented toward the anode (negative pole with black cord). Because DNA is negatively charged, the cut DNA fragments will migrate to the cathode (positive pole with the red cord). Refer to **Figure 4** to see the proper setup of an electrophoretic apparatus.

8. Fill the electrophoresis box with TAE buffer to a level that just covers the gel, about 2 mm. Make sure that all of the wells are filled with the buffer.

Figure 5 Gel loading scheme

Figure 4 Setup of agarose gel unit for DNA electrophoresis

Practicing Gel Loading

Before loading your sample into the wells of the agarose gel, practice this challenging technique. Your instructor will demonstrate the proper method for loading the wells. Each student should practice on a gel that has been prepared earlier by your instructor, not on the gel to be used for running the samples.

1. Load the pipette with 22 μl of loading gel.
2. Hold the pipette with both hands and dip the tip slightly through the buffer covering the gel, with the tip barely in the well.
3. Slowly discharge the contents of the pipette. *Note: The loading gel contains sucrose, which is heavier than the DNA and will pull the sample into the well.*
4. Practice the technique until you are comfortable with it.

Electrophoresing of the Plasmids

1. Add 18 μl of plasmid in the 1X TAE buffer to a new microcentrifuge tube. Then add 4 μl of gel electrophoresis running dye to the tube.
2. Add 18 μl of *Hin*dIII-cut lambda (λ) DNA and 4 μl of the gel electrophoresis running dye. With your glass marking pencil, label this tube

*Hin*dIII. This DNA has been cut into six linear fragments with the *Hin*dIII restriction enzyme. The fragments (bands) are various sizes: 23 kb, 9.4 kb, 6.6 kb, 4.4 kb, 2.3 kb, and 2.0 kb.

3. When the wells are ready to be loaded, make a diagram so that you will know the position of your sample in the agarose gel.
4. Fill the wells by designating the EC-1 samples as odd-numbered groups and EC-2 samples as even-numbered groups, as shown in **Figure 5**.
5. After the samples are loaded into the wells, place the lid on the electrophoresis gel box. Check that the power switch is turned to the "off" position and then attach the electrical leads (red to red and black to black) from the power supply to the box.
6. Turn the power pack on and adjust the rheostat dial to 110V.
7. Electrophorese the gel for 30 to 40 minutes or until the leading edge of the bromphenol blue dye (the dye in the loading gel) has traveled roughly three-fourths of the distance to the edge of the gel.
8. Turn the rheostat to zero and turn off the power. Disconnect the leads and remove the cover from the gel box.

Staining the Gel

1. Put on a pair of disposable laboratory gloves.
2. Lift the gel tray out of the electrophoresis box, and slide the gel into a staining tray containing approximately 100 ml of Carolina Blu stain or 0.025% of methylene blue stain.
3. Allow the gel to remain in the stain for 30 to 40 minutes.

Figure 6 Agarose gel stained with methylene blue following the electrophoresis of plasmid DNA

4. Pour off the stain into a waste beaker. Transfer the gel to a staining tray containing 100 ml of distilled water and allow the gel to decolorize (destain) for another 30 minutes. Frequent destaining with fresh distilled water for 2 minutes increases the intensity of the bands. For best results, let the gel destain overnight in a small volume of water. *Note: If the gel is left overnight in a large volume of water, it may destain too much.*

5. Pour off the water, carefully remove the gel from the staining tray, and place it in a plastic sandwich-size bag or wrap it in a piece of clear plastic wrap. *Note: Be careful to keep the gel flat as you place it in the bag or plastic wrap.*

6. The gel can be placed in the refrigerator until the next lab period.

Figure 6 shows an agarose gel stain with methylene blue following electrophoresis of plasmid DNA.

Observations and Results

1. Tape a millimeter ruler to your light box or to the glass on your overhead projector. If you prefer, you may use a millimeter ruler to measure the migration of the plasmid.

2. Align your gel so that the front end of the well is set at the zero point on the ruler.

3. Measure the migration distances from the front of the well to the front edge of the band and record the distance in the following chart.

4. Prepare a standard curve on the semilog paper provided by plotting the distance traveled in millimeters on the x-axis versus the size of the fragment of *Hin*dIII-cut λ DNA in kilobases. Record your results in the following chart.

   Note: 0.8% agarose gel has pore sizes that will allow the free movement of nucleic acids between 0.5 and 10 kb. Therefore, draw the best-fit straight line for all bands except the 23-kb band.

Migration Distances of Lambda DNA						
Kilobases	23	9.4	6.6	4.4	2.3	2.0
Millimeters						

5. Determine the number of bands in each plasmid and use a ruler to measure the migration distance in centimeters.

Band #	1	2	3	4	5	Total
E. coli-1						
E. coli-2						

6. Draw a diagram of your agarose gel and indicate which bands are linear, closed circular, or nicked circular.

7. Determine the size of linear DNA segments that would migrate the same distance as the various forms of the plasmids, using the standard curve. Record your results below:

Linear DNA	PLASMID DNA	
	E. coli-1	E. coli-2

Review Questions

1. Why is plasmid DNA preferred for genetic engineering studies?

2. What are selectable markers and why are they important to cloning vectors?

3. What is the rationale for using the following solutions for the isolation of plasmids?
   a. EDTA:

   b. Sodium dodecylsulfate (SDS):

   c. Potassium acetate:

(Questions continue)

Isolation of Bacterial Plasmids

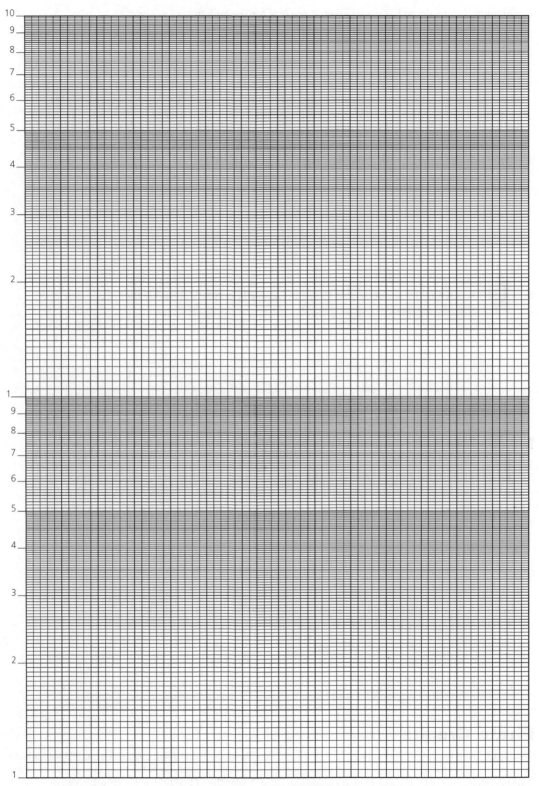

Migration Distance (mm) versus Fragment Size (kb)

4. Alcohol is considered to be a significant reagent for the isolation of nucleic acids (RNA and DNA). Why is this so?

5. What is nicked circular DNA and why is it termed "relaxed"?

6. When might you not be able to use a standard curve to determine the size of a plasmid?

7. When plasmids are isolated from bacterial cells, they may exist in a number of forms.

    a. List the different forms that may be found.

    b. Which do you think would migrate the fastest and farthest in an electrophoresis experiment and why?

Photo Credits

Credits are listed in order of appearance.

Photo 1: L. Brent Selinger, Department of Biological Sciences, University of Lethbridge, Pearson Education

Photo 2: Experiment performed and photographed by L. Brent Selinger, Department of Biological Sciences, University of Lethbridge, Pearson Education

Restriction Analysis and Electrophoretic Separation of Bacteriophage Lambda DNA

Figure 1 Palindrome for *Eco*RI endonuclease

Principle

Through their pioneering work, Werner Arber and Hamilton Smith discovered that bacteria possess enzymes that can act as molecular scissors and cut DNA molecules into smaller fragments. These enzymes, called **endonucleases,** are able to differentiate between DNA endogenous to an organism and foreign DNA, such as that of infecting bacteriophages. Endonucleases can cut foreign DNA, rendering it nonfunctional, which spares the bacterium from infection. For scientists, the discovery of restriction endonucleases has been vital in advancing research over the past 40 years because small DNA fragments are much easier to manipulate than longer DNA strands. Now scientists can accurately map a gene's location on a chromosome and describe its base-pair sequence. **Restriction endonucleases** are also being used to develop DNA recombinants for commercial use, detect genetic defects, map restriction sites on plasmids, and create DNA profiles for use in medicine and forensics.

Endonucleases recognize palindromic sequences, four to six base pairs long, on DNA molecules. In everyday usage, a palindrome is a word that is spelled the same way forward and backward. For example, the word "racecar" is a common palindrome. On a double-stranded DNA molecule, a palindrome is a sequence of base pairs that reads the same on one strand 5′ to 3′ as

it does on the other strand 5′ to 3′. Keep in mind that reading 5′ to 3′ on one strand is the opposite direction of reading 5′ to 3′ on the other. Each endonuclease has its own unique restriction site. **Figure 1** shows an example of a palindromic base-pair sequence and the cutting site for the restriction enzyme *Eco*RI. In the figure, *Eco*RI cuts the molecule between guanine and adenine, producing two fragments with staggered ends.

The key property of endonucleases is that they recognize and digest, or cut, one specific sequence of nucleotides on a DNA molecule and cut this same sequence every time. Several endonucleases make staggered cuts in the double-stranded molecule, producing single strands of DNA with cohesive, or sticky, ends that allows them to combine with complementary single-stranded DNA. Other endonucleases cut DNA sequences straight through both strands, producing blunt ends. **Figure 2** illustrates the restriction sites of some commonly used endonucleases. The arrows indicate the cutting sites on each strand. The endonucleases that produce sticky, staggered ends are clearly distinguishable in Figure 2 from those that produce blunt ends.

DNA fragments cut with the same restriction enzyme can pair with one another. The sticky ends of different strands will join together because of

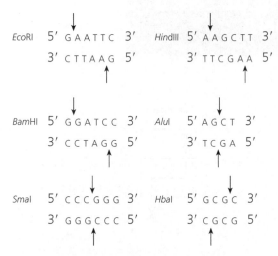

EcoRI	5′ G A A T T C 3′	HindIII	5′ A A G C T T 3′	
	3′ C T T A A G 5′		3′ T T C G A A 5′	
BamHI	5′ G G A T C C 3′	AluI	5′ A G C T 3′	
	3′ C C T A G G 5′		3′ T C G A 5′	
SmaI	5′ C C C G G G 3′	HbaI	5′ G C G C 3′	
	3′ G G G C C C 5′		3′ C G C G 5′	

Figure 2 Illustration of restriction sites for common endonucleases that leave blunt and staggered ends

the formation of hydrogen bonds between complementary bases. However, joined fragments lack phosphodiester bonds between guanine and adenine, and nicks form as a result. These nicks are annealed by DNA ligase enzymes. Under optimum environmental conditions (salt concentration, pH, and temperature), restriction endonucleases will cut a strand of DNA into a number of varying-sized fragments. The exact number and size of the fragments depends on the location and number of restriction sites for the enzyme.

Restriction enzymes are named based on the genus and species of bacteria from which they are obtained. The first letter of the genus name is followed by the first two letters of the species name. For example, an endonuclease from *Escherichia coli* is named *Eco*. If a bacterium produces more than one restriction enzyme, each endonuclease is differentiated by Roman numerals. If the enzyme is coded for on a resistance factor, it is further designated with an "R." Thus *Eco*RI is one of several endonucleases produced by *E. coli* and is coded for on a restriction site. Other widely used endonucleases are obtained from *Haemophilus influenzae D* (*Hind*III, which cuts between adenine bases) and *Bacillus amyloliquefaciens H* (*Bam*HI, which cuts between two guanine bases).

In the following experiment, you will use endonucleases to cut bacteriophage lambda (λ) DNA, containing 48,502 base pairs (48.5 kb), into fragments. You will separate the fragments by using agarose gel electrophoresis, and you will determine the size of each.

CLINICAL APPLICATION

Enzyme Digestion to Isolate Genes of Interest

It was quickly recognized that restriction enzymes would provide a new tool for the investigation of gene organization, function, and expression. Current medical research is examining how restriction enzymes can be used to insert the genes required for insulin production into diabetic patients.

AT THE BENCH

Materials

DNA Source

Bacteriophage λ (200 μl).

Restriction Endonucleases

*Eco*RI, *Hind*III, and *Bam*HI.

Reagents

Tris-acetate buffer, type-specific buffers for *Eco*RI, *Hind*III, and *Bam*HI, electrophoresis loading dye, Carolina Blu or 0.025% methylene blue stain, and 0.8% agarose in 1X TAE buffer.

Equipment

Plastic 1.5-ml microcentrifuge tubes, microcentrifuge, adjustable micropipettes (0.5 to 10 μl), (5 to 10 μl), (10 to 100 μl), large and small fine-point micropipette tips, waterbath, ice bucket, crushed ice, staining tray, disposable gloves, glassware marking pencil, Bunsen burner or hot plate, 250-ml Erlenmeyer flask, beaker for waste, micro test tube racks, electrophoretic apparatus, millimeter ruler, and a light box or overhead projector.

TABLE 1	Microliters (µl) per Digestion Tube						
				ENZYMES			
TUBE	LAMBDA DNA	dH₂O	10X RESTRICTION BUFFER	EcoRI	HinDIII	BamHI	TOTAL VOLUME
B	6	10	2	0	0	2	20
E	6	10	2	2	0	0	20
H	6	10	2	0	2	0	20
L	6	12	2	0	0	0	20

Procedure

Using a Micropipette

Before the start of the experiment, familiarize yourself with the use of a micropipette, the function of which is to accurately deliver microliter volumes of solution. Not all micropipettes work the same way. Some are designed to deliver a fixed volume, while others can deliver variable volumes. Your instructor will demonstrate the proper handling and use of these expensive instruments.

Using samples of colored water, practice using a micropipette, attaching different-sized micropipette tips and delivering various sample volumes to digestion tubes.

1. Set the scale on the pipette to the volume you wish to deliver.

2. Place a tip on the micropipette by pushing it firmly onto the pipette.

3. Depress the plunger to the first stop. This is necessary to remove all of the air from the tip.

4. To load the pipette, dip the pipette tip into the solution and release the plunger slowly to draw up the solution.

5. Touch the end of the tip to the side of the tube to remove any excess solution.

6. To deliver the solution, touch the side of the micropipette tip to the inside of the tube receiving the solution to produce a capillary.

7. Depress the plunger to the *first stop* and then continue depressing the plunger to the *second stop* to deliver the full volume of sample, blowing out the last bit in the tip.

8. Continue depressing the plunger while you remove the pipette tip from the tube. *Note: Releasing the plunger before removing the tip of the pipette from the tube will cause fluid to suck back into the tip.*

Digesting of Lambda (λ) DNA

⚠ Be sure to wear gloves, as enzymes on your skin degrade DNA in the experiment.

1. Obtain a sample of lambda DNA from the instructor.

2. With a glassware marking pencil, label four microcentrifuge tubes with your name or group number followed by an "L" for the uncut DNA, "E" for *Eco*RI, "H" for *Hin*dIII, and "B" for *Bam*HI.

3. Using a new pipette tip for each reagent, add the reagents to the digestion tubes in the following order:

   a. Lambda DNA

   b. Deionized or distilled water (dH₂O)

   c. Restriction enzyme buffer 10X

   d. Restriction endonucleases (10 units/µl)

   Note: The restriction enzyme must be added last to the digestion tubes. Addition of the endonucleases before DNA or buffer may inactivate the endonuclease. Each reagent is added with a new pipette tip to avoid contaminating the digestion tubes.

4. The addition of the reagents to each tube may be made following the scheme in Table 1.

5. Pulse centrifuge or tap your finger on each tube several times to mix the reagents.

6. Place all tubes in a foam rubber test tube rack or a suitable microcentrifuge rack and incubate them in the waterbath at 37°C for 60 minutes.

7. The digestion tubes may be stored in the refrigerator until the next class period. If you are continuing with the experiment now, place the tubes in an ice bucket and proceed to the next step.

Casting the Agarose Gel

Note: Not all casting trays are the same. Your instructor will indicate which type will be used and whether there are special considerations during the setup.

Your instructor prepared the 0.8% agarose gel in a 1X TAE buffer solution before class and maintained it at 55°C in a waterbath. It is ready to pour. One or two drops of Carolina Blu stain was added to the agarose buffer solution to give a small tinge of blue to the gel. At this concentration, the pores that form the gel lattice are such that they allow the free migration of the cut DNA fragments between 0.5 and 10 kb.

1. Place the casting tray inside the casting tray box on a level surface.

2. Close off the ends of the tray with the rubber dams by tightening the knob on the top of the casting tray box.

3. Place a well-forming comb in the first notch at the end of the casting tray.

4. Pour 60–70 ml of agarose solution that has been cooled to 55°C into the tray. Use a toothpick or applicator stick to move the bubbles to the edge of the gel before it solidifies.

5. Allow the gel to solidify completely. It should be firm to the touch after 20 minutes.

6. Slowly remove the rubber dams and *very gently* remove the well-forming comb by pulling it straight up. *Note: Use extreme care not to damage or tear the wells.*

7. Place the gel on the platform in the electrophoresis box so that the formed wells are properly oriented toward the anode (negative pole with black cord). Because DNA is negatively charged, the cut DNA fragments will migrate to the cathode (positive pole with the red cord).

8. Fill the electrophoresis box with TAE buffer to a level that just covers the gel, about 2 mm. Make sure that all of the wells are filled with the buffer.

Practicing Gel Loading

Before loading your sample into the wells of the agarose gel, practice this challenging technique. Your instructor will demonstrate the proper method for loading the wells. Each student should practice on a gel that has been prepared earlier by your instructor, not on the gel to be used for running the samples.

1. Load the pipette with 22 µl of loading gel.

2. Hold the pipette with both hands and dip the tip slightly through the buffer covering the gel, with the tip barely in the well.

3. Slowly discharge the contents of the pipette. *Note: The loading gel contains sucrose, which is heavier than the DNA and will pull the sample into the well.*

4. Practice the technique until you are comfortable with it.

Loading the DNA Digests into the Wells and Electrophoresing the Samples

1. Remove the digestion tubes from the ice bucket and add 4 µl of 6X loading dye to each tube.

2. Pulse centrifuge or tap your finger on each tube several times so that the contents of the tube move to the bottom.

3. Set the dial on the micropipette to deliver 24 µl (20 µl of restriction digests plus 4 µl of loading dye).

4. Deliver each of the four enzyme digests to separate wells in the agarose gel.

5. Remember the order of your samples and the position of each in the agarose gel. Because the gel cannot be marked, you should draw a diagram of the gel and label the position of your samples as shown in **Figure 3**.

6. After the samples are loaded into the wells, place the lid on the electrophoresis gel box. Check that the power switch is turned to the "off" position and then attach the electrical leads (red to red and black to black) from the power supply to the box.

7. Turn the power pack on and adjust the rheostat dial to 110V.

8. Electrophorese the gel for 30 to 40 minutes or until the leading edge of the bromphenol blue dye (the dye in the loading gel) has traveled

Figure 3 Example of gel loading scheme

roughly three-fourths of the distance to the edge of the gel.

9. Turn the rheostat to zero and turn off the power. Disconnect the leads and remove the cover from the gel box.

Staining the Gel

1. Put on a pair of disposable laboratory gloves.

2. Lift the gel tray out of the electrophoresis box, and slide the gel into a staining tray containing approximately 100 ml of Carolina Blu stain.

3. Allow the gel to remain in the stain for 30 to 40 minutes.

4. Pour off the stain into a waste beaker. Transfer the gel to a staining tray containing 100 ml of distilled water and allow the gel to decolorize (destain) for another 30 minutes. Frequent destaining with fresh distilled water for 2 minutes increases the intensity of the bands. For best results, let the gel destain overnight in a small volume of water. *Note: If the gel is left overnight in a large volume of water, it may destain too much.*

5. Pour off the water, carefully remove the gel from the staining tray, and place it in a plastic sandwich-size bag or wrap it in a piece of clear plastic wrap. *Note: Be very careful to keep the gel flat as you place it in the bag or plastic wrap.*

6. The gel can be placed in the refrigerator until the next lab period.

Observations and Results

1. Tape a millimeter ruler to the surface of a light box or to the glass surface of an overhead projector.

2. Place the stained gel (inside plastic bag) next to the zero point on the ruler and measure the distances that each fragment (band) migrated. Measure the distance from the front of the well to the front of the band. Record your results in the following chart.

	Migration Distances of Fragments (mm)					
Uncut λ DNA						
*Bam*HI cut λ DNA						
*Eco*RI cut λ DNA						
*Hin*dIII cut λ DNA						

Linear DNA fragments migrate at rates inversely proportional to the $\log_{10}$ of their molecular weight and base-pair length.

3. A graph (standard curve) can be constructed by plotting known kilobase-pair fragments versus distances migrated from the wells to the front of the fragment. The six kilobase-pair fragment sizes for *Hin*dIII are well established and can be used to plot a standard curve.

4. Once the fragment sizes are measured and distances traveled are plotted on semilog paper a best-fit straight line can be drawn. The size of each unknown fragment can be determined by drawing a vertical line from the migration distance (mm) on the x-axis up to the point on the curve that intersects that straight line. From there, draw a horizontal line to the fragment size on the y-axis.

5. In the following table, the kilobase lengths of *Hind*III are provided. From the standard curve, use the migration distance you have measured to determine the base-pair lengths for the three restriction enzymes. Record your results in the table.

*Hind*III[*]		*Bam*HI		*Eco*RI		λ DNA	
Distance (mm)	Actual kb	Distance (mm)	Calculated kb	Distance (mm)	Calculated kb	Distance (mm)	Calculated kb
	27.4*						
	23.1*						
	9.4						
	6.6						
	4.4						
	2.3						
	2.0						

[*] *Note:* Remember that 0.8% agarose allows the free migration of DNA in the range of 0.5 to 10 kb. Therefore, the 27.4- and 23.1-kb fragments will not be detected.

6. Calculate the fragment lengths of *Eco*RI and *Bam*HI from the standard curve and compare them to the actual kilobase lengths listed in the following chart.

*Hind*III		*Bam*HI			*Eco*RI		
Actual kb	Distance (mm)	Actual kb	Distance (mm)	Calculated Length	Actual kb	Distance (mm)	Calculated Length
27.4*		16.8*			24.6*		
23.1*		12.3			21.2*		
9.4		7.2			7.4		
6.6		6.7*			5.8*		
4.3		6.5*			5.6*		
2.3		5.6*			4.9		
2.0		5.5*			3.5		

Note: These fragments appear as a single band.

7. Compare and contrast your calculated kilobase pair from the standard curve with the actual kilobase pair for the restriction endonucleases.

   a. List those that were most accurate.

   b. List those that were least accurate.

(See Review Questions)

Restriction Analysis and Electrophoretic Separation of Bacteriophage Lambda DNA

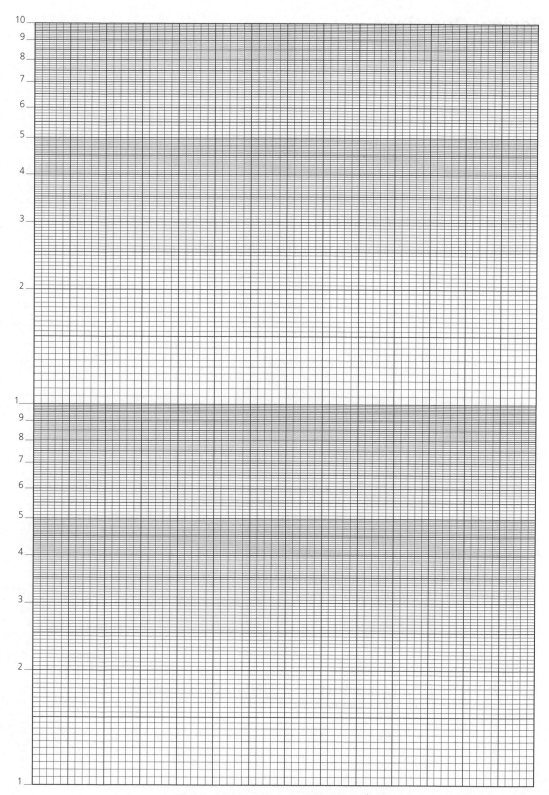

Migration Distance (mm) versus Fragment Size (kb)

Review Questions

1. Why were the DNA digestions carried out at 37°C?

2. Would any or all of these endonucleases cut the DNA of another bacteriophage or bacterium?

3. Why were specific restriction buffers needed for each of the restriction enzyme digests?

4. What could account for low endonuclease activity?

5. Why are the restriction enzymes added last to the digestion mixtures?

6. Assume you have one organism with a gene for ampicillin resistance and another organism with a gene for luciferinase. How would you isolate the gene from one organism and connect it with the gene of the other organism?

7. How would restriction enzymes play a role in having an organism produce a protein that it normally doesn't make?

Illustration Credits

All illustrations by Precision Graphics unless otherwise noted.

1: Carolina Biological Supply Company/Precision Graphics.

Photo Credits

Credits are listed in order of appearance.

Photo 1: L. Brent Selinger, Department of Biological Sciences, University of Lethbridge, Pearson Education

Photo 2: Experiment performed and photographed by L. Brent Selinger, Department of Biological Sciences, University of Lethbridge, Pearson Education

Medical Microbiology

LEARNING OBJECTIVES

Once you have completed the experiments in this section, you should be familiar with the

1. Characteristics and methodology for isolating and identifying selected pathogenic microorganisms.
2. Indigenous microbial flora of selected human anatomical sites.

Introduction

Although microorganisms are ubiquitous and their benefits to humans have been recorded, a small group of organisms remains a focus of concern: They are the pathogens, whose existence makes medical or clinical microbiology an especially important science.

That living agents are capable of inducing infections (*contagium vivum*) was first put forward by the monk Fracastoro in Verona about 500 years ago. In 1659 Kircher reported the presence of minute motile organisms in the blood of plague victims. Two hundred years after Fracastoro developed his initial concept, the germ theory of disease was formulated by Plenciz based on Leeuwenhoek's revolutionary microscopic observation of microorganisms. Perhaps the most important contributions to microbiology were made by Pasteur, Koch, and Lister during the **Golden Era of Microbiology** from 1870 to 1920. These investigators and their students recorded the observations and discoveries that cemented the cornerstone of medical microbiology. The body of knowledge that has accrued since these early years has made clinical microbiology a major component of laboratory or diagnostic medicine. The major responsibility of this science is isolating and identifying infectious pathogens to enable physicians to treat patients with infectious disease prudently, intelligently, and rapidly.

Many of the experiments so far described have application in the field of clinical microbiology. Among these are isolation and identification of unknown cultures, the use of selective and differential media, and biochemical tests used to separate and identify various microorganisms. Although studying all of the bacterial pathogens responsible for human illness is not possible here, routine experiments for isolating and identifying some of the most frequently encountered infectious organisms and microorganisms that constitute the indigenous flora of the human body are included. The pathogens chosen are pyogenic cocci, members of the genera *Staphylococcus* and *Streptococcus*, the *Enterobacteriaceae*, and the organisms suspected in formation of dental caries. Experimental procedures designed for the detection and presumptive identification of microorganisms in blood and urine, which are normally sterile body fluids, have also been incorporated into this section. Organisms that naturally reside in or on body surfaces and constitute the body's **normal flora** are also examined.

The need for the expeditious detection and identification of pathogens has led to the development of rapid testing methods. These are microbiologically and immunologically based and can be performed quickly and without the need for sophisticated and expensive equipment. Some prototypic experiments using these rapid methods are included along with the traditional procedures.

⚠ Many of the organisms that are used, although attenuated by having been subcultured on artificial complex media for many generations, must be viewed as potential pathogens and therefore handled with respect. At this point in your training, your manipulative skills should be sufficiently developed, allowing you to perform aseptically in any medical, hospital, or clinical laboratory setting to prevent infection of yourself and others.

Principle

A variety of microorganisms are known to be involved in the formation of dental caries, including *Lactobacillus acidophilus*, *Streptococcus mutans*, and *Actinomyces odontolyticus*. These organisms in the oral flora produce organic acids, particularly lactic acid, by fermenting carbohydrates that adhere to the surface of the teeth. In the continued presence of lactic acid, dental enamel undergoes decalcification and softening, which result in the formation of tiny perforations called dental caries.

The actual mechanism of action of these organisms is still unclear. However, it has been noted that *S. mutans* excretes an enzyme called **dextransucrase** (glycosyl transferase), which is capable of polymerizing sucroses into a large polymer, dextran, plus the monosaccharide fructose. This polysaccharide clings tenaciously to the teeth and forms dental plaque, in which streptococci reside and ferment fructose with the formation of lactic acid **(Figure 1)**.

Similarly, *L. acidophilus* produces lactic acid as an end product of carbohydrate fermentation. Oral lactobacilli are capable of metabolizing glucose found in the mouth, producing organic acids that reduce the oral acid concentration to a pH of less than 5. At this pH, decalcification occurs and dental decay begins.

One of the best microbiological methods for determining susceptibility to dental caries is the **Snyder test.** This test measures the amount of acid produced by the action of the lactobacilli on glucose. The test employs a differential medium, Snyder agar (pH 4.7), which contains glucose and the pH indicator bromcresol green that gives the medium a green color.

Following incubation, Snyder agar cultures containing lactobacilli from the saliva will show glucose fermentation with the production of acid, which tends to lower the pH to 4.4, the level of acidity at which dental caries form. At this pH the green medium turns yellow. A culture demonstrating a yellow color within 24 to 48 hours is suggestive of the host's susceptibility to the formation of dental caries. A culture that does not change color is indicative of lower susceptibility.

AT THE BENCH

Materials

Cultures

Organisms of the normal oral flora present in saliva.

Media

Per designated student group: two Snyder test agar deep tubes.

Equipment

Bunsen burner, ice-water bath, 1-in. square blocks of paraffin, sterile 1-ml pipettes, mechanical pipetting device, sterile test tubes, and glassware marking pencil.

From Experiment 61 of *Microbiology: A Laboratory Manual*, Tenth Edition. James G. Cappuccino, Natalie Sherman. Copyright © 2014 by Pearson Education, Inc. All rights reserved.

Microbial Flora of the Mouth: Determination of Susceptibility to Dental Caries

CH₂OH ... Sucrose → Sucrase → Glucose + Fructose

Glycosyl transferase

Dextran

Lactic acid

Figure 1 Degradation of sucrose and subsequent conversion of glucose into dextran by *Streptococcus mutans*

Procedure Lab One

1. Melt two appropriately labeled Snyder agar deep tubes and cool to 45°C.

2. Chew one square of paraffin for 3 minutes *without swallowing the saliva*. As saliva develops, collect it in a sterile test tube.

3. Vigorously shake the collected saliva sample and transfer 0.2 ml of saliva with a sterile pipette into one of the Snyder test medium tubes that have been cooled to 45°C. *Note: Don't let the pipette touch the sides of the tubes or the agar.*

4. Mix the contents of the tube thoroughly by rolling the tube between the palms of your hands or by tapping it with your finger.

5. Rapidly cool the inoculated tube of Snyder agar in an ice-water bath.

6. Repeat Steps 3 through 5 to inoculate the second tube.

7. Incubate both tubes for 72 hours at 37°C. Observe cultures at 24, 48, and 72 hours.

Procedure Lab Two

1. Examine the Snyder test cultures daily during the 72-hour incubation period for a change

in the color of the culture medium. Use an uninoculated tube of the medium as a control. **Figure 2** shows a positive and a negative Snyder test.

2. Record the color of the cultures in the Lab Report.

(a)   (b)

Figure 2 Snyder test. (a) No change in the color indicates a negative result. **(b)** The color change to yellow indicates a positive result.

Name: _____

Date: _____ Section: _____

Observations and Results

Using Table 1 to interpret your observations, record your findings about susceptibility to caries in the chart below.

TABLE 1 Assessment of Susceptibility to Dental Caries

CARIES ACTIVITY	HOURS OF INCUBATION		
	24	48	72
Marked	Positive	. . .	. . .
Moderate	Negative	Positive	. . .
Slight	Negative	Negative	Positive
Negative	Negative	Negative	Negative

Source: Courtesy of Difco Laboratories, Inc., Detroit, Michigan.

Positive: Complete color change; green is no longer dominant.
Negative: No color change or a slight color change; medium retains green color throughout.

Tube Number	COLOR OF SNYDER TEST CULTURES			Caries Susceptibility (Yes or No)
	24 hr	48 hr	72 hr	

Review Questions

1. How would you explain the differential nature of the Snyder agar medium as used for the detection of dental caries?

2. How would you explain the mechanism responsible for the formation of dental caries by resident microorganisms?

3. What is the function of the paraffin in this procedure?

4. Based on your results, what is your tendency to form dental caries?

    Is this result consistent with your dental history?

5. Are all members of the resident flora of the mouth capable of initiating dental caries? Explain.

6. What is the ideal time of day to perform this procedure? Why?

Photo Credit

Credits are listed in order of appearance.

Photo 1: Experiment performed and photographed by
L. Brent Selinger, Department of Biological Sciences,
University of Lethbridge, Pearson Education

Normal Microbial Flora of the Throat and Skin

Principle

The normal flora are regularly found in specific areas of the body. This specificity is far from arbitrary and depends on environmental factors such as pH, oxygen concentration, amount of moisture present, and types of secretions associated with each anatomical site. Native microbial flora are broadly located as follows:

1. **Skin:** Staphylococci (predominantly *Staphylococcus epidermidis*), streptococci (alpha-hemolytic, nonhemolytic), enterococci, diphtheroid bacilli, yeasts, and fungi.

2. **Eye conjunctiva:** Staphylococci, streptococci, diphtheroids, and neisseriae.

3. **Upper respiratory tract:** Staphylococci, streptococci (alpha-hemolytic, nonhemolytic, and *Streptococcus pneumoniae*), enterococci, diphtheroids, spirochetes, and members of the genera *Moraxella* (formerly called *Branhamella*), *Neisseria*, and *Haemophilus*.

4. **Mouth and teeth:** Anaerobic spirochetes and vibrios, fusiform bacteria, staphylococci, and anaerobic levan-producing and dextran-producing streptococci responsible for dental caries.

5. **Intestinal tract:** In the upper intestine, predominantly lactobacilli and enterococci. In the lower intestine and colon, 96% to 99% is composed of anaerobes such as members of the genera *Bacteroides*, *Lactobacillus*, *Clostridium*, and *Streptococcus*, and 1% to 4% is composed of aerobes, including coliforms, enterococci, and a small number of *Proteus*, *Pseudomonas*, and *Candida* species.

6. **Genitourinary tract:** Staphylococci, streptococci, lactobacilli, gram-negative enteric bacilli, clostridia, spirochetes, yeasts, and protozoa such as *Trichomonas* species.

In this exercise, you will study the resident flora of the throat and skin. Since these sites represent sources of mixed microbial populations, you will perform streak-plate inoculations to effect their separations. The discrete colonies thus formed can be studied morphologically, biochemically, and microscopically to identify the individual genera of these mixed flora.

The procedure used to identify the native flora of the throat involves the following steps:

1. A *blood agar plate* is inoculated to demonstrate the alpha-hemolytic and beta-hemolytic reactions of some streptococci and staphylococci. Hemolytic reactions on blood agar are shown in **Figure 1**. A distinction between these two genera can be made based on their colonial and microscopic appearances. The streptococci typically form pinpoint colonies on blood agar, whereas the staphylococci form larger pinhead colonies that might show a golden coloration. When viewed under a microscope, the streptococcal cells form chains of varying lengths, whereas the staphylococci are arranged in clusters.

2. A *chocolate agar plate* is inoculated to detect Neisseria spp. by means of the oxidase test. Members of this genus are recognized when the colonies develop coloration that is pink to dark purple upon addition of *p*-aminodimethylaniline oxalate following incubation. **Figure 2** shows colonies growing on chocolate agar from a throat culture.

3. A *Mueller-Hinton tellurite* or *Tinsdale agar plate* is inoculated to demonstrate the presence of diphtheroids, which appear as black, pinpoint colonies on this medium (**Figure 3**). This coloration is due to the diffusion of the

From Experiment 62 of *Microbiology: A Laboratory Manual*, Tenth Edition. James G. Cappuccino, Natalie Sherman.
Copyright © 2014 by Pearson Education, Inc. All rights reserved.

(a) Beta hemolysis

(b) Alpha hemolysis

Figure 1 Beta- and alpha-hemolytic reactions on blood agar

Figure 2 Colony growth on chocolate agar from a throat culture

Figure 3 Mueller-Hinton tellurite agar plate. Growth of black, pinpoint colonies indicates the presence of diphtheroids.

tellurite ions into the bacterial cells and their subsequent reduction to tellurium metal, which precipitates inside the cells.

The procedure used to identify the native flora of the skin involves the following steps:

1. A *blood agar plate* inoculated to determine the presence of hemolytic microorganisms, specifically the staphylococci and streptococci: Differentiation between these two genera may be made as previously described.

2. A *mannitol salt agar plate* inoculated for the isolation of the staphylococci: The generally avirulent staphylococcal species can be differentiated from the pathogenic *Staphylococcus aureus* because the latter is able to ferment mannitol, causing yellow coloration of this medium surrounding the growth. **Figure 4** shows a fermenter and a nonfermenter organism on a mannitol salt agar plate.

3. A *Sabouraud agar plate* inoculated to detect yeasts and molds: Yeast cells will develop pigmented or nonpigmented colonies that are elevated, moist, and glistening. Mold colonies will appear as fuzzy, powdery growths arising from a mycelial mat in the agar medium. **Figure 5** shows yeast colonies and a mold colony.

4. *Chocolate agar plate* inoculated to detect *Neisseria* spp. The presence of *Neisseria* spp. produces pink to purple to black colonies on this medium.

5. *Mueller-Hinton tellurite* or *Tinsdale media* inoculated to detect *Corynebacterium* spp. (diphtheroids). These colonies are black in appearance.

CLINICAL APPLICATION

Skin Flora and Acne

The bacterial population on a single human's skin is about 10^{12} organisms. A normal flora of microorganisms colonizes the human skin at birth as it passes through the birth canal, and typically inhabits the superficial layers of the epidermis and upper parts of the hair follicles. They consist mainly of *Staphylococcus epidermidis*, *Micrococcus*, and corynebacteria such as *Propionibacterium*. *Propionibacterium acnes* is normally found in low concentrations, but overgrows in the anaerobic environment of a blocked hair follicle, producing acne.

Fermenter   Nonfermenter

Figure 4 Mannitol salt agar plate showing a fermenter and a nonfermenter organism

AT THE BENCH

Materials

Media

Per designated student group: two blood agar plates, two mannitol salt agar plates, one chocolate agar plate, one Mueller-Hinton tellurite or Tinsdale agar plate, one Sabouraud agar plate, and two 5-ml sterile saline tubes.

Reagents

Crystal violet, Gram's iodine, safranin, 1% *p*-aminodimethylaniline oxalate, and lactophenol–cotton-blue.

Equipment

Sterile cotton swabs, tongue depressors, desiccator jar with candle, microscope, glass slides, Bunsen burner, glassware marking pencil, and disposable gloves.

Procedure Lab One

⚠ **You must wear disposable gloves in Steps 1–3.**

(a) Yeast colonies

(b) Mold colony

Figure 5 Sabouraud agar plate. (a) Yeast colonies have an elevated, moist, and glistening appearance. **(b)** A mold colony shows fuzzy, powdery growth.

1. Place a tongue depressor on the extended tongue and with a sterile cotton swab, obtain a specimen from the palatine tonsil by rotating the swab vigorously over its surface without touching the tongue, as illustrated.

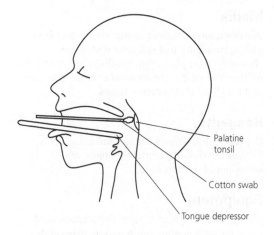

Palatine tonsil

Cotton swab

Tongue depressor

2. Inoculate a tube of sterile saline with the swab and mix until you have a uniform suspension.

3. Using a sterile inoculating loop, inoculate one plate each of blood agar, chocolate agar, mannitol salt agar, and Mueller-Hinton tellurite or Tinsdale agar, all previously labeled with the source of the specimen, by means of a four-way streak inoculation.

4. Using a sterile cotton swab moistened in sterile saline, obtain a specimen from the skin by rubbing the swab vigorously against the palm of your hand.

5. Inoculate a tube of sterile saline with the swab and mix the solution.

6. Inoculate one plate each of blood agar, mannitol salt agar, and Sabouraud agar, as described in Step 3.

7. Incubate the inverted chocolate agar plate in a CO_2 incubator, in a CO_2 incubation bag, or in a candle jar. If you use the candle jar, place a lighted candle in a desiccator jar and cover the jar tightly to effect a 5% to 10% CO_2 environment required for the growth of the *Neisseria*. Incubate the jar for 48 hours at 37°C.

8. Incubate the inverted Sabouraud agar plate for 48 hours at 25°C and the remaining plates for 48 hours at 37°C.

Procedure Lab Two

Selection and Differentiation of Skin and Throat Isolates

1. Examine the blood agar plate cultures for zones of hemolysis (refer to Figure 1).

2. Add the *p*-aminodimethylaniline oxalate to the surface of the growth on the chocolate agar plate. Observe for the appearance of a pink-to-purple-to-black color on the surface of any of the colonies (Figure 2).

3. Examine the Mueller-Hinton tellurite or Tinsdale agar plate for the presence of black colonies (Figure 3).

4. Examine the Sabouraud agar plate for the appearance of moldlike growth (Figure 5).

5. Examine the mannitol salt agar plate for the presence of growth that is indicative of staphylococci. Then examine the color of the medium surrounding the growth. A yellow color is indicative of *S. aureus* (refer to Figure 4).

6. Record your observations in the Lab Report and indicate the types of organisms that may be present in each specimen.

Staining and Morphological Characteristics of Skin and Throat Isolates

1. Prepare two Gram-stained smears from each of the blood agar cultures, choosing well-isolated colonies that differ in their cultural appearances and demonstrate hemolytic activity. Observe microscopically for the Gram reaction and the size, shape, and arrangement of the cells. Record your observations in the Lab Report and attempt to identify each isolate.

2. Prepare two lactophenol–cotton-blue–stained smears of organisms obtained from discrete colonies that differ in appearance on the Sabouraud agar culture. Observe microscopically, draw a representative field in the Lab Report, and attempt to identify the fungi.

Name: _____

Date: _____   Section: _____

Observations and Results

Selection and Differentiation of Skin and Throat Isolates

Cultures	Throat Specimen	Skin Specimen
Blood agar: *Staphylococcus* spp. *Streptococcus* spp. Type of hemolysis: alpha beta		
Chocolate agar: *Neisseria* spp. (+) or (−) pink to purple to black		
Mueller-Hinton tellurite or Tinsdale: *Corynebacterium* spp. (+) or (−) black colonies		
Sabouraud agar: Fungal colonies (+) or (−)		
Mannitol salt agar: *Staphylococcus aureus* Other *Staphylococcus* spp. (*S. epidermidis, S saprophyticus)* (+) or (−) growth Color of medium		
Types of organisms present		

Staining and Morphological Characteristics of Skin and Throat Isolates

Skin Specimen	Isolate 1	Isolate 2
Draw a representative field.		
Gram reaction		
Morphology		
Organism		
Throat Specimen	Isolate 1	Isolate 2
Draw a representative field.		
Gram reaction		
Morphology		
Organism		
Sabouraud Agar Colonies Specimen	Isolate 1	Isolate 2
Draw a representative field.		
Morphology		
Organism		

Review Questions

1. Why are some microorganisms termed "normal flora," and of what value are they to the well-being of the host?

2. A 6-year-old female is taken to her pediatrician for a checkup. As the doctor takes the child's history, her mother reports that the child had a severe sore throat several weeks earlier that regressed without treatment. Upon examination the pediatrician notes that the child has a systolic heart murmur consistent with mitral insufficiency and suspects that she has rheumatic fever.

   a. How was the earlier pharyngitis related to the subsequent development of rheumatic fever?

   b. Rheumatic fever is diagnosed on clinical and serological findings. What test should be done to diagnose rheumatic fever?

   c. How are rheumatic fever patients treated?

3. A 35-year-old female underwent serious abdominal surgery involving extensive bowel resection. She was maintained postoperatively on a regimen of intravenous broad-spectrum antibiotics. Three days postoperative she spiked a fever without a clear source. She complains of vaginal discomfort. Blood cultures reveal the presence of an ovoid cell that reproduced by budding.

   a. Based on this observation, what do you think this organism is?

   b. Is it part of the normal flora in humans?

   c. How did the treatment with broad-spectrum antibiotics predispose the patient to infection with this organism?

Photo Credits

Credits are listed in order of appearance.

Photo 1: Experiment performed and photographed by L. Brent Selinger, Department of Biological Sciences, University of Lethbridge, Pearson Education

Photo 2: Experiment performed and photographed by L. Brent Selinger, Department of Biological Sciences, University of Lethbridge, Pearson Education

Photo 3: James Cappuccino

Photo 4: James Cappuccino

Photo 5: James Cappuccino

Photo 6: Experiment performed and photographed by L. Brent Selinger, Department of Biological Sciences, University of Lethbridge, PearsonEducation

Identification of Human Staphylococcal Pathogens

Once you have completed this experiment, you should understand

1. The medical significance of the staphylococci.

2. Selected laboratory procedures designed to differentiate among the major staphylococcal species.

Figure 1 Streak-plate culture of *Staphylococcus aureus*. Produces colonies that are circular, convex, smooth, and cream-colored to golden yellow in appearance.

Principle

The genus *Staphylococcus* is composed of both pathogenic and nonpathogenic organisms. The three major species are *S. aureus*, *S. saprophyticus*, and *S. epidermidis*. Strains of the last two species are generally avirulent; however, under special circumstances in which a suitable portal of entry is provided, *S. epidermidis* may be the etiological agent for **skin lesions** and **endocarditis**, and *S. saprophyticus* has been implicated in some **urinary tract infections**. **Figure 1** is a streak-plate culture of *Staphylococcus aureus*.

Infections are primarily associated with *S. aureus* pathogenic strains that are often responsible for the formation of **abscesses**, localized pus-producing lesions. These lesions most commonly occur in the skin and its associated structures, resulting in **boils, carbuncles, acne,** and **impetigo.** Infections of internal organs and tissues are not uncommon, however, and include **pneumonia, osteomyelitis** (abscesses in bone and bone marrow), **endocarditis** (inflammation of the endocardium), **cystitis** (inflammation of the urinary bladder), **pyelonephritis** (inflammation of the kidneys), **staphylococcal enteritis** due to enterotoxin contamination of foods, and, on occasion, **septicemia.**

Strains of *S. aureus* produce a variety of metabolic end products, some of which may play roles in the organisms' pathogenicity. Included among these are **coagulase,** which causes clot formation; **leukocidin,** which lyses white blood cells; **hemolysins,** which are active against red blood cells; and **enterotoxin,** which is responsible for a type of gastroenteritis. Additional metabolites of a nontoxic nature are **DNase, lipase, gelatinase,** and the fibrinolysin **staphylokinase.**

When there is a possibility of staphylococcal infection, isolation of *S. aureus* is of clinical importance. These virulent strains can be differentiated from other staphylococci and identified by a variety of laboratory tests, some of which are illustrated in Table 1.

In this exercise you will distinguish among the staphylococcal species by performing traditional test procedures, a computer-assisted multitest procedure, or a newer rapid latex agglutination test.

Traditional Procedures

The traditional procedures involve the following steps:

1. **Mannitol salt agar:** This medium is selective for salt-tolerant organisms such as staphylococci. Differentiation among the staphylococci is predicated on their ability to ferment mannitol.

TABLE 1	Laboratory Tests for Differentiation of Staphylococcal Species		
TEST	*S. aureus*	*S. epidermidis*	*S. saprophyticus*
Mannitol salt agar			
Growth	+	+	+
Fermentation	+	–	–
Colonial pigmentation	Generally golden yellow	White	White
Coagulase	+	–	–
DNase	+	–	–
Hemolysis	Generally beta	–	–
Novobiocin sensitivity	Sensitive	Sensitive	Resistant

Following incubation, mannitol-fermenting organisms, typically *S. aureus* strains, exhibit a yellow halo surrounding their growth, and nonfermenting strains do not. It should be noted that other salt-tolerant microorganisms, such as the enterococci, are capable of growth on mannitol salt agar. These two genera are easily differentiated by performing a catalase test. *Staphylococcus* will grow in the presence of catalase while the enterococci will not.

2. **Coagulase test:** Production of coagulase is indicative of an *S. aureus* strain. The enzyme acts within host tissues to convert fibrinogen to fibrin. It is theorized that the fibrin meshwork that is formed by this conversion surrounds the bacterial cells or infected tissues, protecting the organism from nonspecific host resistance mechanisms such as phagocytosis and the antistaphylococcal activity of normal serum. In the coagulase tube test for bound and free coagulase, a suspension of the test organism in citrated plasma is prepared and the inoculated plasma is then periodically examined for fibrin formation, or coagulation. Clot formation within 4 hours is interpreted as a positive result and indicative of a virulent *S. aureus* strain. The absence of coagulation after 24 hours of incubation is a negative result, indicative of an avirulent strain **(Figure 2)**.

3. **Deoxyribonuclease (DNase) test:** Generally, coagulase-positive staphylococci also produce the hydrolytic enzyme DNase; thus this test can be used to reconfirm the identification of *S. aureus*. The test organism is grown on an agar medium containing DNA. Following incubation, DNase activity is determined by the addition of 0.1% toluidine blue to the surface of the agar. DNase-positive cultures capable of DNA hydrolysis will show a rose-pink halo around the area of growth. The absence of this halo is indicative of a negative result and the inability of the organism to produce DNase **(Figure 3)**.

4. **Novobiocin sensitivity:** This test is used to distinguish *S. epidermidis* from *S. saprophyticus*. The Mueller-Hinton agar plate is heavily seeded with the test organism to produce a confluent growth on the agar surface. After the seeding, a 30-μg novobiocin antibiotic disc is applied to the agar surface. Following incubation, the sensitivity of an organism to the antibiotic is determined by the Kirby-Bauer method as shown in **Figure 4**.

STAPH-IDENT System Procedure

A computer-assisted procedure is the API® (Analytical Profile Index) STAPH-IDENT® system (developed by Analytab Products, Division of Sherwood Medical, Plainview, New York). STAPH-IDENT is a rapid, computer-based micromethod for the separation and identification of the newly proposed 13 species of staphylococci. The system consists of 10 microcupules containing dehydrated substrates for the performance of conventional and chromogenic tests. The addition of a suspension of the test organism serves to hydrate the media and to initiate the biochemical reactions. The identification of the staphylococcal species is made with the aid of the differential charts or the STAPH-IDENT Profile Register that is part of the system (Table 2), or both.

(a) Positive coagulase test

(b) Negative coagulase test

Figure 2 Coagulase test. (a) Clot formation indicates a positive result; **(b)** the absence of coagulation is a negative result.

Latex Agglutination Procedure

The latex agglutination test as a rapid diagnostic slide test for *Staphylococcus aureus*. The Remel BactiStaph® diagnostic kit (Fisher Health Care) uses protein-coated latex particles that are able to detect the clumping factor (bound coagulase and protein A) that causes the *S. aureus* to adhere to the black latex particles, producing a visible agglutination.

Figure 3 DNase test. A rose-pink halo around the area of growth on the left side of the plate indicates a positive result, while the absence of a halo on the right is a negative result.

CLINICAL APPLICATION

Staphyloxanthin

Staphylococcus aureus is one of the most common species of staphylococci to cause human disease, producing many types of skin infections as well as life-threatening diseases like meningitis, osteomyelitis, endocarditis, and toxic shock syndrome. Its pathogenic success is due to its immune-evasive properties, mainly through the production of its yellow pigment staphyloxanthin. This pigment behaves as a virulence factor that helps the organism evade the immune system of the host. Blocking the synthesis of staphyloxanthin may present a unique and vital target for antimicrobials.

AT THE BENCH

Materials

Cultures

24-hour Trypticase soy agar slant cultures of *Staphylococcus epidermidis*, *Staphylococcus saprophyticus* (ATCC 15305), and *Staphylococcus aureus* (ATCC e 27660). Number-coded, 24-hour blood agar cultures of the above organisms for the STAPH-IDENT system.

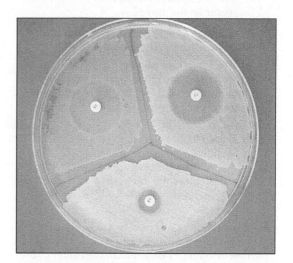

Figure 4 Novobiocin test. *Staphylococcus aureus* and *Staphylococcus epidermidis* (on top) are sensitive to the antibiotic, while *Staphylococcus saprophyticus* (on bottom) is resistant.

Media

Per designated student group: three mannitol salt agar plates, one DNA agar plate, three Mueller-Hinton agar plates, and the STAPH-IDENT system.

Reagents

Citrated human or rabbit plasma, 0.1% toluidine blue, 0.85% saline (pH 5.5–7.0), McFarland barium sulfate standards, and BactiStaph diagnostic kit (latex agglutination test).

Equipment

Bunsen burner, inoculating loop, 13×100-mm test tubes, 15×150-mm test tubes, sterile Pasteur pipettes, 1-ml sterile pipettes, mechanical pipetting device, sterile cotton swabs, 30-µg novobiocin antibiotic discs, glassware marking pencil, metric ruler, forceps, and beaker with 95% ethyl alcohol.

Procedure Lab One

Traditional Procedures

1. Preparation of DNA agar plate culture:
   a. With a glassware marking pencil, divide the bottom of the plate into three sections. Label each section with the name of the organism to be inoculated.
   b. Aseptically make a single line of inoculation of each test organism in its respective sector on the agar plate.

2. Preparation of agar plate cultures for novobiocin sensitivity determination:
   a. Label the three Mueller-Hinton agar plates with the name of the test organism to be inoculated. Inoculate each plate with its respective organism according to the Kirby-Bauer procedure.
   b. Using alcohol-dipped and flamed forceps, aseptically apply a novobiocin antibiotic disc to the surface of each inoculated plate. *Gently* press the discs down with sterile forceps to ensure that they adhere to the agar surface.

3. Preparation of mannitol salt agar plate cultures: Aseptically make a single line of inoculation of each test organism in the center of the appropriately labeled agar plates.

4. Incubation of all plate cultures: Incubate them in an inverted position for 24 to 48 hours at 37°C.

5. Coagulase test procedure:
   a. Label three 13×100-mm test tubes with the name of the organism to be inoculated.
   b. Aseptically add *0.5 ml of a 1:4 dilution of citrated rabbit or human plasma* and 0.1 ml of each test culture to its appropriately labeled test tube.
   c. Examine the bacterial plasma suspensions for clot formation at 5 minutes, 20 minutes, 1 hour, and 4 hours after inoculation by holding the test tubes in a slanted position. Record your observations and results in the Lab Report.
   d. At the end of the laboratory session, place all tubes that are coagulase-negative in an incubator for 20 hours at 37°C.

STAPH-IDENT System Procedure

1. Prepare strip:
   a. Dispense 5 ml of tap water into incubation tray.
   b. Place API strip in incubation tray.

2. Prepare inoculum:
   a. Add 2 ml of 0.85% saline (pH 5.5–7.0) to a sterile 15×150-mm test tube.
   b. Using a sterile swab, pick up a sufficient amount of inoculum to prepare a saline suspension with a final turbidity that is equivalent to a No. 3 McFarland ($BaSO_4$) turbidity standard. *Note: Be sure to use suspension within 15 minutes of preparation.*

3. With a sterile Pasteur pipette, add 2 or 3 drops of the inoculum to each microcupule.

4. Place plastic lid on tray and incubate for 5 hours at 37°C.

Latex Agglutination Procedure

1. Label three of the provided slides (cards) with the name of the organism to be inoculated.

2. Place one drop of *Staphylococcus* latex reagent in the center of the circle on the provided slide.

3. Using an applicator stick or sterile needle, spread one colony of each organism in the reagent of its respective slide.

4. Spread the mixture over the entire circle.

5. Rotate the slide in a circular motion for 60 seconds.

6. Observe all slides for the presence or absence of agglutination. A positive agglutination

reaction usually occurs in 15 seconds and is indicated by a clumping together of the black latex suspension, followed by the loss of the black background. A negative reaction results in little or no agglutination and no loss of the black background within 60 seconds.

7. Record your results as positive (+) or as negative (−) in the chart provided in the Lab Report.

Procedure Lab Two

Traditional Procedures

1. Examine the coagulase-negative tubes, and record your observations in the Lab Report.

2. Examine the mannitol salt agar plate. Note and record the following in the Lab Report.

   a. Presence (+) or absence (−) of growth of each test organism.

   b. Color of the medium surrounding the growth of each test organism.

   c. Whether each test organism is a mannitol fermenter (+) or non–mannitol fermenter (−).

3. Flood the DNA agar plate with 0.1% toluidine blue. Observe for the delayed development of a rose-pink coloration surrounding the growth of each test organism. Record your color observation and indicate the presence (+) or absence (−) of DNase activity in the Lab Report.

4. With a metric ruler, measure the size of the zone of inhibition, if present, surrounding each of the novobiocin discs on the agar plates. A zone of inhibition of 17 mm or less is indicative of novobiocin resistance, whereas a zone greater than 17 mm indicates that the organism is sensitive to this antibiotic. Record the susceptibility of each test organism to novobiocin as sensitive (S) or resistant (R) in the Lab Report.

STAPH-IDENT System Procedure

1. Interpret your STAPH-IDENT system reactions on the basis of the observed color changes in each of the microcupules described in the chart in the Lab Report. Report your color observations and results as (+) or (−) for each test in the Lab Report.

2. Construct a four-digit profile for your unknown organisms using the guidelines provided in the Lab Report.

TABLE 2	API STAPH-IDENT Profile Register				
PROFILE	**IDENTIFICATION**		**PROFILE**	**IDENTIFICATION**	
0 040	STAPH CAPITIS		2 000	STAPH SAPROPHYTICUS	NOVO R
0 060	STAPH HAEMOLYTICUS			STAPH HOMINIS	NOVO S
0 100	STAPH CAPITIS		2 001	STAPH SAPROPHYTICUS	
0 140	STAPH CAPITIS		2 040	STAPH SAPROPHYTICUS	NOVO R
0 200	STAPH COHNII			STAPH HOMINIS	NOVO S
0 240	STAPH CAPITIS		2 041	STAPH SIMULANS	
0 300	STAPH CAPITIS		2 061	STAPH SIMULANS	
0 340	STAPH CAPITIS		2 141	STAPH SIMULANS	
0 440	STAPH HAEMOLYTICUS		2 161	STAPH SIMULANS	
0 460	STAPH HAEMOLYTICUS		2 201	STAPH SAPROPHYTICUS	
0 600	STAPH COHNII		2 241	STAPH SIMULANS	
0 620	STAPH HAEMOLYTICUS		2 261	STAPH SIMULANS	
0 640	STAPH HAEMOLYTICUS		2 341	STAPH SIMULANS	
0 660	STAPH HAEMOLYTICUS		2 361	STAPH SIMULANS	
			2 400	STAPH HOMINIS	NOVO S
1 000	STAPH EPIDERMIDIS			STAPH SAPROPHYTICUS	NOVO R
1 040	STAPH EPIDERMIDIS		2 401	STAPH SAPROPHYTICUS	
1 300	STAPH AUREUS		2 421	STAPH SIMULANS	
1 540	STAPH HYICUS (An)		2 441	STAPH SIMULANS	
1 560	STAPH HYICUS (An)		2 461	STAPH SIMULANS	
2 541	STAPH SIMULANS		6 101	STAPH XYLOSUS	
2 561	STAPH SIMULANS		6 121	STAPH XYLOSUS	

TABLE 2 — API STAPH-IDENT Profile Register (continued)

PROFILE	IDENTIFICATION		PROFILE	IDENTIFICATION	
2 601	STAPH SAPROPHYTICUS		6 221	STAPH XYLOSUS	
2 611	STAPH SAPROPHYTICUS		6 300	STAPH AUREUS	
2 661	STAPH SIMULANS		6 301	STAPH XYLOSUS	
2 721	STAPH COHNII (SSP1)		6 311	STAPH XYLOSUS	
2 741	STAPH SIMULANS		6 321	STAPH XYLOSUS	
2 761	STAPH SIMULANS		6 340	STAPH AUREUS	COAG+
				STAPH WARNERI	COAG−
3 000	STAPH EPIDERMIDIS		6 400	STAPH WARNERI	
3 040	STAPH EPIDERMIDIS		6 401	STAPH XYLOSUS	XYL + ARA+
3 140	STAPH EPIDERMIDIS			STAPH SAPROPHYTICUS	XYL − ARA−
3 540	STAPH HYICUS (An)		6 421	STAPH XYLOSUS	
3 541	STAPH INTERMEDIUS (An)		6 460	STAPH WARNERI	
3 560	STAPH HYICUS (An)		6 501	STAPH XYLOSUS	
3 601	STAPH SIMULANS	NOVO	6 521	STAPH XYLOSUS	
	STAPH SAPROPHYTICUS	NOVO R	6 600	STAPH WARNERI	
			6 601	STAPH SAPROPHYTICUS	XYL − ARA−
4 060	STAPH HAEMOLYTICUS			STAPH XYLOSUS	XYL + ARA+
4 210	STAPH SCIURI		6 611	STAPH XYLOSUS	
4 310	STAPH SCIURI		6 621	STAPH XYLOSUS	
4 420	STAPH HAEMOLYTICUS		6 700	STAPH AUREUS	
4 440	STAPH HAEMOLYTICUS		6 701	STAPH XYLOSUS	
4 460	STAPH HAEMOLYTICUS		6 721	STAPH XYLOSUS	
4 610	STAPH SCIURI		6 731	STAPH XYLOSUS	
4 620	STAPH HAEMOLYTICUS				
4 660	STAPH HAEMOLYTICUS		7 000	STAPH EPIDERMIDIS	
4 700	STAPH AUREUS	COAG+	7 021	STAPH XYLOSUS	
	STAPH SCIURI	COAG−	7 040	STAPH EPIDERMIDIS	
4 710	STAPH SCIURI		7 141	STAPH INTERMEDIUS (An)	
			7 300	STAPH AUREUS	
5 040	STAPH EPIDERMIDIS		7 321	STAPH XYLOSUS	
5 200	STAPH SCIURI		7 340	STAPH AUREUS	COAG−
5 210	STAPH SCIURI	COAG+	7 401	STAPH XYLOSUS	
5 300	STAPH AUREUS	COAG−	7 421	STAPH XYLOSUS	
	STAPH SCIURI		7 501	STAPH INTERMEDIUS (An)	COAG+
5 310	STAPH SCIURI			STAPH XYLOSUS	COAG−
5 600	STAPH SCIURI		7 521	STAPH XYLOSUS	
5 610	STAPH SCIURI	COAG+	7 541	STAPH INTERMEDIUS (An)	
5 700	STAPH AUREUS	COAG−	7 560	STAPH HYICUS (An)	
	STAPH SCIURI		7 601	STAPH XYLOSUS	
5 710	STAPH SCIURI		7 621	STAPH XYLOSUS	
5 740	STAPH AUREUS		7 631	STAPH XYLOSUS	
			7 700	STAPH AUREUS	
6 001	STAPH XYLOSUS	XYL + ARA+	7 701	STAPH XYLOSUS	
	STAPH SAPROPHYTICUS	XYL − ARA−	7 721	STAPH XYLOSUS	
6 011	STAPH XYLOSUS		7 740	STAPH AUREUS	
6 021	STAPH XYLOSUS				

Note: The API STAPH-IDENT Profile Register uses "STAPH" as an abbreviation for Staphylococcus. *The correct scientific abbreviation is* S. aureus, *for example.*

Source: Staph-Ident, Analytab Products, Division of Sherwood Medical, Plainview, New York.

Name: _____

Date: _____ Section: _____

Observations and Results

Traditional Procedures

Staphylococcal Species	APPEARANCE OF PLASMA: CLOTTED (+) OR UNCLOTTED (−)					Coagulase (+) or (−)
	5 min	20 min	1 hr	4 hr	24 hr	
S. aureus						
S. epidermidis						
S. saprophyticus						

Procedure	S. aureus	S. epidermidis	S. saprophyticus
Mannitol salt agar:			
Growth	_____	_____	_____
Color of medium	_____	_____	_____
Fermentation	_____	_____	_____
DNA agar:			
Color of medium	_____	_____	_____
DNase activity	_____	_____	_____
Novobiocin sensitivity:			
Growth inhibition in mm	_____	_____	_____
Susceptibility—(R) or (S)	_____	_____	_____

STAPH-IDENT System Procedure

MICROCUPULE			INTERPRETATION OF REACTIONS		REACTION RESULTS	
No.	Substrate		Positive	Negative	Color	(+) or (−)
1	PHS	p-Nitrophenyl-phosphate, disodium salt	Yellow	Clear or straw-colored		
2	URE	Urea	Purple to red-orange	Yellow or yellow-orange		
3	GLS	p-Nitrophenyl-β-D-glucopyranoside	Yellow	Clear or straw-colored		

→

STAPH-IDENT System Procedure (continued)

MICROCUPULE		INTERPRETATION OF REACTIONS		REACTION RESULTS	
No.	Substrate	Positive	Negative	Color	(+) or (−)
4	MNE Mannose	Yellow or yellow-orange	Red or orange		
5	MAN Mannitol				
6	TRE Trehalose				
7	SAL Salicin				
8	GLC p-Nitrophenyl-β-D-glucuronide	Yellow	Clear or straw-colored		
9	ARG Arginine	Purple to red-orange	Yellow or yellow-orange		
10	NGP 2-Naphthyl-β-D-galactopyranoside	Add 1–2 drops of STAPH-IDENT reagent			
		Plum-purple (mauve)	Yellow or colorless		

Construct a four-digit profile for your unknown organism as follows: A four-digit profile is derived from the results obtained with STAPH-IDENT. The 10 biochemical tests are divided into four groups, as follows:

```
PHS   MNE   SAL   NGP
URE   MAN   GLC
GLS   TRE   ARG
```

Only positive reactions are assigned a numerical value. The value depends on the location within the group.

A value of 1 for the first biochemical in each group (e.g., PHS, MNE)
A value of 2 for the second biochemical in each group (e.g., URE, MAN)
A value of 4 for the third biochemical in each group (e.g., GLS, TRE)
A value of 0 for all negative reactions

A four-digit number is obtained by totaling the values of each of the groups.

Using Table 2 and your four-digit profile number, identify your organism.

Unknown organism: _____

Latex Agglutination Procedure

Record the presence of agglutination as (+), and the absence of agglutination as (−).

	S. aureus	*S. epidermidis*	*S. saprophyticus*
Agglutination			
No agglutination			

Photo Credits

Credits are listed in order of appearance.

Photo 1: Experiment performed and photographed by
L. Brent Selinger, Department of Biological Sciences,
University of Lethbridge, Pearson Education

Photo 2: James Cappuccino

Photo 3: James Cappuccino

Photo 4: James Cappuccino

Identification of Human Streptococcal Pathogens

LEARNING OBJECTIVES

Once you have completed this experiment, you should understand

1. The medical significance of streptococci.

2. Selected laboratory procedures designed to differentiate streptococci on the basis of their hemolytic activity and biochemical patterns associated with the Lancefield group classifications.

Principle

Members of the genus *Streptococcus* are perhaps responsible for a greater number of infectious diseases than any other group of microorganisms. Morphologically, they are cocci that divide in a single plane, forming chains. They form circular, translucent to opaque, pinpoint colonies on solid media. All members of this group are gram-positive, and many are nutritionally fastidious, requiring enriched media such as blood for growth.

The streptococci are classified by means of two major methods: (1) their **hemolytic activity,** and (2) the **serologic classification of Lancefield.** The observed hemolytic reactions on blood agar are of the following three types:

1. **(α) Alpha hemolysis,** an incomplete form of hemolysis, produces a green zone around the colony. α-Hemolytic streptococci, the *Streptococcus viridans* species, are usually nonpathogenic opportunists. In some instances, however, they are capable of inducing human infections such as **subacute endocarditis,** which may precipitate valvular damage and heart failure if untreated. *Streptococcus pneumoniae,* the causative agent of **lobar pneumonia,** will be studied in a separate experiment.

2. **(β) Beta hemolysis,** a complete destruction of red blood cells, exhibits a clear zone of approximately 2 to 4 times the diameter of the colony. The streptococci capable of producing β-hemolysins are most frequently associated with pathogenicity.

3. **(γ) Gamma hemolysis** is indicative of the absence of any hemolysis around the colony. Most commonly, γ-hemolytic streptococci are avirulent.

These hemolytic reactions are shown in **Figure 1.**

Lancefield classified the streptococci into 20 **serogroups,** designated **A** through **V,** omitting **I** and **J,** based on the presence of an antigenic group-specific hapten called the **C-substance.** This method of classification generally implicates the members of Groups A, B, C, and D in human infectious processes.

β-Hemolytic streptococci belonging to **Group A,** and collectively referred to as *Streptococcus pyogenes,* are the human pathogens of prime importance. Members of this group are the main etiological agents of human respiratory infections such as **tonsillitis, bronchopneumonia,** and **scarlet fever,** as well as skin disorders such as **erysipelas** and **cellulitis.** In addition, these organisms are responsible for the development of complicating infections, namely **glomerulonephritis** and **rheumatic fever,** which may surface when primary streptococcal infections either go untreated or are not completely eradicated by antibiotics. The β-hemolytic streptococci found in **Group B** are indigenous to the vaginal mucosa and have been shown to be responsible for **puerperal fever** (childbirth fever), a sometimes-fatal **neonatal meningitis,** and **endocarditis.** Members of **Group C** are also β-hemolytic and have been implicated in **erysipelas, puerperal fever,** and **throat infections.** The enterococci formerly classified as Group D streptococci have been reclassified and are now considered a separate genus. The enterococci differ significantly from other members of Group D, such as *S. bovis,* which may be the etiological agent of urinary tract infections. Enterococci such as *Enterococcus faecalis* may cause infections to the lungs, urinary

From Experiment 64 of *Microbiology: A Laboratory Manual,* Tenth Edition. James G. Cappuccino, Natalie Sherman. Copyright © 2014 by Pearson Education, Inc. All rights reserved.

(a) Alpha hemolysis

(b) Beta hemolysis

(c) Gamma hemolysis

Figure 1 Types of hemolytic reactions on blood agar

tract infections, or bloodstream through an intestinal laceration or poor personal hygiene. The enterococci tend to be antibiotic-resistant, particularly to penicillin and more recently to vancomycin.

The virulence of the streptococci is associated with their ability to produce a wide variety of extracellular metabolites. Included among these are the **hemolysins** (α and β), **leukocidins** that destroy phagocytes, and the **erythrogenic toxin** responsible for the rash of scarlet fever. Also of medical significance are three metabolic end products that facilitate the spread of the organisms, thereby initiating secondary sites of streptococcal infection. These metabolites are **hyaluronidase** (the spreading factor), which hydrolyzes the tissue cement hyaluronic acid; **streptokinase,** a

fibrinolysin; and the **nucleases,** ribonuclease and deoxyribonuclease, which destroy viscous tissue debris.

Although the different groups of streptococci have similar colonial morphology and microscopic appearance, they can be separated and identified by the performance of a variety of laboratory tests. Toward this end, you will perform laboratory procedures to differentiate among the medically significant streptococci on the basis of their Lancefield group classification and their hemolytic patterns. Table 1 will aid in this separation.

Identification of Group A streptococci involves the following procedures:

1. **Bacitracin sensitivity test:** A filter-paper disc impregnated with 0.04 unit of bacitracin

TABLE 1	**Laboratory Differentiation of Streptococci**					
GROUP:	A	B	C	D	K, H, N	
ORGANISMS:	S. pyogenes	S. agalactiae	S. equi	S. bovis NON-ENTEROCOCCI	S. salivarius S. sanguis S. mitis	E. faecalis ENTEROCOCCI
Hemolysis	β	β	β	α → γ	α	α → γ
Bacitracin sensitivity	S	R	R	R	R	R
CAMP test	−	+	−	−	−	−
Bile esculin hydrolysis	−	−	−	+	−	+
6.5% NaCl medium	NG	NG	NG	NG	NG	G
Growth at 10°C	NG	NG	NG	NG	NG	G
Growth at 45°C	NG	NG	NG	NG or G	NG	G

NG = no growth; G = growth; S = sensitive; R = resistant

Figure 2 Bacitracin sensitivity test. Positive for beta-hemolytic Group A streptococci on the left; negative on the right.

CAMP-positive test
Group B streptococci with arrowhead zone of increased hemolysis

Beta-hemolytic *Staphylococcus aureus*

CAMP-negative test
Group A streptococci

Figure 3 CAMP reactions

Figure 4 Positive bile esculin test. A brown-to-black coloration of the medium indicates positive identification of Group D streptococci.

is applied to the surface of a blood agar plate previously streaked with the organism to be identified. Following incubation, the appearance of a zone of growth inhibition surrounding the disc is indicative of Group A streptococci. Absence of this zone suggests a non–Group A organism. **Figure 2** shows the result of a bacitracin sensitivity test.

2. **Directigen™ test:** A rapid, non–growth-dependent immunological procedure for the detection of the Group A antigen, developed by Becton Dickinson and Company. In this test, a clinical specimen is subjected to reagents designed to extract the Group A antigen, which is then mixed with a reactive and a negative control latex. Agglutination with the reactive latex is indicative of Group A streptococci.

Group B streptococci are identified with the **CAMP test** (named for Christie, Atkins, and Munch-Petersen). Group B streptococci produce a peptide, the CAMP substance, that acts in concert with the β-hemolysins produced by some strains of *Staphylococcus aureus*, causing an increased hemolytic effect. Following inoculation and incubation, the resultant effect appears as an arrow-shaped zone of hemolysis adjacent to the central streak of *S. aureus* growth. The non–Group B streptococci do not produce this reaction. **Figure 3** illustrates the CAMP reactions.

Identification of Group D streptococci involves the following:

1. **Bile esculin test:** In the presence of bile, Group D streptococci hydrolyze the glycoside esculin to 6,7-dihydroxy coumarin that reacts

with the iron salts in the medium to produce a brown-to-black coloration of the medium following incubation (**Figure 4**). Lack of this dark coloration is indicative of a non–Group D organism.

2. **6.5% sodium chloride broth:** The enterococci can be separated from the non-enterococci by the ability of the former to grow in this medium. This reaction is shown in **Figure 5**.

Hemolytic activity is identified with a blood agar medium. The pathogenic streptococci, primarily the β-hemolytic, can be separated from the generally avirulent α- and γ-hemolytic streptococci by the type of hemolysis produced on blood agar, as previously described.

CLINICAL APPLICATION

Streptococci Infections

Medically the streptococci are of significant importance because they are responsible for a wide variety of infections, many of which are pyogenic (pus-producing). *Streptococcus agalactiae* (Lancefield group B) may colonize the vagina as well as the upper respiratory tract of humans, and is the most frequent cause of neonatal pneumonia in the United States. Meanwhile, *Streptococcus pyogenes* (Lancefield group A) causes necrotizing fasciitis, a rare but devastating infection that destroys skin, muscle, and underlying tissue. The CAMP test is used to identify Group *A Streptococcus pyogenes* from Group B *Streptococcus agalatiae.*

(a)   (b)

Figure 5 65% sodium chloride test. (a) Growth indicates the presence of Group D enterococci. **(b)** The absence of growth indicates the presence of Group D non-enterococci.

AT THE BENCH

Materials

Cultures

24-hour blood agar slant cultures of *Streptococcus pyogenes* (ATCC 12385), *Enterococcus faecalis*, *Streptococcus bovis*, *Streptococcus agalactiae*, *Streptococcus mitis*, and *Staphylococcus aureus* (ATCC 25923).

Media

Per designated student group: five blood agar plates, three bile esculin agar plates, and three 6.5% sodium chloride broths.

Reagents

Directigen Rapid Group A Strep Test (Becton Dickinson and Company), crystal violet, Gram's iodine, ethyl alcohol, safranin, and Taxo™ A discs (0.04 unit of bacitracin).

Equipment

Bunsen burner, inoculating loop, staining tray, lens paper, bibulous paper, microscope, sterile cotton swabs, glassware marking pencil, sterile 12 × 75-mm test tubes, sterile Pasteur pipettes, sterile applicators, 95% ethyl alcohol in beaker, forceps, and mechanical rotator.

Procedure Lab One

1. Prepare a Gram-stained preparation of each streptococcal culture and observe under oil immersion. Record in the Lab Report your observations of cell morphology and Gram reaction.

2. Prepare the blood agar plate cultures to identify the type of hemolysis as follows:

   a. With a glassware marking pencil, divide the bottoms of two blood agar plates to accommodate the five test organisms. Label each section with the name of the culture to be inoculated.

   b. Using aseptic inoculating technique, make a single line streak of inoculation of each organism in its respective sector on the blood plates.

3. Prepare the blood agar plate cultures for the **bacitracin** test as follows:

   a. With a glassware marking pencil, label the covers of two blood agar plates with the names of the organisms to be inoculated, *S. pyogenes* and *S. agalactiae.*

   b. Using a sterile cotton swab, inoculate the agar surface of each plate with its respective test organism by streaking first in a horizontal direction, then vertically to ensure a heavy growth over the entire surface.

   c. Using alcohol-dipped and flamed forceps, apply a single 0.04-unit bacitracin disc to the surface of each plate. Gently touch each disc to ensure its adherence to the agar surface.

4. Prepare a blood agar plate culture for the **CAMP test** as follows:

    a. Using a sterile inoculating loop, make a single line of inoculation along the center of the plate using the *S. aureus* culture.

    b. With a sterile loop, inoculate *S. pyogenes* on one side and perpendicular to the central *S. aureus* streak, starting about 5 mm from the central streak and extending toward the periphery of the agar plate.

    c. On the opposite side of the central streak, but not directly opposite the *S. pyogenes* line of inoculation, repeat Step 4b using *S. agalactiae*.

5. Prepare the bile esculin agar plate cultures as follows:

    a. Label the three bile esculin plates with the names of the organisms to be inoculated, *S. bovis*, *S. mitis*, and *E. faecalis*.

    b. Aseptically inoculate each plate with its test organism by making several lines of inoculation on the agar surface.

6. Prepare 6.5% sodium chloride broth cultures as follows:

    a. Label three tubes of 6.5% sodium chloride broth with the names of the organisms to be inoculated, *S. bovis*, *E. faecalis*, and *S. mitis*.

    b. With a sterile loop, inoculate each tube with its organism.

7. Conduct the **Directigen test** procedure as follows:

    a. Label two sterile 12×75-mm test tubes as *S. pyogenes* and *S. agalactiae*.

    b. Add 0.3 ml of Reagent 1 to both test tubes.

    c. Using a sterile cotton swab, transfer the test organisms into their respectively labeled test tubes. *Note: These samples will emulate the throat swabs obtained in a clinical solution.*

    d. Add 1 drop of Reagent 2 to each test tube. Mix by rotating the swab against the side of the tube. Allow the swabs to remain in the test tubes for 3 minutes.

    e. Add 1 drop of Reagent 3 to both tubes and mix.

    f. Remove swabs after extracting as much liquid as possible by rolling them against the sides of the tubes.

    g. Place 1 drop of negative antigen control on both circles in Column A of test slide.

    h. Place 1 drop of positive antigen control on both circles in Column B of test slide.

    i. Dispense 1 drop of each streptococcal sample on both circles in Columns C and D, respectively.

    j. Using a new sterile applicator for each specimen, spread each specimen within the confines of both circles in Columns A, B, C, and D.

    k. Add 1 drop of reactive latex to the top row of circles.

    l. Add 1 drop of control latex to the bottom row of circles.

    m. Place the slide on a mechanical rotator for 4 minutes under a moistened humidifying cover.

    n. Compare the agglutination seen in the upper "reactive latex" circles with the consistency of the latex in the bottom "control latex" circles. Any agglutination in the top circles distinct from any background granules seen in the bottom circles indicates Group A streptococci.

8. Incubate all tubes and plates in an inverted position for 24 hours at 37°C.

Procedure Lab Two

1. Examine the two blood agar plates for bacitracin activity. Record in the Lab Report your observations of the presence (+) or absence (−) of a zone of inhibition of any size surrounding the discs.

2. Examine the blood agar plate for the CAMP reaction. Record your observations of the presence (+) or absence (−) of increased arrow-shaped hemolysis.

3. Examine the bile esculin plates for the presence (+) or absence (−) of a brown-black coloration in the medium and record your observations.

4. Observe the 6.5% sodium chloride broth cultures for the presence (+) or absence (−) of growth and record your observations.

5. Examine the two blood agar plates for the presence and type of hemolysis produced by each of the test organisms. Record your observations of the appearance of the medium surrounding the growth and the type of hemolytic reaction that has occurred—α, β, or γ.

6. Observe the Directigen test slide for the presence (+) or absence (−) of agglutination in

the reactive and control latex circles. Based on your observations, indicate the Lancefield group classification of each test organism. Record your results.

7. Based on your observations, classify each test organism according to its Lancefield group.

8. Check that all of your observations have been recorded in the Lab Report.

Observations and Results

Procedure	S. pyogenes	S. agalactiae	S. bovis	E. faecalis	S. mitis
Gram stain: Morphology	_____	_____	_____	_____	_____
Reaction	_____	_____	_____	_____	_____
Bacitracin test: Zone of inhibition	_____	_____	_____	_____	_____
CAMP test: Increased hemolysis	_____	_____	_____	_____	_____
Bile esculin test: Color of medium	_____	_____	_____	_____	_____
Result: (+) or (−)	_____	_____	_____	_____	_____
6.5% NaCl broth: Growth	_____	_____	_____	_____	_____
Hemolytic activity: Appearance of medium	_____	_____	_____	_____	_____
Type of hemolysis	_____	_____	_____	_____	_____

Directigen test:
   Agglutination (+) or (−) in:
      Reactive circle
	_____	_____	_____	_____	_____

Control circle	_____	_____	_____	_____	_____
Lancefield group	_____	_____	_____	_____	_____
Group classification					

Review Questions

1. How do the purposes of the bacitracin and CAMP tests differ?

2. What is the mechanism of the bile esculin test?

3. Why is it important medically to distinguish between the enterococci and the non-enterococci?

4. Why can some streptococci produce secondary sites of infection?

5. The streptococci are known to be fastidious organisms that require an enriched medium for growth. How would you account for the fact that a medium enriched with blood (blood agar) is the medium of preference for growth of these organisms?

Photo Credits

Identification of *Streptococcus pneumoniae*

LEARNING OBJECTIVE

Once you have completed this experiment, you should understand

1. Laboratory procedures to differentiate between *Streptococcus pneumoniae* and other α-hemolytic streptococci.

Figure 1 *Streptococcus pnuemoniae* forms large thick capsules and produces alpha hemolysis on blood agar

Principle

The pneumococcus *Streptococcus pneumoniae* is the major α-hemolytic, streptococcal pathogen in humans. It serves as an etiological agent of **lobar pneumonia,** an infection characterized by acute inflammation of the bronchial and alveolar membranes. These organisms are gram-positive cocci, tapered or lancet-shaped at their edges, that occur in pairs or as short, tight chains. The large, thick **capsules** formed *in vivo* are responsible for antiphagocytic activity, which is believed to enhance the organisms' virulence. In addition, the pneumococci produce α-**hemolysis** on blood agar plates. **Figure 1** shows the effects of *Streptococcus pneumoniae* on blood agar. Because of these properties (short-chain formation, α-hemolysis, and failure of the capsule to stain on Gram staining), the organisms closely resemble *Streptococcus viridans* species. The *S. pneumoniae* can be differentiated from other α-hemolytic streptococci on the basis of the following laboratory tests:

Brief descriptions of the tests and their mechanisms follow:

1. **Bile solubility test:** In the presence of surface-active agents such as **bile** and **bile salts** (sodium desoxycholate or sodium dodecyl sulfate), the cell wall of the pneumococcus undergoes lysis. Other members of the α-hemolytic streptococci will not be lysed by these agents and are bile-insoluble. Following incubation, bile-soluble cultures will appear clear, and bile-insoluble cultures will be turbid.

2. **Optochin sensitivity test:** This is a growth inhibition test in which 6-mm filter-paper discs impregnated with 5 mg of **ethylhydrocupreine hydrochloride** (optochin) and called Taxo P discs are applied to the surface of a blood agar plate streaked with the test organisms. The *S. pneumoniae*, being sensitive to this surface-active agent, are lysed with the resultant formation of a zone of inhibition greater than 15 mm surrounding the P disc. Nonpneumococcal α-hemolytic streptococci are resistant to optochin and fail to show a zone of inhibition or produce a zone less than 15 mm. Sensitivity to optochin is illustrated in **Figure 2.**

Test	S. pneumoniae	S. mitis
Hemolysis	α	α
Bile solubility	+	−
Optochin sensitivity	+	−
Inulin fermentation	+	−
Quellung reaction	+	−
Mouse virulence	+	−

From Experiment 65 of *Microbiology: A Laboratory Manual*, Tenth Edition. James G. Cappuccino, Natalie Sherman. Copyright © 2014 by Pearson Education, Inc. All rights reserved.

Figure 2 Optochin sensitivity test. The formation of a zone of inhibition greater than 15 mm on the left indicates the presence of alpha-hemolytic *S. pneumoniae*. No zone of inhibition on the right indicates the presence of other alpha-hemolytic streptococal species.

In the following experiment, you will use hemolytic patterns, bile solubility, the Quellung reaction, the optochin test, and the inulin fermentation test for laboratory differentiation of *S. pneumoniae* from other α-hemolytic streptococci.

CLINICAL APPLICATION

Pneumococcus Infections

Streptococcus pneumoniae, formerly called *Diplococcus pneumoniae,* appears as a lancet-shaped diplococcus and is unlike all other cocci. The pneumococcus, as it is called, is the causative agent of lobar pneumonia (lung), otitis media (middle ear), and meningitis (meninges) infections. It is currently the leading invasive bacterial disease in children and the elderly. Presently a vaccine is available for people who are designated as high risk for infection with this organism.

AT THE BENCH

Materials

Cultures

24-hour blood agar slant cultures of *Streptococcus pneumoniae* and *Streptococcus mitis.*

Media

Per designated student group: one blood agar plate, two phenol red inulin broth tubes, and four 13×75-mm tubes containing 1 ml of nutrient broth.

Reagents

Crystal violet, Gram's iodine, ethyl alcohol, safranin, methylene blue, 10% sodium desoxycholate, commercially available Taxo P discs (5 mg of optochin), and omnivalent pneumococcal antiserum.

3. **Inulin fermentation:** The pneumococci are capable of fermenting inulin, while most other α-hemolytic streptococci are non–inulin fermenters. Following incubation, the **acid** resulting from inulin fermentation will change the color of the culture from red to yellow. Cultures that are not capable of fermenting inulin will not exhibit a color change, which is a negative test result.

4. **Quellung** (Neufeld) **reaction:** This **capsular swelling** reaction is a sensitive and accurate method of determining the presence of *S. pneumoniae* in sputum. The reaction of the pneumococcal capsular polysaccharide, a hapten antigen, with an omnivalent capsular antiserum (Abcam, Inc.) produces a microscopically visible swollen capsule surrounding the *S. pneumoniae* organisms.

5. **Mouse virulence test:** Laboratory white mice are highly susceptible to infection by *S. pneumoniae* and resistant to other streptococcal infections. Intraperitoneal injection of 0.1 ml of pneumococcus-infected sputum will kill the mouse. Examination of the peritoneal fluid by Gram stain and culture will reveal the presence of *S. pneumoniae.*

Equipment

Bunsen burner, waterbath, inoculating loop, glass slides, coverslips, sterile cotton swabs, sterile 1-ml serological pipettes, mechanical pipetting device, 95% ethyl alcohol in beaker, forceps, and glassware marking pencil.

Procedure Lab One

1. **Bile solubility test**

   a. Label two nutrient broth tubes *S. pneumoniae* and two other tubes *S. mitis*.

   b. Aseptically add 2 loopfuls of the test organisms to the appropriately labeled sterile test tubes to effect a heavy suspension.

   c. Aseptically add 0.5 ml of sodium desoxycholate to one tube of each test culture. The remaining two cultures will serve as controls.

   d. Incubate the tubes in a waterbath at 37°C for 1 hour.

   e. After incubation, examine the tubes for the presence or abence of turbidity in each culture. Record your observations of the appearance (clear or turbid) and bile solubility of each test organism in the Lab Report.

2. **Optochin test**

   a. With a glassware marking pencil, divide the bottom of a blood agar plate into two equal sections and label one section *S. pneumoniae* and the other *S. mitis*.

   b. Using a sterile cotton swab, heavily inoculate the surface of each section with its respective test organism in a horizontal and then vertical direction, being careful to stay within the limits of each section.

   c. Using alcohol-dipped and flamed forceps, apply a single Taxo P disc (optochin) to the surface of the agar in each section of the inoculated plate. Touch each disc slightly to ensure its adherence to the agar surface.

   d. Incubate the plate in an inverted position for 24 to 48 hours at 37°C.

3. **Inulin fermentation test**

   a. Label two phenol red inulin broth tubes with the name of each test organism to be inoculated.

   b. Using aseptic technique and loop inoculation, inoculate each experimental organism in its appropriately labeled tube of medium.

   c. Incubate the tube cultures for 24 to 48 hours at 37°C.

4. **Quellung reaction**

   a. Spread a loopful of each test culture on a separate labeled clean glass slide and allow the slides to air-dry.

   b. Place a loopful of the omnivalent capsular antiserum and a loopful of methylene blue on each of two coverslips.

   c. Place the coverslips over the dried bacterial smears. Prepare a Gram-stained preparation of each test organism and observe under oil immersion. Record your observations of cell morphology and Gram reaction in the Lab Report.

Procedure Lab Two

1. Examine blood agar plates for the presence of hemolysis and optochin activity by measuring the zone of inhibition, if any, surrounding the disc. Record the measurement in the Lab Report and indicate whether each organism is optochin-sensitive (zone of inhibition greater than 15 mm) or optochin-resistant (no zone or less than 15 mm).

2. Observe the inulin fermentation broth cultures containing phenol red and record the color of each culture and whether it is indicative of a positive (+) or negative (−) result in the Lab Report.

3. Examine slides of the Quellung reaction under oil immersion and indicate in the Lab Report the presence (+) or absence (−) of capsular swelling surrounding the blue-stained cells.

Observations and Results

Procedure	*S. pneumoniae*	*S. mitis*

Bile solubility test:
   Appearance of culture
 	
   Bile solubility		

Gram stain:
   Morphology
 	
   Reaction		

Optochin test:
   Zone of inhibition in mm
 	
   Resistant or sensitive		

Inulin fermentation:
   Color of medium
 	
   Fermentation (+) or (−)		

Quellung reaction: Capsular swelling (+) or (−)		

Review Questions

1. Why is it clinically important to distinguish *S. pneumoniae* from other α-hemolytic streptococci?

2. How would you separate *S. pneumoniae* from other α-hemolytic streptococci?

3. What are secondary pneumonias? Why do they develop most frequently following viral infections?

4. Why did it require many years of research to develop an effective, long-term pneumococcal vaccine?

Photo Credits

Credits are listed in order of appearance.

Photo 1: ASM MicrobeLibrary (www.microbelibrary.com)

Photo 2: James Cappuccino

Identification of Enteric Microorganisms Using Computer-Assisted Multitest Microsystems

LEARNING OBJECTIVES

Once you have completed this experiment, you should be familiar with

1. The members of the family Enterobacteriaceae.
2. Laboratory procedures designed to identify enteric pathogens using commercial multitest microsystems.

Principle

The Enterobacteriaceae are a significant group of bacteria that are endogenous to the intestinal tract or that may gain access to this site via a host's ingestion of contaminated food and water. The family consists of a number of genera whose members vary in their capacity to produce disease. The *Salmonella* and *Shigella* are considered to be pathogenic. Members of other genera, particularly *Escherichia* and *Enterobacter*, and to a lesser extent *Klebsiella* and *Proteus*, constitute the natural flora of the intestines and are generally considered to be avirulent. Remember, however, that all can produce disease under appropriate conditions.

The Enterobacteriaceae are gram-negative, short rods. They are mesophilic, nonfastidious organisms that multiply in many foods and water sources. They are all non–spore-formers and susceptible to destruction by common physical and chemical agents. They are resistant to destruction by low temperatures and can therefore frequently survive in soil, sewage, water, and many foods for extended periods.

From a medical point of view, the pathogenic Enterobacteriaceae are salmonellae and shigellae. Salmonellae are responsible for enteric fevers, **typhoid,** the milder **paratyphoid**, and **gastroenteritis.** In typhoid, *Salmonella typhi* penetrates the intestinal mucosa and enters the bloodstream, thus infecting organs such as the gallbladder, intestines, liver, kidney, spleen, and heart. Ulceration

of the intestinal wall, caused by the release of the lipopolysaccharide endotoxin into the blood over a long febrile period, and enteric symptoms are common. **Gastroenteritis** is caused by a number of *Salmonella* species. Symptoms associated with this type of food poisoning include abdominal pain, nausea, vomiting, and diarrhea, which develop within 24 hours of ingestion of contaminated food and last for several days.

Several shigellae are responsible for **shigellosis,** a bacillary dysentery that varies in severity. Ulceration of the large intestine, explosive diarrhea, fever, and dehydration occur in the more severe cases.

Isolation and identification of enteric bacteria from feces, urine, blood, and fecally contaminated materials are of major importance in the diagnosis of enteric infections. Although the Enterobacteriaceae are morphologically alike and in many ways metabolically similar, laboratory procedures for the identification of these bacteria are based on differences in biochemical activities (Figure 1).

In the past, several **multitest systems** have been developed for differentiation and identification of members of the Enterobacteriaceae. They use microtechniques that incorporate a number of media in a single unit. At least six multitest systems are commercially available. The obvious advantages of these units are the need for minimal storage space, the use of less media, the rapidity with which results may be obtained, and the applicability of the results to a computerized system for identification of organisms. There are also certain disadvantages with these systems, including difficulty in obtaining the proper inoculum size since some media require heavy inoculation while others need to be lightly inoculated, the possibility of media carryover from one compartment to another, and the possibility of using inoculum of improper age. Despite these difficulties, when properly correlated with other properties such as Gram stain and colonial morphology on specialized solid media, these systems are acceptable for the identification of Enterobacteriaceae. The most frequently used systems are discussed.

Identification of Enteric Microorganisms Using Computer-Assisted Multitest Microsystems

Figure 1 **Conventional laboratory procedures for isolation and identification of enteric microorganisms**

Enterotube II Multitest System and ENCISE II

The **Enterotube™ II Multitest System** (Roche Diagnostics, Division of Hoffmann-La Roche, Inc.) consists of a single tube containing 12 compartments **(Figure 2a)** and a self-enclosed inoculating needle. This needle can touch a single isolated colony and then in one operation be drawn through all 12 compartments, thereby inoculating all of the test media. In this manner, 15 standard biochemical tests can be performed in one inoculating procedure. Following incubation, the color changes that occur in each of the compartments are interpreted according to the manufacturer's instructions to identify the organisms **(Figure 2b)**. This method has been further refined to permit identification of the enteric bacteria by means of a computer-assisted system called **ENCISE** (Enterobacteriaceae numerical coding and identification system for Enterotube).

Identification of Enteric Microorganisms Using Computer-Assisted Multitest Microsystems

Cap · Handle · Individual compartments · Inoculating needle

(a) Diagram of Enterotube

Inoculated with test organism

Uninoculated control

(b) Inoculated and uninoculated control

Figure 2 Enterotube II multitest system

Plastic strip · Cupule · Microtube · Dehydrated media

(a) Uninoculated control

(b) Inoculated with test organism

Figure 3 The API 20-E system

API (Analytical Profile Index) System

The API® 20-E employs a plastic strip composed of 20 individual microtubes, each containing a dehydrated medium in the bottom and an upper cupule as shown in **Figure 3**. The media become hydrated during inoculation of a suspension of the test organism, and the strip is then incubated in a plastic-covered tray to prevent evaporation. In this manner, 22 biochemical tests are performed. Following incubation, identification of the organism is made by using differential charts supplied by the manufacturer or by means of a computer-assisted system called **PRS** (Profile Recognition System). PRS includes an API coder, profile register, and selector.

In the following experiment, you will inoculate an Enterotube and an API strip with an unknown enteric organism. Following incubation, you will make your identification by two methods: (1) the traditional method of noting the characteristic color changes and interpreting them according to manufacturers' instructions, and (2) the computer-assisted methods illustrated in **Figure 4**.

469

Identification of Enteric Microorganisms Using Computer-Assisted Multitest Microsystems

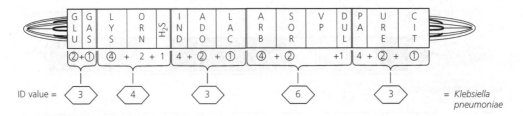

1. Each positive reaction is indicated by circling the number directly below its compartment.
2. The circled numbers in each bracket are added together, and the sum is placed in the box below.
3. The resultant 5-digit number (ID value) is then located in the computer coding manual to identify the organism.

(a) The Enterotube® II

7-digit profile number = | 5 | 1 | 4 | 4 | 5 | 7 | 2 | = *E. coli*

1. The 21 tests are divided into seven groups of three each.
2. A value of 1 is assigned to the first positive test in each group.
3. A value of 2 is assigned to the second positive test in each group.
4. A value of 4 is assigned to the third positive test in each group.
5. A 7-digit number is obtained by totaling the positive values of each of the seven groups of three. This number is located in the analytical profile index to identify the organism.

(b) The API® strip

Figure 4 Computer-assisted techniques for the identification of Enterobacteriaceae

CLINICAL APPLICATION

Enterobacteriacae Infections

The Enterobacteriacae are a very diverse group of bacteria that commonly inhabit the human colon, but can cause a variety of infections throughout the body. In the hospital environment these often result from colonization of intravascular catheters, leading to bacteremia that can progress rapidly to sepsis and septic shock. Once identification of the infectious agent has been made, treatment with effective antimicrobials may be used.

AT THE BENCH

Materials

Cultures

Number-coded, 24-hour Trypticase soy agar streak plates of *Escherichia coli, Salmonella typhimurium, Klebsiella pneumoniae, Enterobacter aerogenes, Shigella dysenteriae,* and *Proteus vulgaris.*

Media

Per designated student group: one Enterotube II, one API 20-E strip, and one 5-ml tube of 0.85% sterile saline.

Reagents

Sterile mineral oil, 10% ferric chloride, Kovac's reagent, VP reagent for API system, nitrate reduction reagents, Barritt's reagent (VP test reagent for Enterotube II system), 1.5% hydrogen peroxide, and 1% p-aminodimethylaniline oxalate (oxidase reagent).

Equipment

Bunsen burner, inoculating loop, 5-ml pipette, mechanical pipetting device, sterile Pasteur pipettes, glassware marking pencil, API profile recognition system and differential identification charts, and Enterotube II ENCISE pads and color reaction charts.

Procedure Lab One

Enterotube II System

1. Familiarize yourself with the components of the system: screw caps at both ends, medium-containing compartments, self-enclosed inoculating needle, plastic side bar, and blue-taped section.

2. Label the Enterotube II with your name and the number of the unknown culture supplied by the instructor.

3. Remove the screw caps from both ends of the Enterotube II. Using the inoculating needle contained in the Enterotube II, aseptically pick some inoculum from an isolated colony on the provided streak-plate culture.

4. Inoculate the Enterotube II as follows:

   a. Twist the needle in a rotary motion and withdraw it slowly through all 12 compartments.

   b. Replace the needle in the tube and with a rotary motion push the needle into the first three compartments (GLU/GAS, LYS, and ORN). The point of the needle should be visible in the H_2S/IND compartment.

   c. Break the needle at the exposed notch by bending, discard the needle remnant, and replace the caps at both ends. The presence of the needle in the three compartments maintains anaerobiosis, which is necessary for glucose fermentation, CO_2 production, and the decarboxylation of lysine and ornithine.

5. Remove the blue tape covering the ADO, LAC, ARB, SOR, VP, DUL/PA, URE, and CIT compartments. Beneath this tape are tiny air vents that provide aerobic conditions in these compartments.

6. Place the clear plastic slide band over the GLU/GAS compartment to contain the wax, which may be spilled by the excessive gas production of some organisms.

7. Incubate the tube on a flat surface for 24 hours at 37°C.

API 20-E System

1. Familiarize yourself with the components of the system: incubation tray, lid, and the strip with its 20 microtubes.

2. Label the elongated flap on the incubation tray with your name and the number of the unknown culture supplied by the instructor.

3. With a pipette, add approximately 5 ml of tap water to the incubation tray.

4. Using a sterilized loop, touch an isolated colony on the provided streak-plate culture, transfer the inoculum to a 5-ml tube of sterile saline, and mix well to effect a uniform suspension.

5. Remove the API strip from its sterile envelope and place it in the incubation tray.

6. Tilt the incubation tray. Using a sterile Pasteur pipette containing the bacterial saline suspension, fill the tube section of each compartment by placing the tip of the pipette against the side of the cupule. Fill the cupules in the CIT, VP, and GEL microtubes with the bacterial suspension.

7. Using a sterile Pasteur pipette, fill the cupules of the AHD, LDC, ODC, and URE microtubes with sterile mineral oil to provide an anaerobic environment.

8. Cover the inoculated strip with the tray lid and incubate for 18 to 24 hours at 37°C.

Procedure Lab Two

Enterotube II System

1. Observe all reactions in the Enterotube II except IND and VP, and interpret your observations using the manufacturer's instructions. Record your observations and results in the Lab Report.

2. Perform the IND and VP tests as follows:

    a. Place the Enterotube II in a rack with the GLU and VP compartments facing downward.

    b. With a needle and a syringe, gently pierce the plastic film of the H_2S/IND compartment and add 2 or 3 drops of Kovac's reagent. Read the results after 1 minute.

    c. As in Step 2b, add 2 drops of Barritt's reagent to the VP compartment and read the results after 20 minutes.

    d. Record your IND and VP observations and results in the Lab Report.

3. Based on your results, identify your unknown organism using the manufacturer's color identification charts.

4. Determine and record in the Lab Report the five-digit ID value as described in **Figure 4a**. Identify your unknown organism by referring to the computer coding manual.

API 20-E System

1. Observe all reactions in the API strip that do not require addition of a test reagent, and interpret your observations using the manufacturer's instructions. Record your observations and results in the Lab Report.

2. Add the required test reagents in the following order: Kovac's reagent to IND, VP reagent to VP (read the result after 15 minutes), ferric chloride to TDA, nitrate reagents to GLU, and oxidase reagent to OXI. Note color changes and interpret your observations according to the manufacturer's instructions. Record your observations and results in the Lab Report.

3. Based on your results, identify your unknown organism using the differential identification chart.

4. Determine and record in the Lab Report the seven-digit profile number as described in **Figure 4b**. Identify your unknown organism by referring to the Profile Recognition System.

Observations and Results

Code	Name	API 20-E		ENTEROTUBE II	
		Appearance (color)	**Result** (+) or (−)	**Appearance** (color)	**Result** (+) or (−)
ONPG	β-Galactosidase				
AHD	Arginine dihydrolase				
LDC/LYS	Lysine decarboxylase				
ODC/ORN	Ornithine decarboxylase				
CIT	Citrate				
H₂S	Hydrogen sulfide				
URE	Urease				
TDA	Tryptophan deaminase				
IND	Indole				
VP	Acetonin				
GEL	Gelatin				
GLU	Glucose				
MAN	Mannitol				
INO	Inositol				
SOR	Sorbitol				
RHA	Rhamnose				
SAC	Sucrose				
MEL	Melibiose				
AMY	Amygdalin				
ARA/ARB	Arabinose				
OXI	Oxidase				
ADO	Adonitol fermentation				
GAS	Gas production				
PHE/PA	Phenylalanine				
LAC	Lactose				
DUL	Dulcitol				
Organism					

Identification of Enteric Microorganisms Using Computer-Assisted Multitest Microsystems

ID value =

Determination of Enterotube II five-digit identification number

Organism _____

Determination of API 20-E seven-digit profile number

Review Questions

1. What are the advantages of multitest systems?

Disadvantages?

2. What Enterobacteriaceae are of medical significance?

List and describe the infections caused by these organisms.

3. Would similar results be obtained by use of the computer-assisted method and the traditional color-change method?

4. What is the clinical justification for the use of a rapid test procedure such as the Enterotube II System for the identification of enteric microorganisms?

Photo Credits

Credits are listed in order of appearance.

Photo 1: Experiment performed and photographed by L. Brent Selinger, Department of Biological Sciences, University of Lethbridge, Pearson Education

Photo 2: Experiment performed and photographed by L. Brent Selinger, Department of Biological Sciences, University of Lethbridge, Pearson Education

Isolation and Presumptive Identification of *Campylobacter*

Principle

Clinicians are aware of the medical significance of *Campylobacter* strains as the etiological agents of enteric infections. The incidence of enteritis caused by *Campylobacter jejuni* equals or exceeds that of salmonellosis or shigellosis. The clinical syndrome, although varying in severity, is generally characterized by acute gastroenteritis accompanied by the rapid onset of fever, headache, muscular pain, malaise, nausea, and vomiting. Twenty-four hours following this acute phase, diarrhea develops that may be mucoid, bloody, bile-stained, and watery. The precise epidemiology of the infection is not clear; however, contact with animals, waterborne organisms, and fecal-oral transmission remain suspect.

The organisms (*campylo*, curved; *bacter*, rod) were formerly called vibrios because of their curved and spiral morphology. In the early 1980s they were reclassified in the genus *Campylobacter*. They are gram-negative and curved or spiral, with a single flagellum located at one or both poles of the cell. In pure culture, two types of colonies have been recognized and designated as Types I and II. The more commonly observed Type I colonies are large, flat, and spread with uneven margins. They are nonhemolytic, watery, and grayish. Type II colonies are also nonhemolytic, but they are smaller (1 to 2 mm), with unbroken edges. They are convex and glistening.

Initially, the isolation of *Campylobacter* organisms from fecal specimens was difficult because of their microaerophilic nature and their 42°C optimal growth temperature. Furthermore, in the absence of selective media, their growth was masked by the overgrowth of other enteric organisms, and they were often overlooked on primary isolation. This situation has been rectified with the development of selective media that are designed specifically for isolating *Campylobacter* species and that inhibit the growth of other enteric organisms. These media are nutritionally enriched and supplemented with 5% to 10% sheep or horse blood. In addition they contain three to five antimicrobial agents, depending on the medium. For example, cephalosporins, one of the antimicrobial agents present in the Campy-BAP medium, is selective for *C. jejuni* and inhibits the species *C. intestinalis*, which is rarely responsible for enteric infections.

The most essential requirement for cultivating campylobacteria is a microaerophilic incubation atmosphere. High concentrations of oxygen are toxic to these organisms, and an atmosphere of 3% to 10% carbon dioxide and 5% to 10% oxygen is optimal for their growth. The incubation temperature for *C. jejuni* is 42°C. At this temperature the organism grows optimally, while growth of *C. intestinalis* is inhibited.

In the experiment to follow, a simulated fecal specimen (a culture containing an attenuated strain of *C. jejuni* and other enteric organisms) is used. You will attempt to isolate the *Campylobacter* organisms by using the following two procedures:

1. A conventional method uses MacConkey agar directly, circumventing enrichment procedures, using a mixed simulated fecal population as the test culture.

2. A special method employs Campy-BAP agar and the CampyPak® and GasPak® jar, which are illustrated in **Figure 1**.

Presumptive identification is made on the basis of colonial morphology and the microscopic appearance of the organisms obtained from a typical isolated colony. You may perform the catalase and oxidase tests for further presumptive identification. In the case of *C. jejuni*, both tests should be positive.

From Experiment 67 of *Microbiology: A Laboratory Manual*, Tenth Edition. James G. Cappuccino, Natalie Sherman. Copyright © 2014 by Pearson Education, Inc. All rights reserved.

medium, *Salmonella typhimurium*, and *Escherichia coli*.

Media

Per designated student group: one Campy-BAP agar plate and one MacConkey agar plate.

Reagents

Crystal violet, Gram's iodine, 95% ethyl alcohol, and 0.8% carbol fuchsin.

Equipment

Bunsen burner, inoculating loop, glassware marking pencil, CampyPak and GasPak jars, and 10-ml pipettes.

Procedure Lab One

1. Aseptically perform a four-way streak inoculation for the isolation of discrete colonies on both appropriately labeled agar plates.

2. Place the inoculated Campy-BAP agar plate in the GasPak jar in an inverted position. Following the manufacturer's instructions, open the CampyPak envelope and place it in the jar. With a pipette, add 10 ml of water to each envelope and immediately seal the jar to establish a microaerophilic environment.

3. Incubate the jar for 48 hours at 42°C.

4. Incubate the MacConkey agar plate culture in an inverted position for 48 hours at 37°C.

Procedure Lab Two

1. Observe both plate cultures for the presence of discrete colonies. Record your observations in the chart provided in the Lab Report.

2. Prepare a Gram stain, using 0.8% carbol fuchsin as the counterstain, of a representative colony agar plate culture. Observe microscopically and record in the Lab Report the microscopic morphology and Gram reaction of each preparation.

3. Based on your observations, identify your isolates and record in the Lab Report.

4. Optional: Perform the catalase and oxidase tests on the representative isolates.

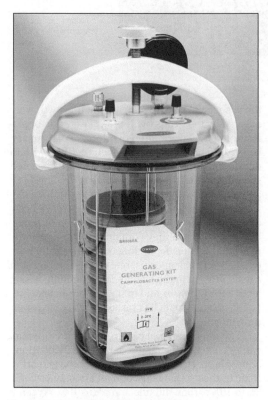

Figure 1 CampyPak and GasPak jar

CLINICAL APPLICATION

Traveler's Diarrhea

Campylobacter is the most common cause of bacterial diarrheal diseases worldwide. It is also referred to as "Traveler's Diarrhea." Poultry and poultry products have been associated with *Campylobacter* infections. Other foods have also been implicated in its transmission. *Campylobacter jejuni* and *Campylobacter coli* are the two most clinically significant and may be isolated from the intestinal tract of poultry. They are slow-growing organisms and are identified by biochemical, immunological, and molecular techniques.

AT THE BENCH

Materials

Cultures

Mixed saline suspensions of *Campylobacter jejuni* cultured on a sheep blood–enriched

Observations and Results

1. In the chart below, diagram the appearance of representative colonies on both plates and describe their colonial characteristics. Also, note and record the color of the medium surrounding the representative colonies on the MacConkey plate.

Plate Culture	Diagram of Colonies	Colonial Characteristics	Color of Medium
Campy-BAP agar			
MacConkey agar			

2. Record your observations of the Gram reactions in the chart below.

| Gram Stain Preparation | Campy-BAP Plate Isolate | MACCONKEY AGAR PLATE | |
		Isolate 1	Isolate 2
Draw a representative field.			
Microscopic morphology			
Gram reaction			

3. Based on your observations, identify your isolates:

   Campy-BAP agar culture isolate: _____

   MacConkey agar culture Isolate 1: _____

   MacConkey agar culture Isolate 2: _____

Review Questions

1. How would you describe the clinical syndrome induced by *C. jejuni*?

2. What are the purposes of the antimicrobial agents present in the selective media used for the isolation of *Campylobacter?*

3. How may *C. jejuni* be separated from *C. intestinalis?*

4. Why might members of *Campylobacter* not be isolated from a stool specimen in a diagnostic laboratory?

Photo Credit

Credits are listed in order of appearance.

Photo 1: Experiment performed and photographed by L. Brent Selinger, Department of Biological Sciences, University of Lethbridge, Pearson Education

Microbiological Analysis of Blood Specimens

LEARNING OBJECTIVES

Once you have completed this experiment, you should be familiar with

1. The microorganisms most frequently associated with septicemia.

2. Laboratory methods for the isolation and presumptive identification of the etiological agents of septicemia.

Principle

Blood is normally a sterile body fluid. This sterility may be breached, however, when microorganisms gain entry into the bloodstream during the course of an infectious process. The transient occurrence of bacteria in the blood is designated as **bacteremia** and implies the presence of nonmultiplying organisms in this body fluid.

Bacteremias may be encountered in the course of some bacterial infections such as pneumonia, meningitis, typhoid fever, and urinary tract infections. A bacteremia of this nature does not present a life-threatening situation because the bacteria are present in low numbers and the activity of the host's innate (nonspecific) immune system is generally capable of preventing further systemic invasion of tissues. A more dangerous and clinically alarming syndrome is **septicemia,** a condition characterized by the rapid multiplication of microorganisms, with the possible elaboration of their toxins into the bloodstream. The clinical picture frequently present in septicemia is that of septic shock, which is recognized by a severe febrile episode with chills, prostration, and a drop in blood pressure.

A large and diverse microbial population has been implicated in septicemia. The major offenders include the following:

1. Gram-negative bacteria, because of their endotoxic properties, are the most frequently encountered etiological agents of the serious complications of septicemia. Among these agents are *Haemophilus influenzae*, *Neisseria meningitidis*, *Serratia marcescens*, *Es-cherichia coli*, *Pseudomonas aeruginosa*, and *Salmonella* spp. Less frequently implicated are *Francisella tularensis* and members of the genera *Campylobacter* and *Brucella*.

2. Gram-positive bacteria that generally do not produce the presenting signs of septic shock include primarily members of the genera *Streptococcus* and *Staphylococcus*.

3. *Candida albicans* is the major fungal invader of the bloodstream.

In the clinical setting, to facilitate the rapid initiation of effective chemotherapy, a culture of the suspect blood sample is required for the isolation and identification of the offending organisms. A blood sample is drawn and cultured in an appropriate medium under both aerobic and anaerobic conditions. Over a period of 3 to 7 days, the cultures are observed for turbidity and Gram-stained smears are prepared to ascertain the presence of microorganisms in the blood. Upon detection of microbial growth in the cultures, transfers onto a variety of specialized agar media are made for the identification of the infectious agent. The schema for this protocol is shown in **Figure 1**.

Two methods are outlined in this exercise. Either method or both methods may be used for the isolation and presumptive identification of the microorganisms in the experimental culture. Both procedures use a simulated blood specimen: a prepared culture containing blood previously seeded with selected microorganisms. The traditional method is a modification of the schema shown in Figure 1. This procedure requires the preparation of Gram-stained smears for the morphological study of the organisms and the inoculation of selected agar media for their isolation and preliminary identification. The alternative method uses the commercially available **BBL Septi-Chek™ System,** a single unit composed of the Septi-Chek culture bottle and the Septi-Chek slide

From Experiment 69 of *Microbiology: A Laboratory Manual*, Tenth Edition. James G. Cappuccino, Natalie Sherman.

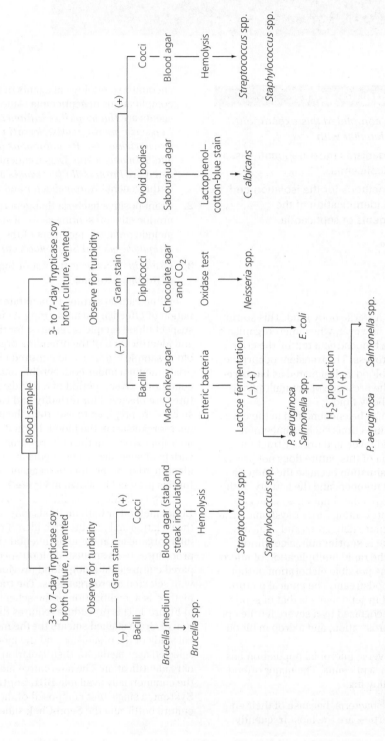

Figure 1 Schema for the isolation and identification of the etiological agents of septicemia

as illustrated in **Figure 2**. The culture-bottle component permits the qualitative determination of the presence of microorganisms in the blood sample, and the slide component is designed for the simultaneous subculturing of the organisms onto a plastic slide containing three differential media (chocolate, MacConkey, and malt agar). Differential growth on these media provides preliminary information as to the nature of the infectious agent and isolated colonies for further study.

Figure 2 Septi-Chek System

AT THE BENCH

Materials

Culture

48- to 72-hour simulated blood culture prepared as follows: 10 ml of citrated blood, obtained from a blood bank, or 10 ml of saline seeded with 2 drops each of *Escherichia coli*, *Neisseria perflava*, and *Saccharomyces cerevisiae*, each adjusted to an absorbance of 0.1 at 600 nm, in 90 ml of Trypticase soy broth containing 0.05% of sodium polyanetholesulfonate (SPS) used to prevent clotting of the blood sample.

Media

Per designated student group: one each of blood agar plate, MacConkey agar plate, chocolate agar plate, Sabouraud agar plate, and Septi-Chek System.

Reagents

Crystal violet, Gram's iodine, 95% ethyl alcohol, safranin, lactophenol–cotton-blue stain, 70% isopropyl alcohol, and 1% *p*-aminodimethylaniline oxalate.

Equipment

Sterile 20-gauge, 1½-inch needles; sterile 1-ml and 10-ml syringes; Bunsen burner; staining tray; inoculating loop; glass microscope slide; lens paper; bibulous paper; microscope; glassware marking pencil; and disposable gloves.

Procedure Lab One

⚠ **Use gloves throughout the procedure.**

1. Swab the rubber stopper of the blood-culture bottle with 70% isopropyl alcohol and allow to air-dry.
2. Using a sterile needle and 1-ml syringe, aseptically remove 0.5 ml of the blood culture by penetrating the rubber stopper.

⚠ **Dispose of the needle and syringe, as a single unit, into the provided puncture-proof receptacle.**

3. To prepare a smear, place a small drop of the culture on a clean glass slide and spread evenly with an inoculating loop.

4. Place 1 drop of culture in one corner of the appropriately labeled blood agar plate and prepare a four-way streak inoculation.

5. Repeat Step 4 to inoculate the MacConkey, chocolate, and Sabouraud agar plates.

6. Incubate the agar plate cultures in an inverted position for 24 to 48 hours as follows: Sabouraud agar culture at 25°C, chocolate agar culture in a 10% CO_2 atmosphere at 37°C, and the remaining cultures at 37°C.

7. Follow the **Septi-Chek System procedure** as follows:

   a. Remove the protective top of the screw cap of the culture bottle, disinfect the rubber stopper with 70% isopropyl alcohol, and allow to air-dry.

   b. Using the 10-ml syringe, aseptically transfer 10 ml of the experimental culture to the appropriately labeled Septi-Chek culture bottle.

   c. Aseptically vent the bottle for aerobic incubation.

   d. Replace the protective top of the screw cap on the bottle.

   e. Gently invert the bottle two or three times to disperse the blood evenly throughout the medium.

   f. Incubate the culture for 4 to 6 hours at 37°C.

   g. Attach the Septi-Chek slide according to the manufacturer's instructions.

   h. Tilt the combined system to a horizontal position and hold until the liquid medium enters the slide chamber and floods the agar surfaces. While maintaining this position, rotate the entire system one complete turn to ensure that all agar surfaces have come in contact with the liquid medium. Return the system to an upright position.

   i. Incubate the system in an upright position at 37°C.

   j. Check the culture bottle daily for turbidity and the slide for visible colony formation.

Procedure Lab Two

1. Examine the blood agar plate culture for the presence (+) or absence (−) of hemolytic activity. If hemolysis is present, determine the type observed. Record your observations in the Lab Report.

2. For the performance of the oxidase test, add p-aminodimethylaniline oxalate to the surface of the growth on the chocolate agar plate. The presence of pink-to-purple colonies is indicative of *Neisseria* spp. Record your observations and the oxidase test results in the Lab Report.

3. Examine the MacConkey agar plate culture for determination of lactose fermentation. Lactose fermenters exhibit a pink-to-red halo in the medium, a red coloration on the surface of their growth, or both a halo and red coloration. Record your observations and indicate the presence or absence of lactose fermenters in the Lab Report.

4. Examine the Sabouraud agar plate culture for the presence of growth. Prepare a lactophenol–cotton-blue–stained smear from an isolated colony. Examine the smear microscopically for the presence of large ovoid bodies indicative of the yeast cells. Record your morphological observations in the Lab Report.

5. Observe the Septi-Chek slide system for the presence of growth on the three agar surfaces. If growth is present on:

   a. Medium 1 (MacConkey agar), examine for fermentative patterns as described in Step 3 and record your observations in the Lab Report.

   b. Medium 2 (chocolate agar), perform the oxidase test as described in Step 2 and record your observations in the Lab Report.

   c. Medium 3 (malt agar), prepare and examine microscopically a lactophenol–cotton-blue–stained smear as described in Step 4. Record your observations in the Lab Report.

Observations and Results

Culture	Traditional Procedure	Septi-Chek System
Blood agar Hemolysis: (+) or (−) Type of hemolysis	_____ _____	_____ _____
Chocolate agar Color of colonies Oxidase test: (+) or (−)	_____ _____	_____ _____
MacConkey agar Color of colonies Color of medium Lactose fermentation: (+) or (−)	_____ _____ _____	_____ _____ _____
Sabouraud or malt agar Cell morphology	_____	_____
Presumptive identification of organisms present	_____	_____

Review Questions

1. Differentiate between septicemia and bacteremia, and explain the medical significance of each.

2. Why are blood samples cultured in both vented and unvented systems?

3. A 15-year-old boy is admitted to the hospital and presents the following symptoms: chills, fever, increased pulse rate, and a drop in blood pressure. The patient indicates that these symptoms have occurred intermittently. The physician suspects a bacteremia and orders a series of three blood cultures over a 24-hour period. Explain the following:

a. Why did the physician order more than one blood culture?

b. Why does blood culture medium contain an anticoagulant?

4. Prior to the introduction of antibiotic therapy, what was the prognosis for patients with septicemia? What significant factors played roles in recovery in the absence of antibiotics?

Photo Credit

Credits are listed in order of appearance.

Photo 1:   Becton dickinson and Company

Microbiological Analysis of Urine Specimens

Principle

The anatomical structure of the mammalian urinary system is such that the external genitalia and the lower aspects of the urethra are normally contaminated with a diverse population of microorganisms. The tissues and organs that compose the remainder of the urinary system, the bladder, ureters, and kidneys, are sterile, and therefore urine that passes through these structures is also sterile. When pathogens gain access to this system, they can establish infection. Some etiological agents of urinary tract diseases are illustrated on this page.

Urinary tract infections may be limited to a single tissue or organ, or they may spread upward and involve the entire system. Infections such as **cystitis** involve the bladder but may spread through the ureters to the kidneys. Infections limited to the ureters and kidneys are called **pyelitis. Glomerulonephritis** is an inflammation that results in the destruction of renal corpuscles; **pyelonephritis** results in the destruction of renal tubules. Organisms other than bacteria may also act as etiological agents of urogenital infections. *Trichomonas vaginalis*, a pathogenic flagellated protozoan, is commonly found in the vagina, and under appropriate conditions, it is responsible for a severe inflammatory **vaginitis.** *Candida albicans*, a pathogenic yeast, is normally found in low numbers in the intestines. Under suitable conditions, such as the use of antibacterial antibiotics, which disrupt the normal intestinal flora and allow *Candida* to proliferate, it can enter the urogenital

systems, where it gives rise to vaginal infections. *Schistosoma haematobium* is a pathogenic fluke, a helminth, responsible for severe bladder infections.

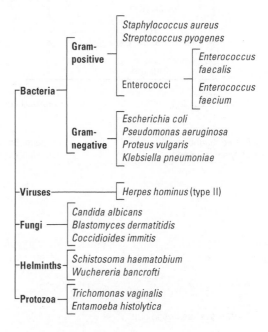

The initial step in diagnosis of a possible urinary tract infection is laboratory examination of a urine specimen. The sample must be collected midstream in a sterile container following adequate cleansing of the external genitalia. It is imperative to culture the freshly voided, unrefrigerated urine sample immediately to avoid growth of normal indigenous organisms, which may overtake the growth of the more slowly growing pathogens. In this event the infectious organism might be overlooked, resulting in an erroneous diagnosis.

Clinical evaluation of the specimen requires a quantitative determination of the microorganisms per ml of urine. Urine in which the bacterial count per ml exceeds 100,000 (10^5) denotes significant **bacteriuria** and is indicative of a urinary tract infection. Urine in which counts range from 0 to 1000 per ml are generally normal.

Microbiological Analysis of Urine Specimens

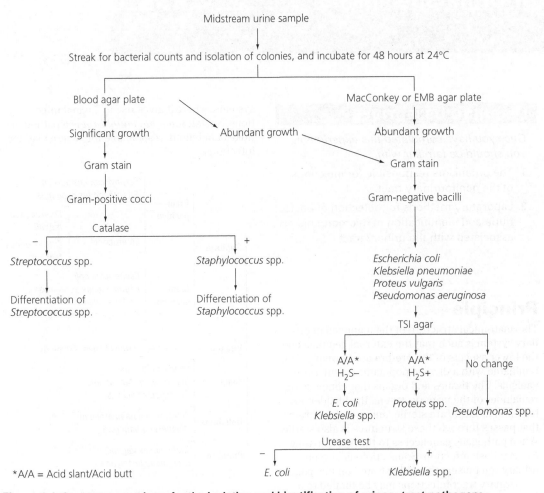

Figure 1 Laboratory procedures for the isolation and identification of urinary tract pathogens

In the conventional method, a urine sample is streaked over the surface of an agar medium with a special loop calibrated to deliver a known volume. Following incubation, the number of isolated colonies present on the plate is determined and multiplied by a factor that converts the volume of urine to 1 ml. The final calculation is then equal to the number of organisms per ml of sample.

Example: Twenty-five colonies were present on a plate inoculated with a loop calibrated to deliver 0.01 ml of a urine specimen.

$$\begin{array}{ccc}
\text{number of} & \text{factor that} & \text{organisms} \\
\text{colonies} \times & \text{converts} = & \text{per ml} \\
& \text{0.01 ml to 1 ml} & \\
\\
25 \times & 100 & = 2500 \text{ organisms} \\
& & \text{per ml}
\end{array}$$

If the specimen is turbid, dilution is necessary prior to culturing. In this case, conventional

10-fold dilutions are prepared in physiological saline to effect a final dilution of 1:1000. Each of the dilutions (10^{-1}, 10^{-2}, and 10^{-3}) is then streaked on the surface of a suitable agar plate medium for isolation of colonies. Following incubation, the number of microorganisms per ml of sample is determined by the following formula:

organisms per ml = number of colonies
  × factor that converts the
    volume of urine to 1 ml
  × dilution factor

Example: Twenty-five colonies were counted on a 10^{-2} dilution plate inoculated with a loop calibrated to deliver 0.01 ml of urine.

Calculation:

$$25 \times 100 \times 100 = 250{,}000 \text{ organisms per ml}$$

488

Microbiological Analysis of Urine Specimens

On determination of bacteriuria, identification of the infectious organism can be accomplished by the laboratory procedures outlined in **Figure 1**.

A newer, less conventional, and less time-consuming method uses a diagnostic urine-culture tube, Bacturcult®, devised by Wampole Laboratories (**Figure 2**). Bacturcult is a sterile, disposable plastic tube coated on the interior with a special medium that allows detection of the bacteriuria and a presumptive class identification of urinary bacteria.

Following incubation of the Bacturcult urine culture, bacteriuria can be detected with a bacterial count. This is performed by placing the counting strip around the Bacturcult tube over an area of even colony distribution and counting the number of colonies within the circle. The average number of colonies counted is interpreted in Table 1.

For the presumptive identification of bacteria, the medium contains two substrates, lactose and urea, and the pH indicator phenol red. Depending on the organism's enzymatic action on these substrates, differentiation of urinary bacteria into three groups following incubation is possible based on observable color changes that occur in the culture:

Group I: *E. coli* and *Enterococcus*—yellow.

Group II: *Klebsiella, Staphylococcus*, and *Streptococcus*—rose to orange.

Group III: *Proteus* and *Pseudomonas*—purplish-red.

Mixed cultures do not always produce clear-cut color changes, however. Therefore, if additional testing is required, the discrete colonies that develop on the medium can be used as the source for subculturing into other media.

Figure 2 Bacturcult culture tube

In this experiment, seeded saline cultures will be used to simulate urine specimens. This is done to minimize the risk of using a potentially infectious body fluid, urine, as the test sample. The conventional procedure performed with the calibrated loop will be used to determine the number of cells in the specimens. The Bacturcult tube will be used for enumeration and presumptive group identification. If your instructor desires to emulate more closely a clinical evaluation of urine, then a mixed seeded culture must be used. Representative colonies isolated from the blood agar streak-plate culture for detection of bacteriuria can then be identified following the schema in Figure 1.

TABLE 1	Bacturcult: Interpretation of Colony Counts	
AVERAGE NUMBER OF COLONIES WITHIN CIRCLE	**APPROXIMATE NUMBER OF BACTERIA PER ML**	**DIAGNOSTIC SIGNIFICANCE**
<25	<25,000	Negative bacteriuria
25 to 50	25,000 to 100,000	Suspicious*
<50	<100,000	Positive bacteriuria

Source: Wampole Laboratories Division, Carter-Wallace, Inc., Cranbury, NJ 08512. Reprinted with permission.

*Additional testing recommended.

The Oldest Clinical Test

Urinary tract infections are among the most frequently occurring problems in clinical medicine. Urine is composed of 95% water with the remainder consisting mainly of urea, uric acid, ammonia, hormones, sloughed squamous cells, proteins, salts, and minerals. Urinalysis is performed for the diagnosis of metabolic or systemic diseases that affect kidney function, for disorders of the kidney and urinary tract, screening for drug abuse, and monitoring patients with diabetes. Urinalysis is considered to be the oldest clinical test, with physical examination of urine for diagnosis having been performed as long as 6000 years ago. Hippocrates, in the 4th century BCE, first realized that urine was a filtrate from the kidneys.

AT THE BENCH

Materials

Cultures

Six saline cultures, each seeded with one of the following 24-hour cultures: *Enterococcus faecalis*, *Staphylococcus aureus*, *Proteus vulgaris*, *Escherichia coli*, *Pseudomonas aeruginosa*, and *Klebsiella pneumoniae*. Optional: Saline culture seeded with a gram-positive and a gram-negative organism.

Media

Per designated student group: three blood agar plates, three sterile 9-ml tubes of saline, and six Bacturcult culture tubes.

Equipment

Bunsen burner, calibrated 0.01-ml platinum loop, glassware marking pencil, sterile 1-ml pipettes, and mechanical pipetting device.

Procedure Lab One

Bacturcult

1. Label each Bacturcult tube with the name of the bacterial organism present in the urine sample.

2. Fill each tube almost to the top with urine.

3. Immediately pour the urine out of each tube, allowing all the fluid to drain for several seconds. Replace the screw cap securely.

4. Immediately prior to incubation, loosen the cap on each tube by turning the screw cap counterclockwise for one-half turn.

5. Incubate the tubes with the caps down for 24 hours at 37°C.

Calibrated Loop for Bacterial Counts

1. Label the three 9-ml sterile saline tubes and the three blood agar plates 10^{-1}, 10^{-2}, and 10^{-3}, respectively.

2. Using the three 9-ml saline blanks, aseptically prepare a 10-fold dilution of the urine sample to effect 10^{-1}, 10^{-2}, and 10^{-3} dilutions.

3. With a calibrated loop, aseptically add 0.01 ml of the 10^{-1} urine dilution to the appropriately labeled blood agar plate and streak for isolation of colonies as illustrated.

4. Repeat Step 3 to inoculate the remaining urine sample dilutions.

5. Incubate all plates in an inverted position for 24 hours at 37°C.

Procedure Lab Two

1. Determine the number of colonies in each of the Bacturcult urine cultures (refer to Lab Report for further instructions).

2. Record your results in the Lab Report.

Observations and Results

Bacturcult Procedure

1. Determine the number of colonies in each of the Bacturcult urine cultures as follows:
   a. Place the counting strip around the tube over an area of even colony distribution and count the number of colonies within the circle.
   b. Repeat the count in another area of the tube.
   c. Average the two counts.
   d. Record in the Lab Report the average number of colonies counted within the circle.
2. Based on your colony count, determine and record in the Lab Report the approximate number of bacteria per ml of each sample and its diagnostic significance as negative bacteriuria, suspicious, or positive bacteriuria.
3. Observe and record in the Lab Report the color of the medium in each of the urine cultures and the presumptive bacterial group.

Urine Culture	Number of Colonies	Number of Bacteria per ml	Diagnostic Significance	Color of Medium	Presumptive Group
E. faecalis					
S. aureus					
K. pneumoniae					
P. vulgaris					
P. aeruginosa					
E. coli					

Calibrated Loop Procedure

Determine the number of colonies on each blood agar culture plate and calculate the number of organisms per ml of the urine. Record your results in the Lab Report.

Urine Sample Dilution	Number of Colonies	Organisms per ml of Sample	Bacteriuria (+) or (−)
10^{-1}			
10^{-2}			
10^{-3}			

Review Questions

1. What types of urinary infections may be caused by different microorganisms?

2. How is a clinical diagnosis of a bacteriuria established?

3. If five colonies were counted on a 10^{-3} dilution plate streaked with 0.01 ml of urine, what was the number of organisms per ml of the original specimen, and is this count indicative of bacteriuria? Explain.

4. How accurate is a laboratory analysis of a 24-hour, unrefrigerated, non-midstream urine sample? Explain.

5. A male patient is diagnosed as having a urinary tract infection. A urine culture is ordered by his physician. She requests that a voided specimen be used rather than a catheterized sample. Why does she make this request?

Species Identification of Unknown Bacterial Cultures

Principle

At this point in the course, you have developed the manipulative skills and the cognitive microbiological knowledge to identify microorganisms beyond their genus classification to the level of their species identification. Therefore, in this experiment, you will use dichotomous keys, *Bergey's Manual of Systematic Bacteriology*, and information accrued from previously performed laboratory procedures to help identify the species of an unknown culture.

Similarly, species identification can be accomplished by using a limited number of carefully selected laboratory procedures. Notice that what appears to be a spurious result in some cases, one that departs from the expected norm for a particular species, may be attributable to strain differences within the given species. These nonconforming results may be verified by the use of *Bergey's Manual* to ascertain the existence of variable biochemical test results for the particular species being studied.

In this experimental procedure, you will receive a mixed culture containing a gram-positive and a gram-negative organism. The protocol will require (1) Gram staining, (2) streak plating for observation of colonial characteristics, (3) use of selective media for the preparation of pure cultures, (4) the performance of appropriate biochemical tests as indicated in the dichotomous keys outlined in **Figure 1** and **Figure 2** and (5) information in *Bergey's Manual.*

CLINICAL APPLICATION

New Molecular Techniques for Rapid Species Identification

Once bacteria from blood or other tissues has been cultured, the organisms must be positively identified. While biochemical and serological tests are the norm for such identification, a recently developed technique of mass spectrometry using matrix-assisted laser desorption/ionization (MALDI) offers a quicker (less than one hour after detection in blood) way to identify organisms. This technique releases key molecules from the organisms in question and, using analysis of the size-to-charge ratios of the molecules and specialized computer software, provides accurate identification of infectious organisms and may provide a future alternative or addition to both biochemical and genomic identification schemes.

AT THE BENCH

Materials

Cultures

Per student: number-coded, 24- to 48-hour mixed Trypticase soy broth cultures each containing a gram-positive and a gram-negative organism selected from the species listed in Figures 1 and 2.

From Experiment 70 of *Microbiology: A Laboratory Manual*, Tenth Edition. James G. Cappuccino, Natalie Sherman.

Species Identification of Unknown Bacterial Cultures

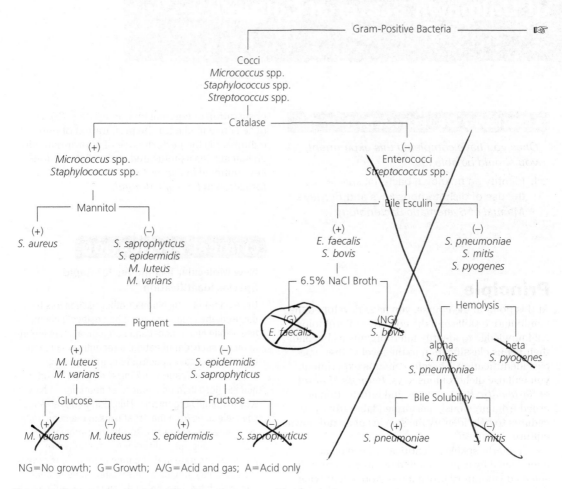

Figure 1 **Schema for the identification of gram-positive bacteria**

NG=No growth; G=Growth; A/G=Acid and gas; A=Acid only

Media

Per student: one Trypticase soy agar plate, two Trypticase soy agar slants, one Trypticase soy broth, one phenylethyl alcohol agar plate, and one MacConkey agar plate.

Required media for the biochemical tests listed in Figures 1 and 2 should be available on your request.

Reagents

Crystal violet, Gram's iodine, 95% ethyl alcohol, safranin, and required reagents for the interpretation of the biochemical reactions listed in Figures 1 and 2.

Equipment

Bunsen burner, inoculating loop and needle, staining tray, immersion oil, lens paper, bibulous paper, microscope, and glassware marking pencil.

Procedure Lab One

Separation of the Bacteria in Mixed Unknown Culture

1. Prepare a Trypticase soy agar broth subculture of the unknown and refrigerate following incubation. You will use this culture if contamination of the test culture is suspected during the identification procedure.

Species Identification of Unknown Bacterial Cultures

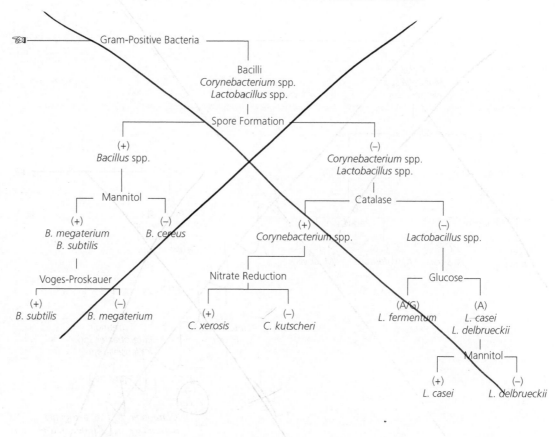

NG= No growth; G= Growth; A/G= Acid and gas; A= Acid only

Figure 1 (continued) Schema for the identification of gram-positive bacteria

2. Prepare a Gram-stained smear of the original unknown culture. Examine the smear and record your observations in the Lab Report.

3. Prepare four-way streak inoculations on the following media for the separation of the microorganisms in the mixed cultures:

    a. Trypticase soy agar for observation of colonial characteristics.

    b. Phenylethyl alcohol agar for isolation of gram-positive bacteria.

    c. MacConkey agar for isolation of gram-negative bacteria.

4. Incubate all the plates in an inverted position and then subculture for 24 to 48 hours at 37°C.

Procedure Lab Two
Preparation of Pure Cultures

1. Isolate a discrete colony on both the phenylethyl alcohol agar plate and the MacConkey agar plate and aseptically transfer each onto a Trypticase soy agar slant.

2. Incubate the Trypticase soy agar slants for 24 to 48 hours at 37°C.

Species Identification of Unknown Bacterial Cultures

Gram-Negative Bacteria ——— ☞

Cocci
Moraxella spp.
Neisseria spp.

Glucose

(+)
Neisseria spp.

(−)
Moraxella spp.

Lactose ——————— ☞

(+)
Citrobacter spp.
Enterobacter spp.
Escherichia spp.
Klebsiella spp.

Nitrate
Reduction

(+)
N. mucosa

(−)
N. sicca

Nitrate
Reduction

(+)
M. catarrhalis

(−)
M. bovis

Indole

(+)
C. intermedius
E. coli

(−)
C. freundii
Enterobacter spp.
Klebsiella spp.

Citrate

(+)
C. intermedius

(−)
E. coli

Methyl Red

(+)
C. freundii
K. ozaenae

(−)
E. aerogenes
K. pneumoniae

H₂S Production

(+)
C. freundii

(−)
K. ozaenae

Urea

(+)
K. pneumoniae

(−)
E. aerogenes

NG=No growth; G=Growth; A/G=Acid and gas; A=Acid only

Figure 2 Schema for the identification of gram-negative bacteria

Procedure Lab Three
Preparation of Pure Cultures

1. Examine the Trypticase soy agar plate for the appearance of discrete colonies. Select two colonies that differ in appearance and record their colonial morphologies in the Lab Report.

2. Examine the phenylethyl alcohol and MacConkey agar plates. Record your observations in the Lab Report.

Identification of Unknown Bacterial Species

1. Prepare a Gram-stained smear from each of the Trypticase soy agar slant cultures to verify their purity by means of the Gram reaction and cellular morphology. Examine the smears and record your observations in the Lab Report.

2. If each Gram-stained preparation is not solely gram-positive or gram-negative, repeat the steps in Labs One and Two, using the

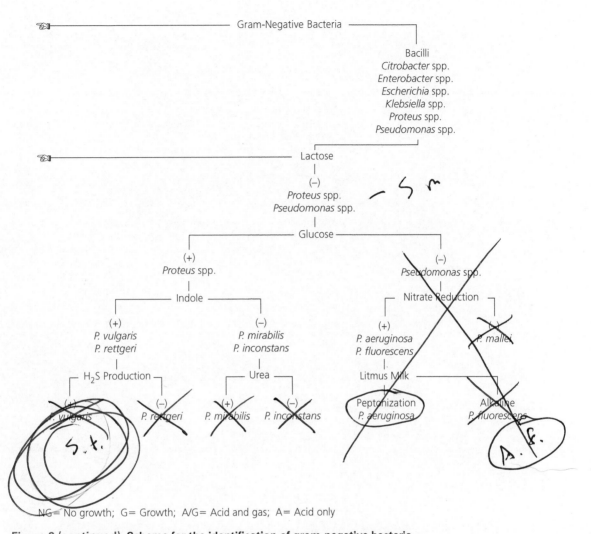

Figure 2 (continued) Schema for the identification of gram-negative bacteria

refrigerated Trypticase soy agar subculture as the test culture.

3. If the isolates are deemed to be pure on the basis of their cultural and cellular morphologies, continue with the identification procedure. During this period and in subsequent sessions, use the dichotomous keys in Figures 1 and 2 to select and perform the necessary biochemical tests on each of your isolates for identification of their species. Incubate all cultures for 24 to 48 hours at 37°C.

Procedure Lab Four

Identification of Unknown Bacterial Species

1. Examine all the biochemical test cultures and record your observation and results in the Lab Report.

Observations and Results

Separation of the Bacteria in Mixed Unknown Culture

Record your observations of the Gram-stained smear of your mixed unknown culture in the chart below.

Organism	Cellular Morphology	Gram Reaction
1		
2		

Preparation of Pure Cultures

1. Select from the Trypticase soy agar plates two colonies that differ in appearance, and record their colonial morphologies.

    Isolate 1:

    Isolate 2:

2. Record your observations of the phenylethyl alcohol and MacConkey agar plates in the chart below.

Medium	Growth (+) or (−)	Colonial Morphology	Coloration of Medium
Phenylethyl alcohol agar			
MacConkey agar			

Identification of Unknown Bacterial Species

1. Record your observations of the Gram-stained smears of the Trypticase soy agar cultures obtained from the phenylethyl alcohol and MacConkey agar plates in the chart below.

Agar Slant From	Cellular Morphology	Gram Reaction
Phenylethyl alcohol agar plate culture		
MacConkey agar plate culture		

Species Identification of Unknown Bacterial Cultures

2. Record your observations and results of all the biochemical tests in the charts below.

GRAM-POSITIVE ISOLATE		
Biochemical Test	Observation	Result

Unknown gram-positive organism: _____

GRAM-NEGATIVE ISOLATE		
Biochemical Test	Observation	Result

Unknown gram-negative organism: _____

Illustration Credits

All illustrations by Precision Graphics unless otherwise noted.

1: Wampole Laboratories Division, Carter-Wallace, Inc., Cranbury, NJ.

Photo Credits

Credits are listed in order of appearance.

Photo 1: Experiment performed and photographed by L. Brent Selinger, Department of Biological Sciences, University of Lethbridge, Pearson Education

Photo 2: Experiment performed and photographed by L. Brent Selinger, Department of Biological Sciences, University of Lethbridge, Pearson Education

Photo 3: Experiment performed and photographed by L. Brent Selinger, Department of Biological Sciences, University of Lethbridge, Pearson Education

Photo 4: James Cappuccino

Photo 5: James Cappuccino

Photo 6: James Cappuccino

Photo 7: Experiment performed and photographed by L. Brent Selinger, Department of Biological Sciences, University of Lethbridge, PearsonEducation

Photo 8: Experiment performed and photographed by L. Brent Selinger, Department of Biological Sciences, University of Lethbridge, Pearson Education

Photo 9: James Cappuccino

Photo 10: James Cappuccino

Photo 11: James Cappuccino

Photo 12: James Cappuccino

Photo 13: Experiment performed and photographed by L. Brent Selinger, Department of Biological Sciences, University of Lethbridge, Pearson Education

Photo 14: James Cappuccino

Photo 15: Experiment performed and photographed by L. Brent Selinger, Department of Biological Sciences, University of Lethbridge, Pearson Education

Photo 16: James Cappuccino

Photo 17: James Cappuccino

Photo 18: ASM MicrobeLibrary (www.microbelibrary.com)

Photo 19: James Cappuccino

Photo 20: Experiment performed and photographed by L. Brent Selinger, Department of Biological Sciences, University of Lethbridge, Pearson Education

Photo 21: Experiment performed and photographed by L. Brent Selinger, Department of Biological Sciences, University of Lethbridge, Pearson Education

Photo 22: Experiment performed and photographed by L. Brent Selinger, Department of Biological Sciences, University of Lethbridge, Pearson Education

Photo 23: Becton dickinson and Company

Immunology

LEARNING OBJECTIVES

Once you have completed the experiments in this section, you should be familiar with

1. The basic principles of nonspecific (innate) and specific (acquired) immunity.
2. Serological procedures that demonstrate immunological reactions of agglutination and precipitin formation.
3. Rapid immunodiagnostic screening procedures.

Introduction

Immunity, or **resistance,** is a state in which a person, either naturally or by some acquired mechanism, is protected from contracting certain diseases or infections. The ability to resist disease may be innate (nonspecific), or it may be adaptive (also called acquired, or specific), when the disease state is stimulated in the host.

Innate immunity is native or natural. It is inborn and provides the basic mechanisms that defend the host against intrusion of foreign substances or agents of disease. This defense is not restricted to a single or specific foreign agent, but it provides the body with the ability to resist many pathological conditions. The mechanisms responsible for this native immunity include the **mechanical barriers,** such as the skin and mucous membranes; **biochemical factors,** such as antimicrobial substances present in the body fluids; and the more sophisticated process of **phagocytosis** and action of the **reticuloendothelial** system.

Adaptive immunity, **cell-mediated** and **humoral,** is acquired by the host in response to the presence of a single or particular foreign substance, usually protein, called an **antigen** (immunogen). In humoral immunity, antigens that penetrate the mechanical barriers of the host, namely the skin and mucous membranes, stimulate formation of **antibodies.** The function of the antibodies is to bind to the specific antigens that are responsible for their production and to inactivate or destroy them. Antibodies are a group of homologous proteins called **immunoglobulins,** which are found in serum and represent five distinct classes: immunoglobulin G (IgG), immunoglobulin A (IgA), immunoglobulin M (IgM), immunoglobulin D (IgD), and immunoglobulin E (IgE).

The primary immunological complexes (antigen + antibody) are as follows:

1. **Agglutination:** This type of reaction uses specific antibodies, **agglutinins,** that are formed in response to the introduction of particulate antigens into host tissues. When these particulate antigens combine with a homologous antiserum, a three-dimensional mosaic complex occurs. This is called an agglutination reaction and can be visualized microscopically and in some cases macroscopically.

2. **Precipitin formation:** This reaction requires specific antibodies, **precipitins,** that are formed in response to the introduction of soluble, nonparticulate antigens into host tissues. These antibodies, when present in serum, form a complex with the specific homologous nonparticulate antigen and result in a visible precipitate.

Advances in chemistry, especially immunochemistry, have enabled us to study the interaction of antigens and immunoglobulins outside the body, in a laboratory setting. These advances have provided an immunological discipline known as **serology,** which studies these *in vitro* reactions that have diagnostic, therapeutic, and epidemiological implications.

In the experiments to follow, you will study several serological procedures based on the principles of agglutination and precipitin formation for the detection of serum antibodies or antigens. The techniques presented in these experiments span a spectrum of methods, ranging from basic reactions to more sophisticated forms of antigen and antibody interactions.

⚠ Note that some of the experimental protocols use positive and negative controls provided in the test kits to demonstrate the desired immunological reactions. These controls do not represent the source of potential pathogens capable of inducing infection in students and instructional staff. The rationale for this design is that body fluids, particularly blood of unknown origin, may serve as a major vehicle for the transmission of infectious viral agents. Thus, our concern with the spread of AIDS and hepatitis precludes the use of blood as a test specimen in a college laboratory.

It is further suggested that your instructor present experiments that use positive and negative control test kits as laboratory demonstrations. This will reduce the cost of the required materials, which may otherwise be prohibitive at many academic institutions, but will still allow you and your fellow students to observe the advances in immunological serology.

Precipitin Reaction: The Ring Test

Principle

The **ring** or **interfacial test** is a simple serological technique that illustrates the precipitin reaction in solution. This antigen-antibody reaction can be demonstrated by the formation of a visible precipitate, a flocculent or granular turbidity, in the test fluid. Antiserum is introduced into a small-diameter test tube, and the antigen is then carefully added to form a distinct upper layer. Following a period of incubation of up to 4 hours, a ring of precipitate forms at the point of contact (interface) in the presence of the antigen-antibody reaction. The rate at which the visible ring forms depends on the concentration of antibodies in the serum and the concentration of the antigen.

To detect the precipitin reaction, a series of dilutions of the antigen is used because both insufficient (zone of antibody excess) and excessive (zone of antigen excess) amounts of antigen will prevent the formation of a visible precipitate (zone of equivalence), as shown in **Figure 1**. In addition, you will be able to determine the optimal antibody:antigen ratio by the presence of a pronounced layer of granulation at the interface of the antiserum and antigen solution. This immunological reaction is illustrated in **Figure 2**.

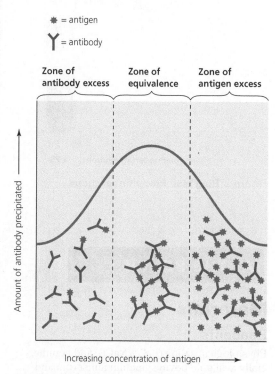

Figure 1 **The precipitin reaction**

Precipitin Reaction: The Ring Test

Bovine serum dilutions: 1:25   1:50   1:75   Control

Figure 2 Ring test: Precipitin reactions

Materials

Reagents

Physiological saline (0.85% NaCl), and commercially available bovine globulin antiserum and normal bovine serum diluted to 1:25, 1:50, and 1:75 with physiological saline. The normal bovine serum contains the antigen (bovine globulin), to which antibodies were made commercially in another animal species and provided as antiserum to bovine globulin.

Equipment

Serological test tubes (8 × 75 mm), 0.5-ml pipettes, serological test tube rack, mechanical pipetting device, glassware marking pencil, and 37°C incubator.

Procedure

1. Label three serological test tubes according to the antigen dilution to be used (1:25, 1:50, and 1:75) and the fourth test tube as a saline control.

2. Using a different 0.5-ml pipette, transfer 0.3 ml of each of the normal bovine serum dilutions into its appropriately labeled test tube.

3. Using a clean 0.5-ml pipette, transfer 0.3 ml of saline into the test tube labeled as control.

4. Carefully overlay all four test tubes with 0.3 ml of bovine globulin antiserum. To prevent mixing of the sera, tilt the test tube and allow the antiserum to run down the side of the test tube.

5. Incubate all test tubes for 30 minutes at 37°C.

6. Examine all test tubes for the development of a ring of precipitation at the interface. Indicate the presence or absence of a ring in the Lab Report.

7. Determine and record the antigen dilution that produced the greatest degree of precipitation; this is indicative of the optimal antibody:antigen ratio.

Observations and Results

Observations and Results

Observations and Results

	ANTIGEN DILUTIONS			
	1:25	**1:50**	**1:75**	**Saline Control**
Presence of interfacial ring: (+) or (−)				

Dilution showing optimal antibody:antigen ratio is _____.

Review Questions

1. How do precipitin and agglutination reactions differ?

2. How would you determine the optimal antigen:antibody ratio by means of the ring test?

3. Why is it essential to use a series of antigen dilutions in this procedure?

4. How would you explain the absence of visible precipitate?

Agglutination Reaction: The Febrile Antibody Test

(a)   (b)

Figure 1 Agglutination reaction. (a) Visible clumping indicates the presence of homologous antibodies in the serum, and a positive reaction. **(b)** The lack of visible clumping indicates the absence of homologous antibodies, and a negative reaction.

Principle

The **febrile antibody test** is used in the diagnosis of diseases that produce febrile (fever) symptoms. Some of the microorganisms responsible for febrile conditions are salmonellae, brucellae, and rickettsiae. **Febrile antigens,** such as endotoxins, enzymes, and other toxic end products, elaborated by these organisms are used specifically to detect or exclude the homologous antibodies that develop in response to these antigens during infection.

In this procedure, the antigen is mixed on a slide with the serum being observed. Cellular clumping is indicative of the presence of homologous antibodies in the serum; the absence of homologous antibodies is indicated when there is no visible clumping. Only the febrile antigens and antibodies of *Salmonella* spp. will be used. **Figure 1** shows a positive and a negative agglutination reaction.

The second part of this experiment is designed to illustrate that agglutination reactions such as the febrile antibody test can be used to identify an unknown microorganism through serotyping. A specific antiserum prepared in a susceptible, immunologically competent laboratory animal is mixed with a variety of unknown bacterial antigen preparations on slides. The bacterial antigen that is agglutinated by the antiserum is identified and confirmed to be the agent of infection.

These tests are strictly qualitative. A quantitative result can be obtained by performing the **antibody titer test,** which measures the concentration of an antibody in the serum and thus allows the physician to follow the course of an infection. The patient's serum is titrated (diluted), and the decreasing concentrations of the antiserum are mixed with a constant concentration of homologous antigen. The end point of the test will occur in the test tube containing the serum having the highest dilution showing agglutination.

CLINICAL APPLICATION

Febrile Disease Diagnosis

Febrile antigens are standardized suspensions of bacteria or bacterial antigens used to qualify or quantify specific serum antibodies that develop during some febrile infections. Based on the Widal Agglutination test for the diagnosis of typhoid fever, serum from patients can be tested for the presence of antibodies correlating to infectious diseases such as brucellosis, salmonellosis, and some rickettsial infections.

From Experiment 72 of *Microbiology: A Laboratory Manual*, Tenth Edition. James G. Cappuccino, Natalie Sherman.

AT THE BENCH

Materials

Cultures

Number-coded, washed saline suspensions of *Escherichia coli*, *Proteus vulgaris*, *Salmonella typhimurium*, and *Shigella dysenteriae*.

Reagents

Physiological saline (0.85% NaCl), commercial preparations of *Salmonella typhimurium* H antigen, and *Salmonella typhimurium* H antiserum (Abcam, Inc.).

Equipment

Bunsen burner, inoculating loop, glass microscope slides, 13×100-mm test tubes, sterile 1-ml pipettes, mechanical pipetting device, applicator sticks, glassware marking pencil, microscope, and waterbath.

Procedure

Febrile Antibody Test

1. With a glassware marking pencil, make two circular areas about ½ inch in diameter on a microscope slide. Label the circles A and B.

2. To Area A, add 1 drop of *S. typhimurium* H antigen and 1 drop of 0.85% saline. Mix the two with an applicator stick.

3. To Area B, add 1 drop of *S. typhimurium* H antigen and 1 drop of *S. typhimurium* H antiserum. Mix the two with a clean applicator stick.

4. Pick up the slide, and with two fingers of one hand, rock the slide back and forth.

5. Observe the slide both macroscopically and microscopically, under low power, for cellular clumping (agglutination).

6. Indicate the presence or absence of macroscopic and microscopic agglutination, and draw a representative field of Areas A and B in the Lab Report.

Serological Identification of an Unknown Organism

1. Prepare two microscope slides as in the previous procedure. Label the four areas on the slides with the numbers of your four unknown cultures.

2. Into each area on both slides, place 1 drop of *S. typhimurium* H antiserum.

3. With a sterile inoculating loop, suspend a loopful of each number-coded unknown culture in the drop of antiserum in its appropriately labeled area on the slides.

4. Pick up the slides and slowly rock them back and forth.

5. Observe both slides macroscopically and microscopically, under low power, for agglutination.

6. In the Lab Report, indicate the presence or absence of macroscopic and microscopic agglutination in each of the suspensions. Also, indicate the suspension that is indicative of a homologous antigen-antibody reaction.

Determination of Antibody Titer

Refer to **Figure 2** when reading the following instructions.

1. Place a row of 10 test tubes (13×100 mm) in a rack and number the tubes 1 through 10.

2. Pipette 1.8 ml of 0.85% saline into the first tube and 1 ml into each of the remaining nine tubes.

3. Into Tube 1, pipette 0.2 ml of *Salmonella typhimurium* H antiserum. Mix thoroughly by pulling the fluid up and down in the pipette. *Note: Avoid vigorous washing.* The antiserum has now been diluted 10 times (1:10).

4. Using a clean pipette, transfer 1 ml from Tube 1 to Tube 2 and mix thoroughly as described. Using the same pipette, transfer 1 ml from Tube 2 to Tube 3. Continue this procedure through Tube 9.

5. Discard 1 ml from Tube 9. Tube 10 will serve as the antigen control and therefore will not contain antiserum.

Agglutination Reaction: The Febrile Antibody Test

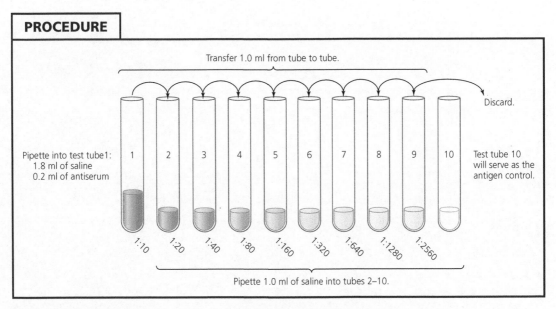

Figure 2 **Antibody titer test.** Serial dilution of *Salmonella typhimurium* H antibody

6. The antiserum has been diluted during this twofold dilution to give final dilutions of 1:10, 1:20, 1:40, 1:80, 1:160, 1:320, 1:640, 1:1280, and 1:2560.

7. Add 1 ml of the *Salmonella typhimurium* H antigen suspension adjusted to an absorbance of 0.5 at 600 nm to all tubes.

8. Mix the contents of the test tubes by shaking the rack vigorously.

9. Incubate the test tubes in a 55°C waterbath for 2 to 3 hours.

10. In the Lab Report, indicate the presence or absence of agglutination in each of the antiserum dilutions. Also, indicate the end point of the reaction.

Name: _____

Date: _____   Section: _____

Observations and Results

Febrile Antibody Test

	Area A	Area B
Draw the appearance of the mixture and of the control.	Saline *S. typhimurium* H antigen	*S. typhimurium* H antiserum *S. typhimurium* H antigen
Macroscopic agglutination (+) or (−)		
Microscopic agglutination (+) or (−)		

Serological Identification of an Unknown Organism

		AGGLUTINATION		
Cell Antigen	**Antiserum**	**Macroscopic (+) or (−)**	**Microscopic (+) or (−)**	**Homologous Antigen-Antibody Reaction**
Unknown No: ____	*S. typhimurium* H			
Unknown No: ____	*S. typhimurium* H			
Unknown No: ____	*S. typhimurium* H			
Unknown No: ____	*S. typhimurium* H			

Determination of Antibody Titer

Tube	Dilution	Agglutination	Titer
1	1:10		
2	1:20		
3	1:40		
4	1:80		
5	1:160		
6	1:320		
7	1:640		
8	1:1280		
9	1:2560		
10	Antigen control		

Review Questions

1. What are febrile antibodies?

   What is their clinical significance?

2. What is the purpose of determining an antibody titer?

3. Why does the antibody titer determination use twofold dilutions of the antiserum rather than 10-fold dilutions?

Photo Credit

Credits are listed in order of appearance.

Photo 1: LeBeau Custom Medical Stock Photo, Newscom

Immunofluorescence

CLINICAL APPLICATION

Diagnosis of Immunobullous Skin Diseases

Immunofluorescence testing is a necessary part of the accurate diagnosis of immunobullous skin diseases and other immune diseases of the skin resulting from autoantibodies to epidermal cells or tissues. Direct immunofluorescence is the diagnostic gold standard in the assessment of patients with these diseases. A fixed and sectioned skin biopsy from a patient's lesion is treated with fluorescent marker conjugated antibodies to human immunoglobulins to test for the presence of autoantibodies.

Principle

The **fluorescent antibody technique,** introduced by Coombs in the mid-1950s, is a rapid and reliable procedure to demonstrate agglutination reactions. It has significant merit for use in the identification of microorganisms or their resultant antibodies. For example, the **fluorescent treponemal antibody-absorption (FTA-ABS) test** is used to diagnose syphilis using *Treponema pallidum* as the antigen for detection of syphilitic antibodies in the patient's serum.

This technique requires the use of a specific antibody that has been tagged at the Fc region with a fluorescent dye, such as fluorescein isocyanate or fluorescein isothiocyanate. When the tagged antibody is applied to the antigen preparation, as in the direct method, or to an antigen-antibody complex, as in the indirect method, a microprecipitate forms at the site of the antigen and exhibits a yellow-green fluorescence when viewed under a fluorescence microscope (**Figure 1**).

In this experiment, you will use the direct immunofluorescence method to demonstrate the antigen-antibody reaction and to identify an unknown antigen. The fluorescein-tagged antibody is added to a heat-fixed bacterial smear. A physiologically buffered saline wash removes any uncombined fluorescent antibody. The resultant agglutination reaction, if present, will be demonstrated by a green fluorescence when viewed under a fluorescence microscope.

AT THE BENCH

Materials

Cultures

24-hour brain heart infusion broth cultures of Group A *Streptococcus pyogenes* and Group D *Enterococcus faecalis;* numbered, unknown mixed broth cultures of Group A *S. pyogenes/ Escherichia coli* and Group D *E. faecalis/ Escherichia coli.*

Reagents

Fluorescent antibody *Streptococcus* Group A (Difco 2318-56-6), fluorescent antibody *Enterococcus* Group D (Difco 2319-56-5), phosphate-buffered saline, and buffered glycerol. *Note: These fluorescent antibodies can also be obtained from Abcam, Inc., Cambridge, Mass.*

Equipment

Microscope slides, coverslips, Petri dishes, U-shaped glass rods to fit into Petri dishes, filter paper, Coplin jar, glassware marking

From Experiment 73 of *Microbiology: A Laboratory Manual,* Tenth Edition. James G. Cappuccino, Natalie Sherman.

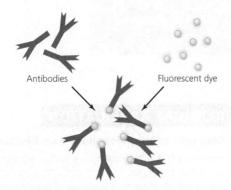

Antibodies   Fluorescent dye

(a) Antibodies are tagged with a fluorescent dye.

Antigens on the cell surface of a bacterium

(b) Tagged antibodies are introduced to a bacterium and attach to antigens on the cell surface.

(c) Photomicrograph of bacterial immunofluorescence. Only bacteria that bind with the antibodies will fluoresce.

Figure 1 Fluorescent antibody technique

pencil, bibulous paper, sterile pipettes, and fluorescence microscope.

Procedure

1. With a glassware marking pencil, label two slides *S. pyogenes* and *E. faecalis*, respectively. Divide the third slide in half and label it as "mixed unknown."

2. Prepare a heat-fixed smear of each known test organism on its appropriately labeled slide. On the slide labeled "mixed unknown," make a smear on each half of the slide using the unknown mixed culture.

3. On the slides labeled *S. pyogenes* and *E. faecalis*, add 1 drop of each respective fluorescent antibody and spread gently over the surface of the smear. On the slide of the mixed unknown smears, label one side FA-A and the other side FA-D, add 1 drop of each fluorescent antibody to its respectively labeled smear, and allow to spread evenly over the smears.

4. Place moistened filter paper in the Petri dishes, insert the U-shaped glass rod (for slide support), and place the prepared slides on the slide supports. Cover the Petri dishes and incubate for 35 minutes at 25°C.

5. Remove the slides from the Petri dishes and wash away excess antibody with 1% phosphate-buffered saline.

6. Immerse the slide in a Coplin jar containing 1% phosphate-buffered saline for 10 minutes at 25°C.

7. Blot the slides dry with bibulous paper.

8. To each slide add 1 drop of buffered glycerol, cover with a coverslip, and examine under a fluorescence microscope as directed by your instructor.

9. Record your observations in the Lab Report.

Name: _____

Date: _____ Section: _____

Observations and Results

1. Based on your microscopic observations, indicate in the chart the color of each smear and the presence (+) or absence (−) of fluorescence.

Culture	Color	Fluorescence (+) or (−)
Group A: *S. pyogenes*		
Group D: *E. faecalis*		
Mixed unknown with Group A antibodies		
Mixed unknown with Group D antibodies		

2. Based on your observations, identify your mixed unknown culture.

   Culture Number:

   Organisms:

Review Questions

1. What does the presence of fluorescence indicate?

2. Why is it necessary to wash away excess labeled antibody before viewing the preparation microscopically?

3. Briefly explain the direct fluorescent antibody procedure.

4. Label all parts of the antibody below, and show where it is tagged with fluorescein isothiocyanate.

5. Aside from syphilis, what diseases can be diagnosed through immunofluorescent techniques?

6. How would you use immunofluorescense to identify Group A *Streptococcus pyogenes* organisms isolated from a patient and differentiate them from other morphologically similar streptococci and staphylococci?

Photo Credit

Credits are listed in order of appearance.

Photo 1: Centers for Disease Control

Enzyme-Linked Immunosorbent Assay

LEARNING OBJECTIVE

Once you have completed this experiment, you should be able to

1. Demonstrate a method for the identification of either an antigen or an antibody by use of an enzyme-labeled antibody test procedure.

Principle

The **enzyme-linked immunosorbent assay (ELISA)** procedure is a widely accepted method that is used for the detection of specific antigens or antibodies. The procedure is predicated on the use of an enzyme-linked (labeled) specific antibody to demonstrate the agglutination reaction for the interpretation of the test result. This test can be performed as a double-antibody technique or as an indirect immunosorbent assay. The former method is used for the detection of test antigens; the latter is used for the detection of the test antibodies. In both methods the reactions are carried out in a well of a plastic microtiter plate.

The double-antibody system requires that the unlabeled antibody be allowed to adsorb to the inner surface of the plastic well in the microtiter plate. Any unbound antibody is then washed away, and a specific test antigen is added to the well. If the antigen binds with the antibody adhering to the walls of the well, this immunocomplex will not be removed by the subsequent washing for the removal of any unbound antigen. An enzyme-linked antibody, specific for the antigen, is now added. If the antigen is present in the well, this labeled antibody binds to the antigen, forming an antibody-antigen-antibody complex. Any unbound enzyme-linked antibody is again removed by

washing. This is followed by the addition of a substrate that is capable of producing a colored end product upon its reaction with the enzyme. The resultant enzymatically produced color change may be observed by eye or spectrophotometrically.

The indirect immunosorbent test procedure is similar to the double-antibody technique in that it requires the use of an enzyme-linked antibody. However, an antigen, rather than an antibody, is adsorbed onto the inner surface of the well.

Enzyme-linked immunosorbent assays are used extensively for the diagnosis of human infectious diseases. Included among these are viral infections such as AIDS, influenza, respiratory syncytial viral infection, and rubella. Bacterial infections such as syphilis, brucellosis, salmonellosis, and cholera can also be ascertained by means of this technique. This procedure also can be used for the detection of drugs in blood or tissues.

In this experiment you will use the **Directigen™ Flu A Test** (Becton, Dickinson and Company) to demonstrate the application of an *in vitro* enzyme immunoassay. This rapid, qualitative test employs an enzyme immunomembrane filter assay to detect influenza A antigen extracted from nasopharyngeal or pharyngeal specimens of symptomatic patients. These specimens are added to a ColorPAC™ test device, and any influenza A antigen present is nonspecifically bound to the membrane surface. Detector enzyme conjugated to monoclonal antibodies specific for the influenza A nucleoprotein antigen is bound to the trapped antigen following its addition to the ColorPAC membrane. Two substrates are then added sequentially and allowed to incubate for 5 to 30 minutes prior to determination of the result.

In the experimental procedure to be followed, the positive control will simulate the nasopharyngeal specimen of a symptomatic patient and will be indicative of a positive result. A pharyngeal swab sample of an asymptomatic individual will be used to illustrate a negative result.

From Experiment 74 of *Microbiology: A Laboratory Manual*, Tenth Edition. James G. Cappuccino, Natalie Sherman.

CLINICAL APPLICATION

Lyme Disease

The ELISA test is commonly used in the diagnosis of Lyme disease for the detection of antibodies to *Borrelia burgdorferi.* Because of the test's sensitivity, it can sometimes produce false positive results and it is not used as the sole basis for diagnosis of Lyme disease. It is generally followed up by a Western Blot test to confirm the diagnosis.

AT THE BENCH

Materials

Cultures

Directigen Flu A positive control and pharyngeal swab specimen from an asymptomatic individual.

Media

Per designated student group or demonstration: one test tube with 2-ml of sterile saline.

Equipment

Directigen Flu A Test kit, sterile cotton swabs, sterile 0.2-ml (200-µl) pipette, mechanical pipetting device, and disposable gloves.

Procedure

Note: This test may be performed as a demonstration for economic reasons or conservation of laboratory time.

⚠ **Wear disposable gloves during the procedure.**

Preparation of Negative Result by Use of a Pharyngeal Specimen

1. Using a sterile cotton swab, obtain a specimen from the palatine tonsil by rotating the swab vigorously over its surface.
2. Immerse the cotton swab into a test tube containing 2 ml of sterile saline. Mix well. Remove as much liquid from the swab as possible by pressing the swab against the inner surface of the tube. Discard the swab into a container of disinfectant.

3. Using a 0.2-ml (200-µl) pipette and a mechanical pipetting device, transfer 124 µl of the pharyngeal specimen into a DispensTube™ provided in the kit.
4. Gently mix and add 8 drops of Reagent A into the DispensTube. Mix well.
5. Insert a tip, provided in the kit, into the DispensTube. Dispense all of the extracted specimen into the ColorPAC test well in drops with the sealed flow controller in position. Allow for complete adsorption.
6. Gently mix and rapidly add drops of Reagent 1 until the test well is filled. Allow sufficient time for complete adsorption.
7. Remove the flow controller from the ColorPAC well and discard it into a container of disinfectant.
8. Gently mix and add 4 drops of Reagent 2 onto the ColorPAC membrane. Allow sufficient time for complete adsorption.
9. Gently mix and add 4 drops of Reagent 3 onto the ColorPAC membrane. Allow sufficient time for complete adsorption. Let stand for 2 minutes.
10. Rapidly add enough drops of Reagent 4 to fill the ColorPAC well. Allow sufficient time for complete adsorption.
11. Gently mix and add 4 drops of Reagent 5 onto the ColorPAC membrane. Allow sufficient time for complete adsorption.
12. Gently mix and add 4 drops of Reagent 6 onto the ColorPAC membrane. Allow sufficient time for complete adsorption. *Note: The membrane will turn yellow.*
13. Gently mix and add 4 drops of Reagent 7 onto the ColorPAC membrane. Allow sufficient time for complete adsorption.
14. Wait at least 5 minutes, but no longer than 30 minutes, and then read the results in a well-lighted area.
15. Observe the appearance of the inner surface of the ColorPAC test wells and record your results in the Lab Report.

Preparation of Positive Result by Use of Positive Control

1. Dispense 4 drops of the positive control, provided in the test kit, into a DispensTube.
2. Repeat Steps 4 through 15 as outlined previously for the preparation of the negative pharyngeal specimen.

Name: _____

Date: _____   Section: _____

Lab Report

Observations and Results

Record your results below based on the following interpretations of your observations:

 Positive test (antigen present): The appearance of a purple triangle (of any intensity) on the ColorPAC membrane indicates the presence of the influenza A antigen in the specimen. A purple dot may be evident in the center of the triangle. The background area should be grayish white.

 Negative test (no antigen detected): The appearance of a purple dot on the ColorPAC membrane indicates the absence of the influenza A antigen in the specimen. The background area should be grayish white.

 Uninterpretable test: The absence of a purple dot, a purple triangle, or an incomplete purple triangle indicates an uninterpretable test.

Negative pharyngeal specimen:

Result

Positive control specimen:

Result

Review Question

1. Why is the ELISA test used to screen human serum for the AIDS virus, while the Western blot procedure is used only as the confirmation test?

521

Sexually Transmitted Diseases: Rapid Immunodiagnostic Procedures

Sexually transmitted diseases (STDs) represent a diverse group of infectious syndromes that share the same mode of transmission, direct sexual contact. Their etiological agents represent a broad spectrum of pathogenic microorganisms that include bacteria, viruses, yeasts, and protozoa. The bacterial STDs include **gonorrhea, syphilis, nongonococcal urethritis,** and **lymphogranuloma venereum.** The representative viral infections are **genital herpes, genital warts, hepatitis B,** and the latest member of this group, **AIDS.** The protozoal and fungal infections, namely **trichomoniasis** and **candidiasis,** are diseases of lesser magnitude in the spectrum of STDs.

The experimental procedures that follow were chosen to demonstrate some of the rapid tests that are currently available for the diagnosis of selected STDs, specifically syphilis, genital herpes, and the chlamydial infections. In the methods that follow, you will perform modified procedures in the absence of clinical specimens. Commercially available positive and negative controls will be used to simulate clinical materials. *It is suggested that any of these tests, if performed, should be done as demonstrations.*

PART A Rapid Plasma Reagin Test for Syphilis

LEARNING OBJECTIVE

Once you have completed this experiment, you should be able to

1. Perform a rapid screening procedure for diagnosis of syphilis.

Principle

Treponema pallidum, the causative agent of **syphilis,** is a tightly coiled, highly motile, delicate spirochete that can be cultivated only in rabbit tissue cultures or rabbit testes. The organisms are resistant to common staining procedures and are best observed under darkfield microscopy.

Syphilis is a systemic infection that, if untreated, progresses through three clinical stages. The first stage, primary syphilis, is characterized by the formation of a painless papule, called a **chancre,** at the site of infection. Secondary syphilis represents the systemic extension of the infection and presents itself in the form of a **maculopapular rash,** malaise, and lymphadenopathy. Following this stage, the disease becomes self-limiting, and the patient appears asymptomatic until the development of tertiary syphilis. In this final stage, life-threatening complications may develop as a result of the extensive cardiovascular and nervous tissue damage that has ensued.

The **rapid plasma reagin (RPR) test,** which has to a large extent replaced the VDRL (Venereal Disease Research Laboratory) agglutination test, determines the presence of **reagin,** the nonspecific antibody present in the plasma of individuals with a syphilitic infection. The reagin appears in the plasma within 2 weeks of infection and will remain at high concentrations until the disease is eradicated. In the RPR test, if the reagin is present in the blood, it will react with a soluble antigen bound to carbon particles to produce a macroscopically visible antigen, or carbon-antibody complex. This procedure has several advantages over the VDRL test:

1. The serum does not require inactivation by heat for 30 minutes.

2. The serum may be obtained from a finger puncture, unlike the VDRL test, which requires a venous blood sample.

3. The required materials, which include the antigen suspension with a dispensing bottle, diagnostic cards, and capillary pipettes, are all contained in individual kits that do not require additional equipment and are disposable.

In the qualitative form of the RPR test, the patient's blood serum and the carbon-bound antigen suspension are mixed within a circle on the diagnostic card. In the presence of a positive

From Experiment 75 of *Microbiology: A Laboratory Manual*, Tenth Edition. James G. Cappuccino, Natalie Sherman.

Reactive   Nonreactive

Figure 1 Test card showing results of the rapid plasma reagin test

(reactive) serum, the antigen-antibody complex will produce a macroscopically visible black agglutination reaction. The macroscopic appearance of a light-gray suspension, devoid of any form of agglutination, is indicative of a negative (nonreactive) serum **(Figure 1)**.

Since this is a nonspecific test, false-positive results may be obtained. It is believed that the reagin is an antibody against tissue lipids in general. Therefore, it may be present in uninfected individuals due to the release of lipids resulting from normally occurring wear and tear of body tissues. It has also been found that serum levels of reagin are elevated during the course of other infectious diseases such as viral pneumonia, lupus erythematosus, infectious mononucleosis, yaws, and pinta. The serum of patients with a reactive RPR result is subjected to additional serological testing, such as the FTA-ABS (fluorescent treponemal antibody-absorption) test, or the TPI (*Treponema pallidum* immobilization) test, using the Treponema pallidum bacterium as an antigen to detect specific antibodies that are also present in the serum during syphilitic infection.

CLINICAL APPLICATION

Spirochetes

The rapid plasma regain (RPR) test detects non-specific antibodies in the blood of patients that may indicate the spirochete *Treponema pallidum* that causes syphilis. This test is used to screen asymptomatic patients, diagnose symptomatic infection, and track the progress of disease over the treatment period. High incidence of false positives due to cross reactivity and false negatives due to low antibody titers requires further testing using the Venereal Disease Research Lab (VDRL) test in many clinical labs.

AT THE BENCH

Materials

Reagents

Commercially prepared syphilitic serum 4+ and nonsyphilitic serum.

Equipment

RPR test kit (Inverness Medical Professional Diagnostics), disposable gloves, and rotating machine (optional).

Procedure

⚠️ **Wear disposable gloves.**

1. Label circles on the diagnostic plastic card as reactive and nonreactive.

2. Using a capillary pipette with an attached rubber bulb, draw the reactive serum up to the indicated mark (0.05 ml).

3. Expel the serum directly onto the card in the circle labeled reactive serum. With a clean applicator stick, spread the serum to fill the entire circle.

4. Repeat Steps 2 and 3 for the nonreactive serum.

5. Shake the dispensing bottle to mix the suspension. Hold the bottle with attached 20-gauge needle in a vertical position and dispense 1 drop onto each circle containing the test serum.

6. If a mechanical rotator is available, place the card on the rotator set at 100 rpm or rotate the card back and forth manually for 8 minutes.

7. In the presence of direct light, while tilting the card back and forth, determine the presence or absence of black clumping in each of the serum-antigen mixtures. Record your observations and the reaction as (+) or (−) in the Lab Report.

Genital Herpes:
Isolation and Identification of Herpes Simplex Virus

LEARNING OBJECTIVE

Once you have completed this experiment, you should be able to

1. Perform a tissue culture procedure for the growth and identification of the herpes simplex virus.

Principle

The double-stranded DNA herpes simplex virus (HSV) is the etiological agent of a variety of human infections. Included among these are **herpes labialis,** fever blisters around the lips; **keratoconjunctivitis,** infection of the eyes; **herpes genitalis,** eruptions on the genitalia; **herpes encephalitis,** a severe infection of the brain; and **neonatal herpes.** The herpes simplex virus is divided into two antigenically distinct groups, **HSV-1** and **HSV-2.** The former is most frequently implicated with infections above the waist, whereas the latter is predominantly responsible for genital infections.

Primary infection with HSV-2 manifests itself with the appearance of vesicular lesions, characterized by itching, tingling, or burning sensations on or within the male and female genitalia. These vesicles regress spontaneously within 2 weeks. Following this symptomatic phase, however, the virus reverts to a latent state in the sacral nerves and remains quiescent until exacerbated by some environmental factor. With no chemotherapeutic cure presently available, recurrent genital herpes with subclinical symptoms is common.

Detection of the herpes simplex virus requires the use of tissue culture techniques. The presence of the virus is then determined by the development of cytopathogenic effects in these cultures, such as the detection of intranuclear inclusion bodies. In recent years, these time-consuming, specialized procedures have been greatly facilitated by the availability of immunoenzymatic reagents for the identification of this clinically significant virus.

The **Cellmatics™ HSV Detection System** is a self-contained system providing for both the growth and identification of the virus from clinical specimens. In this procedure, the provided tissue culture tubes are inoculated with the clinical sample. Following a 24-hour incubation period and fixation, the presence of HSV antigens is determined by the addition of anti-HSV antibodies, which specifically bind to the HSV antigens. To demonstrate this antigen-antibody complex, a secondary antibody, substrate, and chromogen are added. Following this staining process, HSV-positive cultures viewed microscopically will exhibit brown-black areas of viral infection on a clear background of unstained cells.

In this exercise, you will perform a modified procedure. In the absence of a clinical specimen, the actual culturing and fixation process will not be performed. Instead, the positive and negative commercially available controls will be used to simulate the clinical samples.

CLINICAL APPLICATION

Culturing HSV

Genital herpes is caused by herpes simplex-2 virus (HSV-2). It is spread from person to person during sexual contact. The infection is transmitted by means of viral shedding, which may occur even when no signs or symptoms appear. A swab sample of a vesicular lesion or from the site of a previous lesion is taken from the patient and sent to the clinical or infectious disease lab for identification. This virus can only be grown in tissue culture and not cultivated on or in other laboratory media.

AT THE BENCH

Materials

Cultures

Cellmatics HSV Positive and Negative Control Tubes.

Reagents

Cellmatics Immunodiagnostic Reagents Kit, distilled water (Difco Labs).

Equipment

5-ml pipettes, mechanical pipetting device, and microscope.

Procedure

1. Warm immunodiagnostic reagents to room temperature.

2. Drain all fluid from the positive and negative control tubes.

3. Using a 5-ml pipette, wash the culture tubes twice with 5 ml of distilled water and drain. *Note: When washing, exercise care to prevent disruption of the monolayer.*

4. Add 10 drops of primary antiserum (Vial 1). *Note: When adding reagents, hold the vials vertically to ensure proper delivery.*

5. Incubate the *tightly capped* tubes in a *horizontal* position for 15 minutes at 37°C. To ensure complete coverage of the monolayer, occasionally rock the tubes gently during incubation.

6. Wash three times with 5 ml of distilled water and drain.

7. Add 10 drops of secondary antibody (Vial 2).

8. Incubate for 15 minutes at 37°C as described in Step 5.

9. Wash three times with 5 ml of distilled water and drain.

10. Add 10 drops of substrate (Vial 3) and 2 drops of chromogen (Vial 4). Mix gently.

11. Incubate for 15 minutes at 37°C as described in Step 5.

12. Wash three times with 5 ml of distilled water and drain.

13. Examine microscopically for the presence of stained cells at 40× and 100× magnifications. Scan the entire stained monolayer of both culture tubes for the presence of brown to blackish-brown stained cells. HSV infection is indicated by the presence of dark-colored cells when viewed against an unstained background of normal cells.

14. Record your observations in the Lab Report.

PART C Detection of Sexually Transmitted Chlamydial Diseases

LEARNING OBJECTIVE

Once you have completed this experiment, you should be able to

1. Perform an immunofluorescent procedure for diagnosis of *Chlamydia* infections.

Principle

Members of the genus ***Chlamydia*** are a group of obligate intracellular parasites. Although they were once believed to be viruses, their morphological and physiological characteristics more closely resemble bacteria, so they are now considered small bacteria. Chlamydiae are gram-negative, nonmotile, thick-walled, spherical organisms possessing both DNA and RNA that reproduce by means of binary fission. Their dependence on living tissues for cultivation and their lack of an ATP-generating system emulate the characteristics of viruses, but their bacterial nature is further affirmed by their sensitivity to antibiotic therapy. *Chlamydia trachomatis*, the human pathogen, is now recognized to be responsible for two sexually transmitted diseases, **nongonococcal urethritis** (NGU) and **lymphogranuloma venereum** (LGV). The incidence of both diseases in contemporary society is increasing dramatically.

NGU is a urethritis (inflammation of the urethra) with symptoms similar to, but less severe than, those of gonorrhea. Undiagnosed and untreated infections may lead to **epididymitis** and **proctitis** in men and **cervicitis, salpingitis,** and **pelvic inflammatory disease** in women. Nongonococcal urethritis is also caused by other bacteria such as *Ureaplasma urealyticum,* and

Mycoplasma hominis, as well as the protozoan *Trichomonas vaginalis.* LGV, the most severe of the genital chlamydial infections, initially develops with a painless lesion at the portal of entry, the genitalia. Systemic involvement is evidenced by swelling of the regional lymph nodes, which become tender and suppurative before disseminating the organisms to other tissues. In the absence of chemotherapeutic intervention, scarring of the lymphatic vessels can cause their obstruction, leading to **elephantiasis,** enlargement of the external genitalia in men, and narrowing of the rectum in women.

The **MicroTrak® Direct Specimen Test** is a rapid, immunofluorescent procedure for the detection of *C. trachomatis.* The procedure circumvents the need to culture these organisms in susceptible tissues prior to their identification. This slide test is designed to detect elementary bodies, the infectious particles produced during the life cycle of this organism, by the use of a staining reagent, a fluorescein-labeled monoclonal antibody specific for the principal protein of the *C. trachomatis* outer-membrane. In this procedure, a slide smear is prepared from the clinical specimen. Following fixation, when the slide is exposed to the Direct Specimen Reagent, the antibody binds to the organisms. Their presence is then determined by the appearance of apple-green chlamydiae against a red background of counterstained cells when viewed under a fluorescent microscope.

CLINICAL APPLICATION

Treating Chlamydia

Chlamydial infections are the most commonly reported sexually transmitted diseases. More than fifty million infections occur worldwide with three million cases occurring in the United States annually. Any sexually active person can contract Chlamydia, but it most frequently occurs in teenagers and young adults. The incidence appears higher in females than in males. Chlamydia may be transmitted by an infected mother to her newborn during birth. If a mother's medical or sexual history indicates possible exposure, a urogenital swab will be used to collect a sample for testing.

AT THE BENCH

Materials

Cultures

Commercially prepared positive and negative control slides.

Reagents

MicroTrak Direct Specimen Test for *Chlamydia trachomatis* (VWR Scientific).

Equipment

Fluorescent microscope.

Procedure

1. Stain the positive and negative control slides with the MicroTrak reagent for 15 minutes.
2. Incubate slides for 15 minutes.
3. Rinse the slides with distilled water.
4. Air-dry the slides.
5. Examine the slides under a fluorescent microscope for the presence of apple-green particles indicative of chlamydiae. The particles are evident against a reddish background of counterstained cells.
6. Record your results in the Lab Report.

Observations and Results

PART A: Rapid Plasma Reagin Test for Syphilis

	Reactive Serum	**Nonreactive Serum**
Appearance of serum-antigen mixture		
Reaction (+) or (−)		
Draw the observed reaction.		

PART B: Genital Herpes: Isolation and Identification of Herpes Simplex Virus

Indicate in the chart below the presence (+) or absence (−) of dark-stained patches.

CONTROL CULTURES			
Negative		**Positive**	
40×	100×	40×	100×

PART C: Detection of Sexually Transmitted Chlamydial Diseases

Record your results below, indicating the presence (+) or absence (−) of the apple-green chlamydiae on each of the slides.

Positive control slide: _____

Negative control slide: _____

Review Questions

1. Why is an adult who has a high antibody titer to herpes simplex virus 2 (HSV-2) subject to recurrent genital herpes infections?

2. A 20-year-old college student was informed following a physical examination that her blood test for syphilis was reactive. She indicated that she was a virgin and had never received a blood transfusion. A repeat RPR test was positive, but the TPI test was negative. How would you explain these bizarre results, and what is the clinical status of this patient?

Photo Credits

Credits are listed in order of appearance.

Photo 1: LeBeau Custom Medical Stock Photo, Newscom

Photo 2: Centers for Disease Control

Scientific Notation

APPENDIX

Microbiologists are required to perform a variety of laboratory techniques, including preparing and diluting solutions; expressing concentrations of chemicals, antibiotics, and antiseptics in solution; making quantitative determinations of cell populations based on the standard method for plate counting; and making serial dilutions to accommodate the latter procedure. These techniques commonly involve the use of very large or very small numbers (e.g., 9,000,000,000 or 0.0000000009), which can be so cumbersome to manipulate that errors may result. Therefore, it is essential for microbiologists to have a good command of scientific exponential notation known as **scientific notation**.

The basis for this system is predicated on the fact that all numbers can be expressed as the product of two numbers, one of which is the power of the number 10. In scientific notation, the small superscript number next to the 10 is called the **exponent**. Positive exponents tell us how many times the number must be multiplied by 10, while negative exponents indicate how many times a number must be divided by 10 (that is, multiplied by one-tenth).

For example, a number written using the exponential form designated as scientific notation would appear as 7.5×10^3, meaning that $7.5 \times 10 \times 10 = 7500$. Appendix Table 1 shows both large and small numbers written in the exponential form.

Appendix Table 1	Scientific (Exponential) Notation
NUMBERS GREATER THAN ONE	**NUMBERS LESS THAN ONE**
$1{,}000{,}000{,}000 = 1 \times 10^9$	$0.000\,000\,001 = 1 \times 10^{-9}$
$100{,}000{,}000 = 1 \times 10^8$	$0.000\,000\,01 = 1 \times 10^{-8}$
$10{,}000{,}000 = 1 \times 10^7$	$0.000\,000\,1 = 1 \times 10^{-7}$
$1{,}000{,}000 = 1 \times 10^6$	$0.000\,001 = 1 \times 10^{-6}$
$100{,}000 = 1 \times 10^5$	$0.000\,01 = 1 \times 10^{-5}$
$10{,}000 = 1 \times 10^4$	$0.000\,1 = 1 \times 10^{-4}$
$1000 = 1 \times 10^3$	$0.001 = 1 \times 10^{-3}$
$100 = 1 \times 10^2$	$0.01 = 1 \times 10^{-2}$
$10 = 1 \times 10^1$	$0.1 = 1 \times 10^{-1}$
$1 = 1 \times 10^0$	$1 = 1 \times 10^0$

Note: The exponent to which the power of 10 is raised is equal to the number of zeros to the right of 1.

Note: The exponent to which the power of 10 is raised is equal to the number of zeros to the left of 1 plus 1.

From Appendix 1 of *Microbiology: A Laboratory Manual*, Tenth Edition. James G. Cappuccino, Natalie Sherman.

Multiplication

Rule: To multiply two numbers that are written in scientific notation (exponential form) you must **add** the exponents.

Using numbers larger than 1:

$$75 \times 1200 = 90,000$$

Scientific notation: $(7.5 \times 10^1) \times (1.2 \times 10^3) = 9 \times 10^4$

Addition of exponents: $1 + 3 = 4$

Using numbers less than 1:

$$0.75 \times 1200 = 900$$

Scientific notation: $(7.5 \times 10^{-1}) \times (1.200 \times 10^3) = 9 \times 10^2$

Addition of exponents: $(-1 + 3 = 2)$

$$0.75 \times 0.12 = 0.09$$

Scientific notation: $(7.5 \times 10^{-1}) \times (1.2 \times 10^{-1}) = 9 \times 10^{-2}$

Addition of exponents: $(-1) + (-1) = -2$

Division

Rule: To divide two numbers in scientific notation, you must **subtract** the exponents.

$$75,000 \div 1,200,000 = 0.0625$$

Scientific notation: $(7.5 \times 10^4) \div (1.2 \times 10^6) = 6.25 \times 10^{-2}$

Subtraction of exponents: $(4 - 6 = -2)$

$$7,500 \div .012 = 625,000$$

Scientific notation: $(7.5 \times 10^3) \div (1.2 \times 10^{-2}) = 6.25 \times 10^5$

Subtraction of exponents: $3 - (-2) = 5$

As you practice the use of scientific notation with large and small numbers, you will become more proficient and more comfortable with this system of scientific calculation.

In microbiology laboratories as in other science laboratories, solutions must be diluted to achieve a desired final concentration of the active material contained in that solution. A **solution** may be defined as a mixture of two or more substances (**solute**) in which the molecules of the solute are evenly distributed and will not separate on standing, or precipitate from the solution. Solutes are dissolved in a solvent or diluent, such as water, alcohol, or some other vehicle in which the solute is soluble. Solutions are usually referred to as stock solutions and may be diluted by a variety of methods, depending upon the experimental requirements. Some of these methods are listed as follows:

1. A **dilution factor** must be determined first in order to dilute a solution. This dilution factor tells us how many times a solution must be diluted and is calculated by dividing the **initial concentration (IC)** of the solution by the **final concentration (FC)** desired.

$$IC \div FC = \text{dilution factor}$$

   Example: You wish to dilute a 10% stock solution to a final concentration of 2%.

$$10\% \div 2\% = 5 \,(\text{dilution factor})$$

   Take 1.0 ml of the 10% stock solution plus 4.0 ml of diluent (solvent), which equals a total of 5.0 ml. Thus each ml of the final solution will contain 2% solute.

2. Another method is used when a specific volume composed of a specific concentration is required.

   a. $\dfrac{IC}{FC} = 10 \,(\text{dilution factor})$

   b. $\dfrac{\text{volume needed}}{\text{concentration required}} = \dfrac{\text{amount of initial}}{\text{solution needed}}$

   c. volume needed − amount of initial solution = amount of diluent

Example: You have a 50% concentrated solution and you need 200 ml of a 5% solution.

   a. $\dfrac{IC}{FC} = \dfrac{50\%}{5\%} = 10 \,(\text{dilution factor})$

   b. $\dfrac{\text{volume needed}}{\text{concentration required}} = \dfrac{200\,\text{ml}}{5\%} = 40\,\text{ml}$

   c. 40 ml of 50% IC + 160 ml of diluent = 200 ml of a solution such that each ml will contain 5% solute rather than the original 50% in the stock solution

3. The ability to prepare large dilutions is absolutely essential for work in the microbiology laboratory. This method requires that large dilutions be prepared in two steps.

Example: A solution contains 1.0 g per ml of an active material and needs to be diluted to a final concentration of 1.0 μg per ml. A 1,000,000 (1×10^6)-fold dilution must be made. It is not practical to make such a dilution in one step since 999,999 ml of diluent would be required. This type of dilution is made as follows:

   a. Dilute 1 ml of the stock solution 1000 times:
      1.0 ml + 999 ml of diluent = 1000 μg/ml

   b. Dilute the solution containing 1000 μg/ml another 1000 times:
      1 ml of 1000 μg/ml + 999 ml diluent = 1.0 μg/ml

4. When working with large molecules such as proteins, there will be times when you will be required to make large dilutions of the sample to be contained in a specific volume.

Example: You need to make 50 ml of a 1/20,000 dilution of albumin.

   $\dfrac{\text{final dilution}}{\text{volume needed}} = \dfrac{20,000}{50} = 400 \,(\text{dilution factor})$

   a. $\dfrac{1.0\,\text{ml of}}{\text{albumin}} + \dfrac{399\,\text{ml of}}{\text{diluent}} = 1/400 \text{ dilution}$

Methods for the Preparation of Dilutions

b. $\dfrac{1.0\text{ ml of}}{\text{a 1/400}} + \dfrac{49\text{ ml of}}{\text{diluent}} = \dfrac{50\text{ ml of a}}{\text{soution; each ml}}$
$\text{dilution} \qquad\qquad \text{contains 1/20,000}$
of albumin.

$$50\,(\text{volume}) \times 400\,(\text{dilution factor}) = 20{,}000$$

5. Perhaps the most useful type of dilution used in microbiology and immunology is the **serial dilution**. This is essential when small volumes of material are needed. This type of dilution procedure has many uses in the microbiology laboratory, especially for the determination of the total number of cells in culture the number of viral plaques found in suspensions of viruses the antibody titer and in other immunological studies. The procedure requires the use of dilution blanks containing a known volume of diluent (distilled water, saline, etc.) to which a specific volume of the sample is added. To facilitate the ease of calculations, dilutions are usually made in multiples of 10. For example: 1.0 ml of a sample is added to a 9.0-ml dilution blank (1.0 ml + 9.0 ml = 10) and is recorded as a 1:10 dilution.

It has been statistically determined that greater accuracy is achieved with very large dilutions made from a series of smaller dilutions. For the convenience of the student, it is illustrated in **Appendix Figure 1**:

1. All dilution blanks contain 9.0 ml of diluent.
2. A fresh pipette is used for each dilution, and the used pipettes are placed in a beaker of disinfectant.
3. After delivery of the sample, the tubes are mixed thoroughly before the next dilution is made.
4. Pippetting by mouth is not allowed. Only mechanical pipette aspirators may be used.

The stock solution in Appendix Figure 1 has been diluted 1 million times. In other words, 1.0 ml from Tube 6 will contain 1/1,000,000 of the sample contained in the stock solution.

Appendix Figure 1 Serial dilution

Microbiological Media

The formulas of the media used in the exercises are listed alphabetically in grams per liter of distilled water unless otherwise specified. Sterilization of the media is accomplished by autoclaving at 15 lb pressure for 15 minutes unless otherwise specified. Most of the media are available commercially in powdered form, with specific instructions for their preparation and sterilization.

Ammonium sulfate broth (pH 7.3)

Ammonium sulfate	2.0
Magnesium sulfate $\cdot$ 7H$_2$O	0.5
Ferric sulfate $\cdot$ 7H$_2$O	0.03
Sodium chloride	0.3
Magnesium carbonate	10.0
Dipotassium hydrogen phosphate	1.0

Bacteriophage broth 10× (pH 7.6)

Peptone	100.0
Beef extract	30.0
Yeast extract	50.0
Sodium chloride	25.0
Potassium dihydrogen phosphate	80.0

Basal salts agar* and broth (pH 7.0)

0.5 M sodium diphosphate	100.0 ml
1.0 M potassium dihydrogen phosphate	100.0 ml
Distilled water	800.0 ml
0.1 M calcium chloride	1.0 ml
1.0 M magnesium sulfate	1.0 ml
Ammonium sulfate	2.0
*Agar	15.0

Note: Swirl until completely dissolved, autoclave, and cool. Aseptically add 10.0 ml of 1% sterile glucose.

Bile esculin (pH 6.6)

Beef extract	3.0
Peptone	5.0
Esculin	1.0
Oxgall	40.0
Ferric citrate	0.5
Agar	15.0

Blood agar (pH 7.3)

Infusion from beef heart	500.0
Tryptose	10.0
Sodium chloride	5.0
Agar	15.0

Note: Dissolve the above ingredients and autoclave. Cool the sterile blood agar base to 45°C to 50°C. Aseptically add 50 ml of sterile defibrinated blood. Mix thoroughly, avoiding accumulation of air bubbles. Dispense into sterile tubes or plates while liquid.

Brain heart infusion (pH 7.4)

Infusion from calf brain	200.0
Infusion from beef heart	250.0
Peptone	10.0
Dextrose	2.0
Sodium chloride	5.0
Disodium phosphate	2.5
Agar	1.0

Bromcresol purple dextrose fermentation broth (pH 7.2)

Bacto® casitone	10
Dextrose	5
Bromcresol purple (0.2%)	0.01

Bromcresol purple (0.2%) is made separately and filter sterilized. 5 ml is aseptically added to the medium.

Note: Autoclave at 12 lb pressure for 15 minutes.

Bromcresol purple lactose fermentation broth (pH 7.2)

Bacto casitone	10
Lactose	5
Bromcresol purple (0.2%)	0.01

Bromcresol purple (0.2%) is made separately and filter sterilized. 5 ml is aseptically added to the above medium.
Note: Autoclave at 12 lb pressure for 15 minutes.

Bromcresol purple maltose fermentation broth (pH 7.2)

Bacto casitone	10
Maltose	5
Bromcresol purple (0.2%)	0.01

Bromcresol purple (0.2%) is made separately and filter sterilized. 5 ml is aseptically added to the medium.
Note: Autoclave at 12 lb pressure for 15 minutes.

Bromcresol purple sucrose fermentation broth (pH 7.2)

Bacto casitone	10
Sucrose	5
Bromcresol purple (0.2%)	0.01

Bromcresol purple (0.2%) is made separately and filter sterilized. 5 ml is added to the medium aseptically.
Note: Autoclave at 12 lb pressure for 15 minutes.

Campy-BAP agar (pH 7.0)

Trypticase peptone	10.0
Thiotone™	10.0
Dextrose	1.0
Yeast extract	2.0
Sodium chloride	5.0
Sodium bisulfide	0.1
Agar	15.0
Vancomycin	10.0 mg
Trimethoprim lactate	5.0 mg
Polymyxin B sulfate	2500.0 IU
Amphotericin B	2.0 mg
Cephalothin	15.0 mg
Defibrinated sheep blood	10.0%

Note: Aseptically add the antibiotics and defibrinated sheep blood to the sterile, molten, and cooled agar.

Chocolate agar (pH 7.0)

Proteose peptone	20.0
Dextrose	0.5
Sodium chloride	5.0
Disodium phosphate	5.0
Agar	15.0

Note: Aseptically add 5.0% defibrinated sheep blood to the sterile and molten agar. Heat at 80°C until a chocolate color develops.

Crystal violet agar (pH 7.0)

Bacto beef extract	3
Bacto peptone	5
Bacto crystal violet	0.00014
Bacto agar	15

Note: 1.0 ml of a crystal violet stock solution may be added to the base medium. Stock solution: 14 mg of crystal violet dye dissolved in 100 ml of distilled water.

Decarboxylase broth (Moeller) (pH 6.0)

Peptone	5.0
Beef extract	5.0
Dextrose	0.5
Bromcresol purple	0.01
Cresol red	0.005
Pyridoxal	0.005
Distilled water	1000.0 ml

To make amino acid–specific medium, add one of the amino acids below; dispense in 3- to 4-ml amounts and autoclave at 121°C for 10 minutes.

L-lysine dihydrochloride or L-arginine monohydrochloride or L-ornithine dihydrochloride	10 g/l

Deoxyribonuclease (DNase) agar (pH 7.3)

Deoxyribonucleic acid	2.0
Phytane	5.0
Sodium chloride	5.0
Trypticase	15.0
Agar	15.0

Endo agar (pH 7.5)

Peptone	10.0
Lactose	10.0
Dipotassium phosphate	3.5
Sodium sulfite	2.5
Basic fuchsin	0.4
Agar	15.0

Eosin–methylene blue agar (Levine) (pH 7.2)

Peptone	10.0
Lactose	5.0
Dipotassium phosphate	2.0
Agar	13.5
Eosin Y	0.4
Methylene blue	0.065

Gel diffusion agar

Sodium barbital buffer	100.0 ml
Noble agar	0.8

Glucose acetate yeast sporulation agar (pH 5.5)

Glucose	1
Yeast extract	2
Sodium acetate (with $3H_2O$)	5
Bacto agar	15

Glucose salts broth (pH 7.2)

Dextrose	5.0
Sodium chloride	5.0
Magnesium sulfate	0.2
Ammonium dihydrogen phosphate	1.0
Dipotassium hydrogen phosphate	1.0

Glycerol yeast extract agar supplemented with aureomycin (pH 7.0)

Glycerol	5.0 ml
Yeast extract	2.0
Dipotassium phosphate	1.0
Agar	15.0

Note: Aseptically add aureomycin, 10 μg per ml, to the sterile, molten, and cooled agar.

Grape juice broth

Commercial grape or apple juice	
Ammonium biphosphate	0.25%

Note: Sterilization not required when using a large yeast inoculum.

Hay infusion broth

Hay infusion broth preparations are prepared 1 week ahead of the laboratory session in which they will be used. Into a 2000-ml beaker place about 800 ml of water and two to three handfuls of dry grass or hay (obtained from a farm or storage barn). During the incubation period, the infusion should be aerated by passing air through a rubber tube attached to an air supply. This preparation is sufficient for a class and can be dispensed in 50-ml beakers.

Hektoen enteric agar (pH 7.1)

Peptic digest of animal tissue	12.0
Yeast extract	3.0
Bile salt	9.0
Lactose	12.0
Sucrose	12.0
Salicin	2.0
Sodium chloride	5.0
Sodium thiosulfate	5.0
Ferric ammonium citrate	1.5
Bromthymol blue	0.064
Acid fuchsin	0.5
Agar	13.5

Inorganic synthetic broth (pH 7.2)

Sodium chloride	5.0
Magnesium sulfate	0.2
Ammonium dihydrogen phosphate	1.0
Dipotassium hydrogen phosphate	1.0

KF broth (pH 7.2)

Polypeptone	10.0
Yeast extract	10.0
Sodium chloride	5.0
Sodium glycerophosphate	10.0
Sodium carbonate	0.636
Maltose	20.0
Lactose	1.0
Sodium azide	0.4
Phenol red	0.018

Lactose fermentation broth 1× and 2×* (pH 6.9)

Beef extract	3.0
Peptone	5.0
Lactose	5.0

*For 2× broth use twice the concentration of the ingredients.

Litmus milk (pH 6.8)

Skim milk powder	100.0
Litmus	0.075

Note: Autoclave at 12 lb pressure for 15 minutes.

Luria-Bertani (Miller) agar base (pH 7.0)

Pancreatic digest of casein	10.0
Yeast extract	5.0
Sodium chloride	0.5
Agar	15.0

Luria-Bertani (Miller) broth (pH 7.0)

Tryptone	10.0
Yeast extract	5.0
Sodium chloride	10.0

MacConkey agar (pH 7.1)

Bacto peptone	17.0
Proteose peptone	3.0
Lactose	10.0
Bile salts mixture	1.5
Sodium chloride	5.0
Agar	13.5
Neutral red	0.03
Crystal violet	0.001

Mannitol salt agar (pH 7.4)

Beef extract	1.0
Peptone	10.0
Sodium chloride	75.0
d-Mannitol	10.0
Agar	15.0
Phenol red	0.025

m-Endo broth (pH 7.5)

Yeast extract	6.0
Thiotone peptone	20.0
Lactose	25.0
Dipotassium phoshate	7.0
Sodium sulfite	2.5
Basic fuchsin	1.0

Note: Heat until boiling; do not autoclave.

m-FC broth (pH 7.4)

Biosate™ peptone	10.0
Polypeptone peptone	5.0
Yeast extract	3.0
Sodium chloride	5.0
Lactose	12.5
Bile salts	1.5
Aniline blue	0.1

Note: Add 10 ml of rosolic acid (1% in 0.2N sodium hydroxide). Heat to boiling with agitation; do not autoclave.

Milk agar (pH 7.2)

Skim-milk powder	100.0
Peptone	5.0
Agar	15.0

Note: Autoclave at 12 lb pressure for 15 minutes.

Minimal agar (pH 7.0)
Minimal agar, supplemented with streptomycin and thiamine*

Solution A (pH 7.0)

Potassium dihydrogen phosphate	3.0
Disodium hydrogen phosphate	6.0
Ammonium chloride	2.0
Sodium chloride	5.0
Distilled water	800.0 ml

Solution B (pH 7.0)

Glucose	8.0
Magnesium sulfate · 7H$_2$O	0.1
Agar	15.0
Distilled water	200.0 ml

Note: Autoclave Solutions A and B separately and combine.

*To Solution B, add 0.001 g of thiamine prior to autoclaving. To the combined sterile and molten medium, add 50 mg (1 ml of 50 mg per ml) sterile streptomycin solution before pouring agar plates.

MR-VP broth (pH 6.9)

Peptone	7.0
Dextrose	5.0
Potassium phosphate	5.0

Mueller-Hinton agar (pH 7.4)

Beef, infusion	300.0
Casamino acids	17.5
Starch	1.5
Agar	17.0

Mueller-Hinton tellurite agar (pH 7.4)

Casamino acids	20.0
Casein	5.0
L-tryptophan	0.05
Potassium dihydrogen phosphate	0.3
Magnesium sulfate	0.1
Agar	20.0

Note: Aseptically add 12.5 ml of tellurite serum to the sterile, 50°C molten agar.

Nitrate broth (pH 7.2)

Peptone	5.0
Beef extract	3.0
Potassium nitrate	5.0

Nitrite broth (pH 7.3)

Sodium nitrite	2.0
Magnesium sulfate · 7H$_2$O	0.5
Ferric sulfate · 7H$_2$O	0.03
Sodium chloride	0.3
Sodium carbonate	1.0
Dipotassium hydrogen sulfate	1.0

Nitrogen-free mannitol agar* and broth (pH 7.3)

Mannitol	15.0
Dipotassium hydrogen phosphate	0.5
Magnesium sulfate	0.2
Calcium sulfate	0.1
Sodium chloride	0.2
Calcium carbonate	5.0
*Agar	15.0

Nutrient agar* and broth (pH 7.0)

Peptone	5.0
Beef extract	3.0
*Agar	15.0

Nutrient gelatin (pH 6.8)

Peptone	5.0
Beef extract	3.0
Gelatin	120.0

Peptone broth (pH 7.2)

Peptone	4.0

Phenol red dextrose broth (pH 7.3)

Trypticase	10.0
Dextrose	5.0
Sodium chloride	5.0
Phenol red	0.018

Note: Autoclave at 12 lb pressure for 15 minutes.

Phenol red inulin broth (pH 7.3)

Trypticase	10.0
Inulin	5.0
Sodium chloride	5.0
Phenol red	0.018

Note: Autoclave at 12 lb pressure for 15 minutes.

Phenol red lactose broth (pH 7.3)

Trypticase	10.0
Lactose	5.0
Sodium chloride	5.0
Phenol red	0.018

Note: Autoclave at 12 lb pressure for 15 minutes.

Phenol red sucrose broth (pH 7.3)

Trypticase	10.0
Sucrose	5.0
Sodium chloride	5.0
Phenol red	0.018

Note: Autoclave at 12 lb pressure for 15 minutes.

Phenylalanine agar (pH 7.3)

Yeast extract	3.0
Dipotassium phosphate	1.0
Sodium chloride	5.0
DL-phenylalanine	2.0
Bacto agar	12.0
Distilled water	1000.0 ml

Note: Completely dissolve ingredients in boiling water. Dispense in tubes, autoclave, and cool in slanted position.

Phenylethyl alcohol agar (pH 7.3)

Trypticase	15.0
Phytane	5.0
Sodium chloride	5.0
β-Phenylethyl alcohol	2.0
Agar	15.0

Potato dextrose agar (pH 5.6)

Infusion from potatoes	200.0
Bacto dextrose	20.0
Bacto agar	15.0

Sabouraud agar (pH 5.6)
Sabouraud agar supplemented with chlortetracycline (Aureomycin)*

Peptone	10.0
Dextrose	40.0
Agar	15.0

*Aseptically add Aureomycin, 10 μg per ml, to the sterile, molten, and cooled medium.

Salt medium — *Halobacterium*

Sodium chloride	250.0
Magnesium sulfate · 7H$_2$O	10.0
Potassium chloride	5.0
Calcium chloride · 6H$_2$O	0.2
Yeast extract	10.0
Tryptone	2.5
Agar	20.0

Note: The quantities given are for preparation of 1-liter final volume of the medium. In preparation, make up two solutions, one involving the yeast extract and tryptone and the other the salts. Adjust the pH of the nutrient solution to 7. Sterilize separately. Mix and dispense aseptically.

SIM agar (pH 7.3)

Peptone	30.0
Beef extract	3.0
Ferrous ammonium sulfate	0.2
Sodium thiosulfate	0.025
Agar	3.0

Simmons citrate agar (pH 6.9)

Ammonium dihydrogen phosphate	1.0
Dipotassium phosphate	1.0
Sodium chloride	5.0
Sodium citrate	2.0
Magnesium sulfate	0.2
Agar	15.0
Bromthymol blue	0.08

Snyder test agar (pH 4.8)

Tryptone	20.0
Dextrose	20.0
Sodium chloride	5.0
Bromcresol green	0.02
Agar	20.0

Sodium chloride agar, 7.5% (pH 7.0)

Bacto beef extract	3.0
Bacto peptone	5.0
Sodium chloride	7.5
Bacto agar	15.0

Microbiological Media

Sodium chloride broth, 6.5% (pH 7.0)
Brain heart infusion broth	100.0 ml
Sodium chloride	6.5

Starch agar (pH 7.0)
Peptone	5.0
Beef extract	3.0
Starch (soluble)	2.0
Agar	15.0

Thioglycollate, fluid (pH 7.1)
Peptone	15.0
Yeast extract	5.0
Dextrose	5.0
L-cystine	0.75
Thioglycollic acid	0.3 ml
Agar	0.75
Sodium chloride	2.5
Resazurin	0.001

Tinsdale agar (pH 7.4)
Proteose peptone, No. 3	20.0
Sodium chloride	5.0
Agar	20.0

Note: Following boiling, distribute in 100-ml flasks. Autoclave, cool to 55°C, add 15 ml of rehydrated Tinsdale enrichment to each 100 ml, and mix thoroughly before dispensing.

Top agar (for Ames test)
Sodium chloride	5.0
Agar	6.0

Tributyrin agar (pH 7.2)
Peptone	5.0
Beef extract	3.0
Agar	15.0
Tributyrin	10.0

Note: Dissolve peptone, beef extract, and agar while heating. Cool to 90°C, add the tributyrin, and emulsify in a blender.

Triple sugar–iron agar (pH 7.4)
Beef extract	3.0
Yeast extract	3.0
Peptone	15.0
Proteose peptone	5.0
Lactose	10.0
Saccharose	10.0
Dextrose	1.0
Ferrous sulfate	0.2
Sodium chloride	5.0
Sodium thiosulfate	0.3
Phenol red	0.024
Agar	12.0

Trypticase nitrate broth (pH 7.2)
Trypticase	20.0
Disodium phosphate	2.0
Dextrose	1.0
Agar	1.0
Potassium nitrate	1.0

Trypticase soy agar (pH 7.3)
Trypticase	15.0
Phytane	5.0
Sodium chloride	5.0
Agar	15.0

Tryptone agar* and broth
Tryptone	10.0
Calcium chloride (reagent)	0.01–0.03 M
Sodium chloride	5.0
*Agar	11.0

Tryptone soft agar
Tryptone	10.0
Potassium chloride (reagent)	5.0 ml
Agar	9.0

Urea broth
Urea broth concentrate (filter-sterilized solution)	10.0 ml
Sterile distilled water	90.0 ml

Note: Aseptically add the urea broth concentrate to the sterilized and cooled distilled water. Under aseptic conditions, dispense 3-ml amounts into sterile tubes.

Yeast extract broth (pH 7.0)
Peptone	5.0
Beef extract	3.0
Sodium chloride	5.0
Yeast extract	5.0

Biochemical Test Reagents

Agarose gel, for Electrophoresis

Agarose	1 g
Tris-borate buffer (1×)	125 ml

Note: Melt agarose, being careful not to overboil. Cover loosely with foil and hold at room temperature, or place in 60°C waterbath until ready for use.

Barritt's reagent, for detection of acetylmethylcarbinol

Solution A

Alpha-naphthol	5.0 g
Ethanol, absolute	95.0 ml

Note: Dissolve the alpha-naphthol in the ethanol with constant stirring.

Solution B

Potassium hydroxide	40.0 g
Creatine	0.3 g
Distilled water	100.0 ml

Note: Dissolve the potassium hydroxide in 75 ml of distilled water. The solution will become warm. Allow to cool to room temperature. Add the creatine and stir to dissolve. Add the remaining water. Store in a refrigerator.

Biotin-histidine solution, for Ames test

L-Histidine HCl	0.5 mM
Biotin	0.5 mM
Distilled water	10.0 ml

Buffered glycerol (pH 7.2), for immunofluorescence

Glycerin	90.0 ml
Phosphate buffered saline	10.0 ml

Diphenylamine reagent, for detection of nitrates

Dissolve 0.7 g diphenylamine in a mixture of 60 ml concentrated sulfuric acid and 28.8 ml of distilled water. Cool and slowly add 11.3 ml of concentrated hydrochloric acid. Allow to stand for 12 hours. Sedimentation indicates that the reagent is saturated.

Endonuclease buffers

Buffer 1: EcoRI buffer

Tris-HCl (pH 7.5)	50 mM
$MgCl_2$	10 mM
NaCl	100 mM
Triton® X-100	0.02%
BSA	0.1 mg/ml

Buffer 2: HindIII buffer

Tris-HCl (pH 8.5)	10 mM
$MgCl_2$	10 mM
KCl	100 mM
BSA	0.1 mg/ml

Buffer 3: BamHI buffer

Tris-HCl (pH 8.0)	10 mM
$MgCl_2$	5 mM
KCl	100 mM
2-Mercaptoethanol	1 mM
Triton X-100	0.02%
BSA	0.1 mg/ml

Ferric chloride reagent

Ferric chloride	10.0 g
Distilled water	100.0 ml

Gram's iodine, for detection of starch

As in Gram's stain

Hydrogen peroxide, 3%, for detection of catalase activity

Note: Refrigerate when not in use.

Kovac's reagent, for detection of indole

p-Dimethylaminobenzaldehyde	5.0 g
Amyl alcohol	75.0 ml
Hydrochloric acid (concentrated)	25.0 ml

Note: Dissolve the p-dimethylaminobenzaldehyde in the amyl alcohol. Add the hydrochloric acid.

Loading Dye 6×, for gel electrophoresis

Glycerol (50%)	6 ml
Bromphenol blue (2%)	1 ml
Xylene cyanol (2%)	1 ml
Distilled water	1000 ml

Note: This can be stored in the refrigerator indefinitely.

McFarland Barium Sulfate Standards,
for API Staph-Ident procedure

Prepare 1% aqueous barium chloride and 1% aqueous sulfuric acid solutions. Using the following table, add the amounts of barium chloride and sulfuric acid to clean 15- × 150-mm screw-capped test tubes. Label the tubes 1 through 10.

Preparation of McFarland Standards

Tube	Barium Chloride 1% (ml)	Sulfuric Acid 1% (ml)	Corresponding Approximate Density of Bacteria (million/ml)
1	0.1	9.9	300
2	0.2	9.8	600
3	0.3	9.7	900
4	0.4	9.6	1200
5	0.5	9.5	1500
6	0.6	9.4	1800
7	0.7	9.3	2100
8	0.8	9.2	2400
9	0.9	9.1	2700
10	1.0	9.0	3000

Methyl cellulose, for microscopic observation of protozoa

Methyl cellulose	10.0 g
Distilled water	90.0 ml

Methylene blue stain (0.025%)

Methylene blue 1% stock solution (1 g + 99 ml distilled H_2O)	10 ml
Distilled water	390 ml

Methyl red solution, for detection of acid

Methyl red	0.1 g
Ethyl alcohol	300.0 ml
Distilled water	200.0 ml

Note: Dissolve the methyl red in the 95% ethyl alcohol. Dilute to 500 ml with distilled water.

Nessler's reagent, for detection of ammonia

Potassium iodide	50.0 g
Distilled water (ammonia-free)	35.0 ml

Add saturated aqueous solution of mercuric chloride until a slight precipitate persists.

Potassium hydroxide (50% aqueous)	400.0 ml

Note: Dilute to 1000 ml with ammonia-free distilled water. Let stand for 1 week, decant supernatant liquid, and store in a tightly capped amber bottle.

Nitrate test solution, for detection of nitrites

Solution A, Sulfanilic acid

Sulfanilic acid	8.0 g
Acetic acid, 5 N: 1 part glacial acetic acid to 2.5 parts distilled water	1000.0 ml

Solution B, Alpha-naphthylamine

Alpha-naphthylamine	5.0 g
Acetic acid, 5 N	1000.0 ml

Oxidase Reagent

Tetramethyl-*p*-phenylene diamine dihydrochloride	1.0 g
Distilled water	100 ml

Orthonitrophenyl-β-D-galactoside (ONPG),
for enzyme induction

0.1 M sodium phosphate buffer (pH 7.0)	50.0 ml
ONPG (8×10^{-4} M)	12.5 mg

p-Aminodimethylaniline oxalate,
for detection of oxidase activity

p-Aminodimethylaniline oxalate	0.5 g
Distilled water	50.0 ml

Note: To dissolve fully, gently warm the solution.

Phosphate-buffered saline, 1% (pH 7.2–7.4),
for immunofluorescence

Solution A

Disodium phosphate	1.4 g
Distilled water	100.0 ml

Solution B

Sodium dihydrogen phosphate	1.4 g
Distilled water	100.0 ml

Note: Add 84.1 ml of Solution A to 15.9 ml of Solution B. Add 8.5 g of sodium chloride and enough distilled water to make 1 liter.

Biochemical Test Reagents

Rabbit plasma, for detection of coagulase activity

Note: Store vials at 2°C to 8°C. Reconstitute by the addition of 7.5 ml of sterile water.

Sodium barbital buffer, for immunofluorescence

Sodium barbital	6.98 g
Sodium chloride	6.0 g
1 N hydrochloric acid	27.0 ml
Distilled water, to fill to 1000 ml	

Toluidine blue solution, 0.1%, for detection of DNase activity

1% toluidine blue solution	0.1 ml
Distilled water	99.9 ml

Tris-acetate buffer 10×

Tris base	48.4 g
Glacial acetic acid	11 g
EDTA (0.5 M)	20 ml
Distilled water	1000 ml

Note: Add ingredients to 1 liter volumetric flask and then add water to volume.

Tris-acetate buffer 1×

Tris-acetate buffer 10× (see previous entry)	100 ml
Distilled water	900 ml

Note: Buffer can be stored indefinitely at room temperature.

Tris-borate buffer 5×

Tris base	54 g
Boric acid	27.5 g
EDTA (0.5M, pH 8.0)	20 ml
Distilled water	1000 ml

Tris-borate buffer 1× working solution

Tris-borate buffer 5× (see previous entry)	200 ml
Distilled water	800 ml

Staining Reagents

Acid-Fast Stain

Carbol fuchsin (Ziehl's)
Solution A

Basic fuchsin (90% dye content)	0.3 g
Ethyl alcohol (95%)	10.0 ml

Solution B

Phenol	5.0 g
Distilled water	95.0 ml

Note: Mix Solutions A and B. Add 2 drops of Triton X per 100 ml of stain for use in heatless method.

Acid Alcohol

Ethyl alcohol (95%)	97.0 ml
Hydrochloric acid	3.0 ml

Methylene blue

Methylene blue	0.3 g
Distilled water	100.0 ml

Capsule Stain

Crystal violet (1%)

Crystal violet (85% dye content)	1.0 g
Distilled water	100.0 ml

Copper sulfate solution (20%)

Copper sulfate ($CuSO_4 \cdot 5H_2O$)	20.0 g
Distilled water	80.0 ml

Fungal Stains

Lactophenol–cotton-blue solution

Lactic acid	20.0 ml
Phenol	20.0 g
Glycerol	40.0 ml
Distilled water	20.0 ml
Aniline blue	0.05 g

Note: Heat gently in hot water (double boiler) to dissolve; then add aniline blue dye.

Water-iodine solution

Gram's iodine (as in Gram's stain)	10.0 ml
Distilled water	30.0 ml

Gram Stain

Crystal violet (Hucker's)
Solution A

Crystal violet (90% dye content)	2.0 g
Ethyl alcohol (95%)	20.0 ml

Solution B

Ammonium oxalate	0.8 g
Distilled water	80.0 ml

Note: Mix Solutions A and B.

Gram's iodine

Iodine	1.0 g
Potassium iodide	2.0 g
Distilled water	300.0 ml

Ethyl alcohol (95%)

Ethyl alcohol (100%)	95.0 ml
Distilled water	5.0 ml

Safranin

Safranin O	0.25 ml
Ethyl alcohol (95%)	10.0 ml
Distilled water	100.0 ml

Negative Stain

Nigrosin

Nigrosin, water-soluble	10.0 g
Distilled water	100.0 ml

Note: Immerse in boiling waterbath for 30 minutes.

Formalin	0.5 ml

Note: Filter twice through double filter paper.

Spore Stain

Malachite green

Malachite green	5.0 g
Distilled water	100.0 ml

Safranin
Same as in Gram stain

From Appendix 5 of *Microbiology: A Laboratory Manual*, Tenth Edition. James G. Cappuccino, Natalie Sherman.

LABORATORY SAFETY RULES AND REGULATIONS

The following basic safety rules should be observed at all times in the laboratory.

1. Upon entering the laboratory, place coats, books, and other paraphernalia in specified locations—never on bench tops.

2. Keep doors and windows closed during the laboratory session to prevent contamination from air currents.

3. At the beginning and termination of each laboratory session, wipe bench tops with a disinfectant solution provided by the instructor.

4. Do not place contaminated instruments, such as inoculating loops, needles, and pipettes, on bench tops. Loops and needles should be sterilized by incineration, and pipettes should be disposed of in designated receptacles.

5. On completion of the laboratory session, place all cultures and materials in the disposal area as designated by the instructor.

6. Rapid and efficient manipulation of fungal cultures is required to prevent the dissemination of their reproductive spores in the laboratory environment.

7. Wash your hands with liquid detergent, rinse with 95% ethyl alcohol, and dry them with paper towels upon entering and prior to leaving the laboratory.

8. Wear a paper cap or tie back long hair to minimize its exposure to open flames.

9. Wear a laboratory coat/apron and disposable gloves, as determined by your instructor, to protect your clothing and hands from contamination and from coming into direct contact with staining solutions.

10. Closed shoes should be worn at all times in the laboratory setting.

11. Never apply cosmetics or insert contact lenses in the laboratory.

12. Do not smoke, eat, or drink in the laboratory. These activities are absolutely prohibited.

13. Carry cultures in a test-tube rack when moving around the laboratory. Likewise, keep cultures in a test-tube rack on the bench tops when not in use. This serves a dual purpose: to prevent accidents and to avoid contamination of yourself and the environment.

14. Never remove media, equipment, or, especially, microbial cultures from the laboratory. Doing so is absolutely prohibited.

15. Immediately cover spilled cultures or broken culture tubes with paper towels and then saturate them with disinfectant solution. After 15 minutes of reaction time, remove the towels and dispose of them in a manner indicated by the instructor.

16. Report accidental cuts or burns to the instructor immediately.

17. Never pipette by mouth any broth cultures or chemical reagents. Doing so is strictly prohibited. Pipetting is to be carried out with the aid of a mechanical pipetting device only.

18. Do not lick labels. Use only self-stick labels for the identification of experimental cultures.

19. Speak quietly and avoid unnecessary movement around the laboratory to prevent distractions that may cause accidents.

Additional precautions for handling body fluids:

20. Disposable gloves must be worn during the manipulation of these test materials.

21. Immediate hand washing is required if contact with any of these fluids occurs and also upon removal of gloves.

22. Masks, safety goggles, and laboratory coats should be worn if an aerosol might be formed or splattering of these fluids is likely to occur.

23. Spilled body fluids should be decontaminated with a 1:10 dilution of household bleach, covered with paper toweling, and allowed to react for 10 minutes before removal.

24. Test specimens and supplies in contact with these fluids must be placed into a container of disinfectant prior to autoclaving.

From Inside Covers of *Microbiology: A Laboratory Manual*, Tenth Edition. James G. Cappuccino, Natalie Sherman.

SERIAL DILUTION

This figure illustrates the basic steps of serial dilution and appears here as a convenient reference for this commonly used technique. Turn back to this figure whenever you need a quick reminder of the procedure.

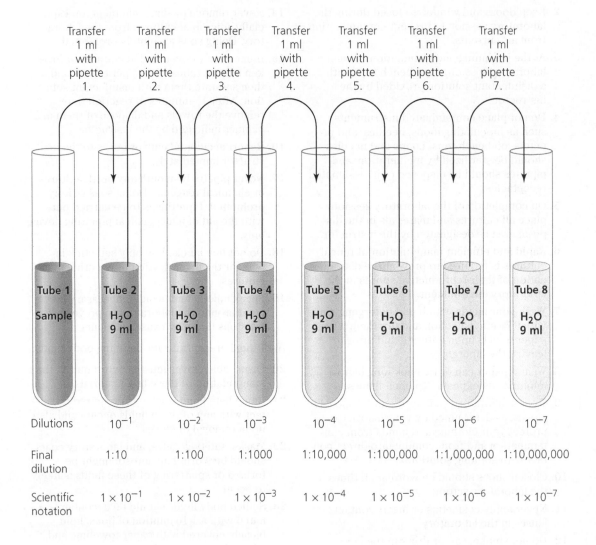

Index

555

Potatoes, 539
poultry, 347, 478
Pour plates, 341
Pour-plate technique, 20, 140-141, 143, 356
povidone-iodine, 320
Precipitate, 191-192, 320, 408, 453, 504, 505, 508, 533, 542
Precipitates, 106, 319-320, 339, 410, 436
Precipitation, 175, 200, 320, 410, 506
Precipitin formation, 503-504
Precipitins, 504
Pre-erythrocytic stage, 237
Pressure, 2-3, 36, 232, 287-288, 289-290, 295-296, 298, 481, 486, 535-539
Primary infection, 525
Primary stain, 75-77, 79-80, 81, 85, 87-89, 94-95
    acid-fast stain, 81
    capsule stain, 89
    gram stain, 75-77, 80, 81
    spore stain, 87-88
Primary syphilis, 523
Probability, 345
Proctitis, 526
    chlamydial, 526
Producers, 361
Product, 160, 175, 182, 184, 195, 206, 209, 217-218, 258, 333, 431, 519, 531
Production, 117-118, 123, 140, 159-160, 161, 169-172, 175-177, 180-183, 191-194, 199, 209, 211, 213, 215, 218, 221, 225, 227, 267, 272, 299, 327, 333-334, 336, 339, 342, 354, 367, 387, 418, 431, 444-445, 471, 473, 496-497, 503
Product(s), 160
Products, 105, 118, 127, 141, 149, 159-160, 166, 169-171, 175, 180-182, 184, 190, 195, 199-200, 207, 217-219, 223, 247, 287-288, 290, 298, 327-328, 329-330, 332, 336, 354, 367, 391, 401, 431, 443-444, 448, 454, 478, 509
Prokaryotic cells, 52, 312, 385
Promoter, 376
Properties, 1, 19, 55, 100, 106, 159, 163, 179, 257, 295, 321, 445, 461, 467, 481
Prophage, 273
    induction, 273
Propionibacterium, 437
Propionibacterium acnes, 437
Protease, 162
Proteases, 162, 354
Protein, 76, 97, 99, 117, 123, 140, 162-164, 200, 217, 271-273, 288, 300, 303, 307, 319, 354, 373, 376, 399, 426, 445, 503, 527
    denaturation, 117, 319
    structural, 97, 162, 272, 376
    structure, 117, 271, 288, 303, 319, 373
    synthesis, 97, 162, 217, 271, 288, 300, 303, 307, 354, 445
    viral, 271, 273
Protein A, 445
Protein breakdown, 123
protein denaturation, 319
Protein hydrolysis, 162
Protein synthesis, 97, 288, 300, 303, 307, 354
    inhibition of, 303
    inhibitors, 307
    transcription, 300
Proteins, 55, 59, 97, 124, 126, 159, 161-163, 172, 199-200, 204, 288, 289, 319-321, 353-354, 410, 490, 503, 533
    denaturation, 319-320
    digestion of, 200
    functions, 97
    membrane, 161-162, 320-321
    metabolic pathways for, 162
    simple, 55
    structure, 288, 319
    structure and function of, 288
    synthesis of, 159, 161-162, 353-354
Proteolysis, 162, 164, 199-201
Proteolytic enzymes, 200
Proteus, 45, 160, 176, 179, 192, 195, 198, 217-220, 224, 229, 305, 327, 435, 467-468, 470, 487-490, 497, 510
    P. mirabilis, 176, 497
    P. vulgaris, 176, 497
Proteus spp., 176, 468, 488, 497
Proteus vulgaris, 45, 160, 179, 192, 195, 220, 224, 305, 470, 487-488, 490, 510
    hydrogen sulfide test, 192

Kirby-Bauer antibiotic sensitivity test, 305
    phenylalanine deaminase test, 220
    urease test, 160, 195, 488
Protists, 229
Protoplast, 287
Protozoa, 45, 52-53, 229, 231-236, 237-242, 244-245, 334, 337, 355, 435, 487, 523, 542
    classification, 229
    in soil, 237, 355
    intestinal, 237, 244, 337, 435, 487
    motility, 45, 229
    nutrition, 229
    parasitic, 229, 237-242, 244-245, 337
    pond water, 45, 231, 233
    reproduction, 229, 232
    sizes of, 52
    taxonomy, 229
Protozoans, 229, 231
Providencia, 219
Pseudomembranous colitis, 88
Pseudomonadales, 355
Pseudomonads, 171, 367
Pseudomonas, 31, 45, 119, 121, 160, 163, 176, 179, 200, 206, 213, 224, 264, 305, 307, 309, 327, 354, 361, 367-369, 372, 435, 468, 481, 487-490, 497
    P. aeruginosa, 163, 497
    P. fluorescens, 497
Pseudomonas aeruginosa, 31, 45, 160, 163, 179, 200, 206, 213, 224, 264, 305, 307, 361, 481, 487-488, 490
    biochemical characteristics, 224
    cultural characteristics, 31, 224, 264
    experiments, 160, 179
    Kirby-Bauer antibiotic sensitivity test, 305
Pseudomonas spp., 488, 497
Pseudopods, 229, 232, 235, 238
Psychrophile, 117, 122
Psychrophiles, 118-119
Public health, 198, 327, 337, 344
Puerperal fever, 7, 453
Puffballs, 247-248
Pulse, 419-420, 486
Pure culture, 1-2, 23, 27-28, 225, 265, 369, 477
Pure cultures, 1-2, 19-23, 26-28, 141, 493, 495-496, 499
    defined, 2
Purines, 304
Pus, 322, 443, 456
Pyelitis, 487
Pyelonephritis, 443, 487
Pyrimidine, 304
    synthesis, 304
Pyrimidines, 299
Pyrogallic acid technique, 134
Pyruvate, 169, 185
    in fermentation, 169
    metabolism, 169
Pyruvic acid, 169-170, 172, 174, 180, 184-185, 190, 192, 199, 333
    fermentation of, 199, 333
    in fermentation, 169
    Krebs cycle and, 184

Q

Quanta, 299
Quantitative data, 313
Quebec colony counter, 8, 140-142, 144, 151, 356, 358, 403
Quellung (Neufeld) reaction, 462
Quellung reaction, 461-463, 465
Quinolone, 303

R

R plasmids, 408
Rabbit, 446, 523, 543
Radiation, 3, 87, 272, 287-288, 299-302
    in microbial control, 288
    ionizing, 3, 272, 288, 299, 301
    sterilization, 3, 288, 299-301
    wavelengths, 299
radicals, 299
Rapid plasma reagin (RPR) test, 523
Rapid testing methods, 430
Rash, 454, 523
Raw materials, 159
Rays, 35-36, 38-39, 162, 299, 301
Reading frame, 391

Reagents, 6, 59, 66, 75-77, 79, 81, 83, 87, 89, 91, 183, 185, 205-206, 220, 225, 259, 334, 341, 368, 376, 392, 408, 418-419, 437, 446, 455-456, 462, 471-472, 478, 483, 494, 506, 510, 515, 524-527, 541-543, 545, 547
    Barritt's, 185
    Kovac's, 185
Reagin, 523-524
Receptacles, 547
Receptor, 271-272, 274
Receptor sites, 271-272, 274
Recombinant DNA, 397, 407-408
Recombinant DNA technology, 397
    applications of, 397
Recombinants, 381, 417
Recombination, 381, 385, 399, 401
    homologous, 381, 399
Rectal swab, 468
Red blood cells, 107, 237-239, 241, 443, 453
    hemolysis, 107, 453
Red wine, 333
Reduction, 7, 9, 11, 107, 133, 160, 180, 191, 199-201, 205-206, 208, 224-225, 227, 319, 321, 333, 369, 371, 436, 471, 495-497
    reduction reactions, 199
refractive index, 36, 39, 45
Refrigeration, 118
Refrigerators, 2
    laboratory, 2
Regulation, 98
    enzyme activity, 98
Regulatory gene, 375
Release, 76, 200, 272-274, 280, 408-409, 419, 467, 524
Releasing, 377, 399, 409-410, 419
Renal tubules, 487
Rennet curd, 200
Rennin, 200
Repair, 300
    DNA, 300
Replication, 271-273, 288, 300, 401, 407
    origin of, 407
    plasmid, 401, 407
    viral, 271, 273
    viral nucleic acid, 271
Repressor, 376
Repressor protein, 376
Reproduction, 87, 117, 229, 232, 247, 257-259, 262-264, 287, 295, 321, 353
    eukaryotic, 229, 247
    fungal, 247
    microbial, 117, 287, 295, 353
Reproductive spores, 247, 547
Resazurin, 134, 540
Research, 21, 36, 118, 256, 270, 307, 313, 373, 375, 391, 397, 399, 408, 417-418, 466, 523-524
resistance, 140, 150, 209, 219, 289, 293, 303, 306, 313, 322, 361, 382, 387-389, 401, 407-408, 418, 426, 444, 447, 503
    development of, 303, 387, 447
    innate immunity, 503
    mechanisms of, 303
    multiple, 407
Resistance genes, 407
resistant bacteria, 150, 281, 307
Resolution, 37-39
Resorcinol, 319
Respiration, 98, 127, 133, 161, 169-171, 173, 191, 205, 209, 213
    aerobic, 127, 133, 161, 169, 171, 205, 209, 213
    anaerobic, 98, 127, 133, 169, 191, 205
    cellular respiration, 127, 133, 169
    process of, 98, 161
Respiratory infection, 86
Respiratory infections, 453
Respiratory tract, 327, 435, 456
    normal flora, 435
Restriction analysis, 417-421, 424-426
Restriction endonucleases, 397-398, 417-419, 424
Restriction enzyme, 397, 411, 417-419, 426
Restriction enzymes, 418, 424, 426
Restriction sites, 417-418
Reticuloendothelial system, 503
Revertant, 391
Revolving nosepiece, 38
Rheumatic fever, 441, 453
Rhizobium, 354
Rhizoids, 265
Rhizopus, 248, 250-254, 265, 268, 327, 354, 355